DITERRANEVM

Africe pars

Gades
Calix

Caput S.
Vincetij

Cartagena

Granata

Granata

Ifpalis

Sibilla

Maiorica

Minorica

HISPANIA

Lifbona

Tagus fl:

Toletū

Portugallia

Mare Ligufticum

Barfalona

Catalonia

Aragonia

Iber fl:

Castilia

Sala
manca

Narbon

Nauarra

Saragoza

Panpzlona

Burgos

Gallicia

Prouincia

Pyrenæi mõtes

Bizcdid

Asturia

S.Iacob

Marfilia

Tolofa

Gnafconia

Finis terrę

Lägendock

Garūna fl:

Delphinat

Auernia

Aquitania

Rodanus

Lugdunū

Limofin

Subaudia

GALLIA

eluetia

Turonia

Burgundia

Ligeris fls

Bafilea

Sequana fl:

Britānia

Argēti

Paris

NIA

FRANCIA

Normādia

Treueris

Brabantia

Hannonia

Antwerp

Picardia

Rhenus fl:

Flandria

Artois

Mare Anglicum

OCEANVS

alia

Cornubia

Lõdon

fia

Tamefis fl:

wallia

ANGLIA

Ganaforda

Mare Septētrionale

Tueda fl:

HIBERNIA

Scotiæ pars

WATERFORD TREASURES

A guide to the
historical and archaeological
treasures of Waterford City

Published by Waterford Museum of Treasures in May 2004

Produced by Terry Murphy Photography & Design

Copyright © Waterford Museum of Treasures

A catalogue record of this book is available from
the British Library.

ISBN 0-9547335-0-9

Printed in Ireland by M.Y. Gallaghers of Waterford Limited

Typeset in Times New Roman

Origination by Linda Murphy

Waterford Museum of Treasures
The Granary
Merchants Quay
Waterford
Ireland

CONTENTS

FOREWORD

As Minister for the Environment, Heritage and Local Government, I am particularly pleased to commission this splendid panorama of the remarkable historic and archaeological treasures of Waterford. The treasures are used imaginatively as both mileposts and signposts to help us negotiate the thousand-year history of the city. Some pieces link us to great events while others illuminate the dark recesses almost forgotten by the passage of time. The authors have treated the objects almost like hostages from the past, forcing them to recount their part in the dramatic story of a city that has stood the test of time and has continued to re-invent itself.

For me as a Waterfordian, having strong family connections with the port and overseas trade, the most striking feature of the collection is its international dimension; be it the Scandinavian influence on Viking age jewellery or the remarkable French, German and Flemish pottery. The collection reflects the diverse origins and activities of the inhabitants of this great port. The objects associated with the Wyses of Waterford, an Anglo-Norman landed and mercantile family, best exemplify this cosmopolitanism. The sword and cap of maintenance were given to William Wyse by King Henry VIII of England in 1536; Wyse's descendant was the last grand prior of the English-speaking chapter of the Knights of St John of Jerusalem who ruled Malta until 1798, while another descendant married the emperor Napoleon Bonaparte's niece and became the first British ambassador to Greece.

Trade was not the only medium of cultural exchange. The Christianisation of Waterford in the eleventh century brought the city into the ambit of the Rome-based international family connecting every parish in Christendom. It reached its apogee in the Renaissance as reflected in the magnificent cloth of gold vestments, material symbols of cultural co-operation. The cloth of gold came from a Florentine loom in 1480 and the decorated panels, which are wonderful paintings in silk, are really sermons in the universal language of the visual and testimony to the skill of Flemish embroiderers.

In a world often characterised by distrust and fear of the otherness of others this volume affords an opportunity to focus positively on the contribution of those who, in their time, were considered outsiders. The Vikings, Anglo-Normans and Welsh, the Italians, English, Huguenot refugees from France, the Dutch settlers, have all left their mark on the city. The 1736 view of Waterford, the earliest landscape painting of the city, is by the great artist William van der Hagen and so to this day, the image we have of our eighteenth century city is as it was seen through the eyes of this Dutch artist.

Conversely the Irish diaspora is also featured in the generosity with which the emigrants endowed the land of their forefathers. This is illustrated by the wonderful Spanish silver gifts from Waterford émigrés who settled in the eighteenth century in Cadiz, then one of the leading ports in the world. The transatlantic diaspora is also featured - those who went to Newfoundland and the United States. Their gifts, so beautifully illustrated in this book, show us that these migrants enriched immeasurably their countries of adoption without forgetting the land of their birth. Clearly in the past political borders were not insurmountable impediments to trade and cultural interchange and Ireland's heritage is so much the richer for this. This book is proof that cultural diversity is a potent and positive force.

The idea of a New Europe linked by trade and commerce, every participant influencing and being influenced by others, is not so novel. In many ways the New Europe that we are creating is just a more formal reiteration of the centuries old feeling of a common European heritage evolving, not through isolation, but by contact. It is fitting

4

that this volume should be published to coincide with the meeting, in Waterford, of the enlarged Council of the twenty-five member states of the European Union. As we endeavour to forge that new Europe - new bonds of friendship founded on a sense of common purpose - we do so in the full knowledge that diversity is enriching and therefore we are all winners. As Minister whose portfolio also includes heritage and local government, I commend Waterford City Council for its commitment to the protection and promotion of the city's heritage. The editors, contributors and photographer have produced for Waterford a book that will instil pride in its citizens and furnish visitors with a lasting and treasured reminder of Urbs Intacta.

Martin Cullen, T.D.
President of the Council of the European Union (Environment)
Minister for the Environment, Heritage and Local Government

14 May 2004

AN ROINN COMHSHAOIL, OIDHREACHTA AGUS RIALTAIS ÁITIÚIL
DEPARTMENT OF THE ENVIRONMENT, HERITAGE
AND LOCAL GOVERNMENT

PREFACE

Waterford Museum of Treasures has a special relationship with the National Museum of Ireland not least because it is one of the twelve designated museums in Ireland. Its designation in July 2001 marked an important milestone for the museum. Designated museums have reached a standard of professional curatorial management that facilitates the acquisition of objects on loan from the National Museum's collections. The National Museum has been and will be happy in future to loan objects to Waterford Museum, and we feel these loans have and will continue to make a significant contribution to the success of the museum.

I have a special affinity with Waterford where between 1986 and 1992 over a fifth of the early historic city was archaeologically excavated. This is because of my own work at Wood Quay in Dublin and my gratitude to Waterford City Council for their praiseworthy publication of the results. The Viking Age houses uncovered particularly in Peter Street are internationally important and complement the corpus of knowledge garnered from our work on the Dublin excavations. Waterford Museum has on display a spectacular kite brooch dating from c1100, one of the great finds of the city excavations. The display also features a trial or motif piece, a game board and a ringed pin of slightly earlier date. It is important that objects from excavations be seen in the city in which they were recovered. I must compliment Waterford City Council again on its commitment to the museum and on the manner in which the material is presented.

The Great Charter Roll of 1373, one of the great treasures of fourteenth century Ireland, is also on display at Waterford Museum. This remarkable document, almost four metres long, is a testament to the power and wealth of the city in the middle ages when it rivalled Dublin in the volume of its overseas trade. Unusually, it illustrates not only town life and officialdom but even the clothes, fashions and accessories of fourteenth century Ireland. And it is not just about the Vikings and the middle ages; the origins of the eponymous glass and historical figures including Thomas Francis Meagher also deservedly feature prominently.

The museum has won several major awards and has used modern technology to broaden the appeal of the exhibits. Waterford Museum of Treasures is one of the most successful museums outside Dublin, attracting each year visitor numbers equivalent to over half Waterford's own population. One of the keys to its success is that it does not try to replicate a national museum but instead has taken a theme - the story of its own city - and highlighted it in all its aspects to the highest standards.

In congratulating Waterford City Council and Eamonn McEneaney on the fifth anniversary of the Museum's foundation, I am delighted to be associated with a publication that brings over a hundred of the city's treasures into this special focus. The reader will have a real encounter with Waterford's past by visiting the museum and acquiring this guidebook as a souvenir of his or her visit.

Dr Patrick F Wallace
Director
National Museum of Ireland

INTRODUCTION AND ACKNOWLEDGMENTS

Waterford has been particularly fortunate in the survival of so much of its cultural heritage. The sheer scope and diversity of that inheritance is remarkable for an Irish city and includes Viking age jewellery, medieval illuminated manuscripts, renaissance cloth-of-gold vestments and eighteenth century glass. Over one hundred treasures of Waterford are assembled in this guide, beautifully photographed by Terry Murphy.

This book is an attempt to introduce these fascinating riches to the wider public. To this end we have endeavoured to place each object in its historic context and to convey each one's story, why it is important and what key it holds to the secret treasure chest of our past.

The museum is greatly indebted to the wider community, locally, nationally and indeed internationally, whose generosity of spirit has been remarkable. Nearly half the objects featured in this book are on long-term loan to the museum - this speaks volumes for their owners. The artefacts so kindly loaned are not only important for the history of Waterford, but are themselves beautiful works of art and we are always conscious of the great privilege it is for us to have them in our care. All the churches in the city have been overwhelming in their generosity - this support is indeed appropriate as religion has been central to the history of the city throughout the centuries. The Friends of Waterford Museum of Treasures, individual and corporate, provide not just moral support and constant encouragement but also much-needed funds for ongoing purchase and conservation. Similarly the Dublin-based Friends of the National Collections of Ireland, the Heritage Council and the Ireland Newfoundland Partnership are valued and esteemed benefactors.

National institutions, in particular the National Museum of Ireland and the National Gallery of Ireland, have been more than generous and supportive. As a museum we have many dealings with the curatorial staff of both institutions and we have always found them enthusiastic and forthcoming with their expertise and time. Both the Director of the National Museum, Patrick Wallace and the Director of the National Gallery, Raymond Keaveney have been unstinting in their support.

As editors of this book we would like to publicly acknowledge the trojan work of the staff of Waterford Museum of Treasures, Linda Keane, Mairin Claridge, Bernie Sexton, Jim Nugent, Michael Phelan and of our part-time staff members. Their constant professionalism and enthusiasm are major factors in the museum's success.

We thank all of the contributors to this volume. Not only have they made this book possible but over the years have been willing to share their immense knowledge of history and archaeology with us. The quality and integrity of their contributions here is remarkable; this guide, and indeed Waterford city, is the richer for the way in which they share their scholarship with the ease of true academics. In writing both the introductory chapters and the individual essays we have drawn heavily on the works of many historians, art historians, archaeologists and other specialists. We would like to acknowledge the use of material, published and unpublished, including Olga Bonaparte Wyse, John Bradley, Michael Brennan, Eugene Broderick, Jack Burtchaell, Cyril Byrne, Niall Byrne, Jennifer Cochran, Des Cowman, Cliodna Devitt, Mairead Dunlevy, Annie Fletcher, T N Fewer, John M Hearne, Bill Irish, Joan Johnson, James Lydon, Catriona MacLeod, John Mannion, Ben Murtagh, Conor O'Brien, Raghnall Ó Floinn, Tadhg O'Keeffe, Timothy O'Neill, Gillian Smith, David Smith, Patrick Wallace, Julian Walton and Audrey Whitty.

This guide draws heavily on that great *magnum opus* published in 1997 by Waterford Corporation, *Late Viking and Medieval Waterford Excavations 1986-1992*. To the authors of that volume, Maurice Hurley, Orla Scully with Sarah McCutcheon, we are forever indebted. We have relied almost completely on the specialist reports in the above publication for information on the archaeological objects discussed here, in particular the work of Terry

Barry, Audrey Gahan, Andrew Halpin, J G Hurst, Michael Kenny, Ronald Lightbown, Clare McCutcheon, Elizabeth Okasha, Uainín O'Meadhra, Brian Spencer, Niamh Whitfield and Elizabeth Wincott Heckett.

The Mayor of Waterford, Councillor Thomas Cunningham and Members of Waterford City Council stand out among elected local representatives in Ireland for their dedicated commitment to the protection and promotion of the city's heritage. Their continued support and enthusiasm ensures a central place for the museum in the life of the city. The backing of City Manager Conn Murray and Director of Services Colette Byrne make our task of managing and promoting the museum both pleasant and fulfilling. Our colleagues Jane Cantwell, City Librarian, Donal Moore, City Archivist and Conor Nolan, Arts Officer are valued collaborators.

In today's world we often underestimate the importance of patronage, taking for granted the generosity of our benefactor's commitment to the promotion of the arts or a particular aspect of our heritage. The patrons of art in the middle ages were highly regarded, to such an extent that they were historically depicted kneeling to the right or left of the Virgin Mary or a saint. Minister Martin Cullen TD, by his vision in commissioning this publication, has afforded us a wonderful opportunity to present to the public some of the treasures of this historic city and for this we are deeply indebted. We hope that this guide will help connect the reader to Waterford's past and one thousand years of history.

Eamonn McEneaney
Director
Waterford Museum of Treasures

Rosemary Ryan
Education Officer
Waterford Museum of Treasures

Contributors

Dr Eugene Broderick

Cliodna Devitt

Dr John M Hearne

Eamonn McEneaney

Ben Murtagh

Raghnall Ó Floinn

Rosemary Ryan

Orla Scully

Julian Walton

MUSEUM ORIGINS

As early as 1835 Thomas Wyse, MP for Waterford, at a meeting organised by the Waterford Mechanics Society in the Assembly Rooms, City Hall, called on the government to provide funding towards erecting a building suitable 'for the ordinary objects of an institute, a museum and a gallery of design'.[1] However his words went unheeded until 1897 when the Waterford and South-East Archaeological Society opened in the city a small museum 'on the same lines as the Science and Art Museum in Dublin where visitors and tourists could come and inspect a collection of objects equal to any in Ireland'.[2] This museum was established in the free library at number one Adelphi Terrace, a house built by the Penrose family, now the site of the Tower Hotel. The museum moved to Lady Lane in the early twentieth century and the collection substantially added to, most notably by Canon Power, Waterford historian and scholar.[3] In 1954 material from this museum was transferred to Reginald's Tower when its interior was re-modelled for that purpose. The new exhibition there was supplemented by objects from the municipal collection.

Then in 1978 Waterford City Council set a primary objective in the city development plan of that year to 'provide assistance for site assembly at High Street, Arundel Square and Peter Street to effect major shopping redevelopment proposals'. In July 1986 the council invited developers to submit proposals for the site, with the condition that the developer should archaeologically resolve the area. In 1987, Maurice Hurley was appointed by Waterford Corporation as Senior Archaeologist in charge of co-ordinating excavations. He continued in this role until 1991 when he was replaced by Orla Scully, who had been with the project from the outset. Over a six-year period a team of archaeologists resolved some six thousand square metres - a fifth of the old Viking city.[4] This undertaking of the city centre archaeological excavations in preparation for the development of City Square Shopping Centre was one of the most exciting developments in twentieth century Waterford. The developers put a new heart into the old city as the dereliction and decay of decades was wiped away. The excavations also transformed the whole perception of the history and archaeology of the city, creating a real sense of uncovering our Viking past, discovering our roots with all the romantic and heroic associations that this conjured up.

For six years archaeologists mined the rich seams of late medieval, Anglo-Norman and late Viking age Waterford. Outside this hoarded compound of history the people of Waterford went on with their lives as they had for over a thousand years before and when the opportunity arose, an open gate, a removed piece of hoarding, they peered into the site to snatch a fleeting glimpse of the uncovering of their city's past. The elected members of Waterford City Council fully supported the development under the management of Michael Doody, City Manager and the Assistant Town Clerk, Terry O'Sullivan. The developer, John Sisk and Sons Limited, financed the excavation and post excavation work, greatly assisting the endeavour.

At first objects from the site were displayed in Reginald's Tower. Then as the number, range and quality of the artefacts unearthed surpassed all expectations, Waterford Corporation in 1988 acquired the Methodist church in Greyfriars Street for conversion to a museum. This was an ideal arrangement; as the small Methodist community no longer required the building it ensured that the beautiful turn of the century gothic church would continue to serve a useful purpose. The material from the excavation was proudly displayed at Greyfriars Heritage Centre until 1999 giving the people of Waterford access to their recently discovered archaeological heritage.

1992 saw the completion of the excavations and the beginning of the work of cataloguing, synthesising the information and writing the excavation report. It also saw the city council engage consultants from York in England, that other great Viking city with strong links to Waterford, to devise a heritage tourism plan for the city which was later adopted by the council. The same year the present writer

was employed by the corporation to advise on heritage matters and assist in moving forward some of the recommendations made by the consultants. Waterford Corporation now purchased the grain store in Hanover Street, known locally as the Granary, from G H Hall. It had been built in 1872, a rebuilding of an earlier grain and bacon store which stood on the site but was destroyed by fire. This was the same site where the first catholic mayor of Waterford since the seventeenth century, Newfoundland-born Thomas Meagher had a warehouse. So the Granary has long associations with the city's mercantile past, being an important physical link with the role of Waterford as a port purveying the bounty of the hinterland by ship to distant lands.

In 1993 work began on the conservation of Reginald's Tower. This was a major undertaking, as the interior walls had been cement rendered in the 1950s, totally obscuring the interior historic features. Some of the material from the historic municipal collection displayed in the tower was now transferred to Greyfriars where it was displayed alongside the archaeological artefacts. This period also saw the beginning of a programme of conservation work on the municipal collection. In 1995 Duchas, the Heritage Service took over the guardianship of Reginald's Tower and work on the interior was completed by 1999 when an exhibition was installed.

The work of converting the Granary building into a museum began in 1997. The building had been almost derelict since vacated by R & H Hall in the 1960s. Conversion work was completed early in 1999 and a new exhibition, which had been over two years in preparation, was officially opened by the Mayor Cllr Brian Swift. Waterford City Council and City Manager, Edward Breen had given the project their full backing and were successful in securing major ERDF funding (through Bord Fáilte and South-East Tourism), urban renewal funding from the Department of the Environment and Local Government and a very generous donation from Waterford Crystal Ltd. The city council provided the remainder of the funding, which amounted to over fifty per cent of the total project cost. Following the opening of Waterford Museum of Treasures, the Greyfriars centre was converted to the Municipal Art Gallery.

The collection on display in the museum dates from the Viking age to the end of the nineteenth century and is presented in a themed format, telling the story of Waterford chronologically. Central to our philosophy in developing the exhibition was that the collection be accessible and welcoming to the public. The building is fully wheelchair accessible. On an intellectual level every effort had been made to appeal to as broad an audience as possible: there are sound guides pitched both at adult and child level

while computer inter-actives and audio-visual presentations are extensively used. Foreign visitors are also catered for with sound guides in six languages. Curriculum based programmes for schools, lifelong learning, after-dark events and community outreach are all part of the museum's activities.

To date the museum has won a number of important awards, the Irish Museum of the Year Award 1999 and the Irish American Cultural Institute Award 2000. It was one of six museums to receive a special commendation in the European Museum of the Year Awards 2002. In 2001, the Minister for Arts, Heritage, the Gaeltacht and the Islands designated the museum under the National Monuments legislation. The following year, among the many objects loaned to the museum by Henry Bonaparte Wyse, was a painting by Henrietta Wyse of her brother Thomas, the same man who almost one hundred and seventy years ago first mooted the idea of a museum for Waterford.

Eamonn McEneaney
Director
Waterford Museum of Treasures

Reginald's Tower

'Reginald's tower - a massive hinge of stone connecting the two great outspread wings, the Quay and the Mall, within which lay the body of the city'.

T.F. Meagher 1843[1]

The origins of Reginald's Tower are obscure. An account dated 860 states that the Norse at Waterford were attacked by the men of Leinster who drove them 'back into a small place with a small fortification'[2] This suggests that the Vikings had some form of ninth century fortification at Waterford, however in the absence of archaeological evidence it would be presumptuous to associate this fortification with the site of the present tower. Following the arrival of the Viking warlord Ragnall, grandson of Ivor the Boneless in 914, it is logical to assume that a fortified base existed and certainly by 1088 the Annals of Ireland are referring to a *Dun* or fort at Waterford.[3]

At the time of the Anglo-Norman siege of the city in 1170 a Gaelic account refers to this *Dun* while the Anglo-Norman chronicler Giraldus Cambrensis refers to 'Raghenald's Tower'.[4] It has been suggested that the tower derives its name from Ragnall mac Gillemaire, a leading figure in the Hiberno-Norse government of Waterford, who was imprisoned in the tower when the city fell to Strongbow and the Anglo-Normans in 1170[5] In 1463 the two names Dundory and Reginald's Tower appear in the Rolls of the Irish Parliament then meeting in Waterford[6] This suggests that those of Irish and Hiberno-Norse descent used the name Dundory while the Old English, those of Anglo-Norman descent, called it Reginald's Tower. The name Dundory survives into the late eighteenth century on deeds and refers to the whole area from Reginald's Tower to Christ Church Cathedral. In 1784 John Roberts and a consortium leased 'a plot of ground, formerly a garden, under Dunderry wall' as a site for a playhouse and assembly hall.[7]

When King Henry II arrived in Waterford in 1171 he committed Robert Fitzstephen to Reginald's Tower giving it the distinction of being the oldest royal prison in Ireland. During the medieval period the tower probably fulfilled the role of a royal castle in Ireland and it is safe to assume that the first two floors of the present structure were built in the late twelfth or early thirteenth century. The early Waterford mints may well have been sited in the tower, but we know for certain that the 1463 mint was because it is recorded in the Rolls of the Irish Parliament. It is probable that the tower was used as an arsenal in 1394 when King Richard II landed in Waterford at the head of a huge armada. A contemporary illustration of the visit shows what appear to be cannon balls being unloaded from Richard's ships. If this interpretation is correct, then this is the earliest depiction of artillery being imported into Ireland.[8] In 1495 the supporters of the pretender Perkin Warbeck laid siege to Waterford. The assault was in retaliation for the city's refusal to recognise him as king. The citizens, using canonn lodged in Reginald's Tower 'bulged or drowned with the ordinance shot out of

Reginald's Tower

Dundore', one of Warbeck's ships.[9] After eleven days the siege was lifted making this the first successful use of artillery by an Irish city. At the time of the siege the monument probably stood at its present height, for two new floors were added to the earlier structure some time in the late middle ages. In the decades prior to the Warbeck siege there are many references in the city's Great Parchment Book to the strengthening and repair of the defences and to the availability of 'guns both great and small' in the city. We must assume that these modifications were carried out to accommodate and facilitate the use of cannon.[10]

The strategic importance of the tower, standing as it did at the confluence of the river Suir and its tributary the St John's river, was underlined and later undermined during the reign of Elizabeth I. The developments in artillery coupled with the fears of a Spanish invasion led to the erection of a blockhouse built onto the east of the tower between 1560 and 1568 to accommodate larger cannon.[11] It was at this time that the present entrance door was constructed to give access to the blockhouse. The original entrance would have been on the opposite side - from within the walled city. A map dating from c1590 shows both the tower and the blockhouse extending out into the river with the cannon projecting from the blockhouse clearly visible. (p127) The building of the blockhouse to accommodate the changing technology of warfare marked

the beginning of the end of the tower as the pivotal point in the city's defences and guardian of the city's quays. The days of the walled town were numbered. However despite their advances blockhouses were not impregnable and in 1570 Stucley, an English pirate, believed by some contemporaries to be the illegitimate son of Henry VIII, came with Venetian pirates to Waterford and under cover of dark they stole the cannon from the blockhouse![12]

What is not obvious today is that Reginald's Tower was part of a whole series of walls and towers encircling the city. In 1586 Don Diego Ortiz, a Spanish spy wrote 'the town is surrounded by a stone wall about a mile in circumference with seventeen towers and cannon on them to keep off the savages'.[13] Today Reginald's Tower is the finest of the six surviving towers which as a group constitute the largest collection in Ireland of medieval urban defences. In 1649 Oliver Cromwell unsuccessfully laid siege to the city. However in 1650, parliamentary forces launched a second siege, this time featuring parliamentary frigates which bombarded the city from the river Suir. A cannon ball, still lodged in the north-facing wall of the tower is a potent reminder of the siege and fall of the city. Three years after the restoration of King Charles II (1660-1685) the tower was used as an arsenal 'for keeping the kings stores'.[14]

Reginald's Tower

Twenty years later c1683 Stanhope described the fortifications at Reginald's Tower: 'The lower platform lying near the river is well fortified with seven or eight great gunns, well mounted. The upper part of the [Reginald's] tower is also furnished with several brasse gunns of great length, which command the adjacent country on all sides'.[15] About the year 1700 the city council had begun removing the walls and towers protecting the quays; as part of this process the block house adjoining the tower was demolished in 1711. Fortunately, Reginald's Tower survived and by the mid-eighteenth century was in the possession of the storekeeper of the fort of Duncannon in county Wexford who was engaged in the defence of the harbour.[16]

By 1730 the St John's river that entered the Suir next to the tower was diverted and the Mall and bowling- green then occupied the area where the river once flowed. Charles Smith wrote in 1746 that the 'bowling-green makes this part of the town very agreeable'.[17] The strategic importance of the tower at the confluence of the two rivers was now lost forever. As the walls connecting it to the other towers on the circuit were demolished it became the isolated monument it is today. The sheer bulk of the tower and its perceived antiquity

helped to save it from a fate similar to those other towers protecting the quays. In 1819 it was converted for use as a debtors' prison 'a place of correction for vagrants and sturdy beggars'. After 1861 it was the home of the High Constable of the city. In 1954 the last resident departed and it was converted to a museum. In 1993 work began on the restoration and conservation of the monument. Following the completion of the interior conservation works, an exhibition was installed in 1997 telling the fascinating story of the tower and its pivotal position in the circuit of medieval walls and towers that once enclosed the city.

By the nineteenth century the tower had become something of a Waterford icon when a limestone plaque placed on the monument stated that it was built in 1003. In 2003 the city celebrated the tower's millennium. To highlight the importance of both the tower and the remaining sections of town wall as historic monuments, the City Council in conjunction with the Department of the Environment, Heritage and Local Government hosted the 13th International Walled Towns Symposium. The week-long event attracted over one hundred delegates from eleven European countries including five of the accession countries to the enlarged

Reginald's Tower

European Union. The highpoint was a sound and light show based on the story of Reginald's Tower performed by Spraoi, the city's street theatre company. Today Waterford City Council and the Department of the Environment, Heritage and Local Government jointly manage the monument.

VIKING AGE

WATERFORD

The period known as the Viking Age extended from the ninth to the eleventh centuries. This was a time of the Viking movements overseas, when Viking ships sailed from the Scandinavian heartland out across the northern hemisphere on voyages of piracy and invasion and journeys of commerce, exploration and settlement. The world of the Vikings consisted of a loose grouping of the Scandinavian homelands and new overseas colonies, linked by sea routes that reached across the Baltic and the North Sea, spanning even the Atlantic. Viking settlements were to be encountered from Newfoundland to Novgorod and from the North Cape of Norway to Normandy in the Frankish Empire. Viking ships sailed the northern waters from the Labrador to the White Seas; they harried the Atlantic coasts of Europe to the Straits of Gibraltar, even penetrating the western Mediterranean. The Dnieper and the Volga brought their merchant craft to the Black Sea and the Caspian and so into direct contact with the world of Byzantium and Islam. The rivers of the Continent and the British Isles carried their warships deep into the heart of Europe.[1]

In Ireland the Vikings first appeared in 795 and in the following centuries laid the foundations of Ireland's oldest towns and cities. Founded by Viking warlords in 914, Waterford is Ireland's oldest centre of continuous urban settlement. It is also the only Irish city to retain its Old Norse-derived place-name, Waterford being a corruption of *Vedrarfjordr*. The first element of the place-name has its root in the Old Norse *Vedr*, a noun meaning 'wind or weather', and refers to the fact that this inlet of the river Suir or fjord to the Scandinavians, was often exposed to the wind and that this settlement offered a safe haven in any storm.[2] The city also has the distinction of being older than all of the north European capitals except London and Paris. After Dublin it was the most important city in Ireland up until the end of the seventeenth century.

While as yet no conclusive evidence has been found of any significant pre-Viking settlement at Waterford, there are many references in the Irish Annals to suggest that,

like Dublin, Waterford had ninth century origins. In the annals the 'settlement' is called *Port Láirge*, named, it is believed, after Laraig a ninth century Viking.[3] In 858 the annals record the defeat of the fleet of *Port Láirge*.[4] A later eleventh century source records the arrival at *Port Láirge* in 860 of a Norse group and an attack on them by the men of Munster who drove them into 'a small place with a small fortification'.[5] A reference in 891 to an army which included the foreigners of *Port Láirge* also suggests settlement;[6] however, we cannot be certain if these bases were permanent or indeed even located on the site of the present city.

The most dramatic event in terms of developing a permanent Viking settlement in Waterford occurred in 914 when several annals record that a great Scandinavian fleet landed in Waterford under the leadership of Ragnall, grandson of Ivor the Boneless. This fleet originated in northern France and having failed to gain a foothold on the Severn estuary, it landed in Waterford, where a stronghold was erected from which the Vikings initiated a new phase of plundering activity.[7] Munster was devastaed in 915 and two years later Dublin was re-established following its abandonment in 902 when the Irish 'drove out the foreigners' though the full extent of this expulsion has yet to be determined.

In 914 Ragnall became King of Waterford and in 917 Niall Glúndub, High King of Ireland, besieged Waterford but failed to take it. The following year Ragnall with the Waterford Norse defeated the Scots on the banks of the Tyne and established himself as King of York. Ragnall's family provided kings for tenth century Waterford and Dublin and kings for York until 952.[8] Both as plunderers and plundered, the Vikings of Waterford were drawn into Irish dynastic politics. Their settlement, with its great fleet, was highly prized by Gaelic kings struggling for control of their provinces or indeed for the high kingship of Ireland.

The rise to power of the Uí Briain dynasty in Munster

after 976 saw them become overlords in Waterford. In 984 Waterford was the venue for a meeting between the king - Brian Bóroma (Boru) and the sons of Aralt, the Norse king of Limerick. Brian was trying to enlist the aid of the Limerick fleet for a projected attack on Dublin and when it finally did come at Clontarf in 1014, both Hiberno-Norse Limerick and Waterford were allies of Brian. Although Brian was killed in the battle at Clontarf, he had, in the course of his long reign, managed to force his authority over much of the country. In so doing, he made great use of the naval power supplied by his 'allies' the Hiberno-Norse of Waterford who helped defeat one of the main contenders for the high-kingship, Máel Sechnaill.[9] This defeat highlights the importance of the port towns in Irish politics and the close relationship existing between the native population and the descendants of the original Viking settlers.

Clearly, Waterford, like Dublin, was a prize to be won for an aspiring Irish dynasty. Waterford moved out of the Uí Briain, Munster sphere into that of the kingdom of Leinster when in 1037 it was captured by Diarmait mac Máel na mBó, King of Uí Chennselaig, under whose aegis, it has been suggested, coins were later minted in Waterford.[10] The capture of Waterford was part of Diarmait's bid to be king of Leinster, an ambition he achieved in 1042. On Diarmait's death thirty years later his former ally Toirdelbach ua Briain now took control of the kingdom of Leinster, marching on Dublin where he installed his son Muirchertach as king.[11] The Munster men now controlled Leinster and Dublin and so Waterford was now back under the control and influence of Toirdelbach Ua Briain of Munster, grandson of Brian Boru.

In 1086 Toirdelbach Ua Briain was succeeded by his son Muirchertach who reigned as high-king, with opposition, from 1093 to 1114; he was the most powerful king in Ireland of his day. In 1096 he installed his brother Diarmait as *dux*, or leader, of Waterford.[12] Yet despite Muirchertach's power the political landscape could still be fluid, particularly as Waterford is geographically situated right on the border between Munster and Leinster. In 1088 Waterford was the target of an unsuccessful attack by a rival claimant to the kingdom of Leinster - the annals tell us that the attackers captured the town but failed to take the royal stronghold.[13] Presumably this stronghold is the fort referred to in later documents as Dundory, a small fortified area at the confluence of the St John's river and the river Suir. Waterford remained under Muirchertach Ua Briain's influence until 1114 when he was deposed by his brother Diarmait who ruled until his death in 1118. It is not clear who controlled Waterford after his death but by 1137 King Cormac MacCarthaig of Desmond is reported to have defended the town when attacked by the combined forces of Diarmait Mac Murchada of Leinster and Conchobar Ua Briain of Thomond (county Clare).[14] The sources tell us that Diarmait Mac Murchada's army was assisted by the foreigners of Dublin and Wexford who brought to the siege two hundred ships. One source states that MacCarthaig forces turned them away and Waterford was saved. MacCarthaig's victory was short-lived as he was murdered the following year at the behest of Diarmait Mac Murchada.[15] Evidence uncovered during the city centre excavations revealed that either immediately before or after this attack in 1137 the city's western defences were upgraded when the ditch and earthen bank surmounted by a timber palisade were replaced by a finely-coursed stone wall.[16]

The murdered Diarmait Mac Carthaig was succeeded by his son, also called Diarmait, Waterford remaining under his control until 1170 when he failed to prevent its capture by Strongbow, the Anglo-Norman ally of Diarmait Mac Murchada, King of Leinster. Strongbow's victory brought Viking age Waterford to an end. On Mac Murchada's death in 1171, the stage was occupied by a new and for-midable figure the Angevin King of England, Henry II, who arrived in Waterford the same year. When Diarmait Mac Carthaig, King of Desmond submitted to Henry in the city he had once controlled, a new chapter in the history of Waterford and Ireland had begun.

The Viking contribution to Irish history has been described as that of catalyst. They introduced new styles which were to influence craftsmen working with stone, leather, bone, metal and parchment while they in turn were influenced by Irish craftsmen. It was a two way process reflected in the material culture of the Hiberno-Norse towns and in the commissions of leading churchmen and great Gaelic princes. Evidence of Waterford's part in this fusion of cultures was unearthed during the large-scale archaeological excavations carried out from 1986 to 1992. The area excavated constituted about a fifth of the historic Viking settlement and gives an insight into the town when Muirchertach Ua Briain (1086-1114) High King of Ireland, with opposition, was overlord of Waterford.

The interplay of political and cultural influences and Waterford's role in this is very evident in 1096 when under the influence of Muirchertach Ua Briain the christianised inhabitants of Waterford had their first bishop consecrated by Anselm, Archbishop of Canterbury (1093-1109). The archbishop wished to put church reform on the agenda - bringing the Irish church more into line with Rome - and by so doing possibly extend his own influence in Ireland. A reformed Irish church could also work to the advantage of Muirchertach Ua Briain in that an organised and centralised church would give credibility, substance and legitimacy to his claim to the high-kingship of Ireland.[17]

The life and work of Waterford's first bishop Malchus, an Irish monk educated in Winchester and consecrated in Canterbury, illustrates just how the Hiberno-Norse or Viking age towns could be catalysts in the fusion of cultures. The excavations in Waterford revealed the foundations of St Peter's Church, probably begun within a decade of the arrival of Bishop Malchus in 1096. Its dedication to St Peter would have been a conscious effort to reflect the new bonds being forged with Rome.[18] So too was its architecture novel, a tripartite plan type with an English Romanesque-style apse which connects it very firmly to the early twelfth century English Romanesque style tradition. It is the only twelfth century parish church in Ireland with a semi-circular apse.[19] The suggestion by Dr Tadhg O'Keeffe that the church may have had the only known Irish example of a *sacrarium*, a drain to take away the water after the priest had washed the vessels during mass, is particularly interesting for if the feature is so interpreted it may have been influenced by that in St Mary's Church in Winchester where Malchus received his training.[20]

When Malchus arrived a national council gathered, probably in Waterford, in a response to the urgings of Anselm for reform of the church in Ireland. Within five years, Muirchertach Ua Briain would call a second council or synod at Cashel also with the purpose of reforming the Irish church and bringing it closer to Rome. In a very political move, Ua Briain made a grant of Cashel, St Patrick's Rock, to the church. In one fell swoop he gained much prestige for himself and deprived a rival dynasty of their *caput* or headquarters.[21] The most famous of the twelfth century synods was held in Ráith Bressail sometime between 1106 and 1114. By this time, Malchus was now archbishop of Cashel. The Bishop of Lismore attened the council and probably took with him the famous Lismore Crosier (on display in the National Museum of Ireland). It is one of the great examples of twelfth century Irish metalwork - made about 1110 - yet many of the motifs used in the decoration reflect the popularity of the Scandinavian-inspired decoration called the Urnes style. It has been suggested that it was taken to the synod to highlight the independence of Lismore and counter growing rumours that the See of Waterford may have been about to make a takeover bid.[22] At the time the crosier was being crafted, possibly at Lismore, another craftsman some forty miles away in Waterford was busy making the famous Waterford kite brooch, one of the finest pieces of twelfth century Irish secular jewellery to survive. The kite brooch is very much in the native Irish tradition, yet its maker drew on a broad repertoire of Irish, Anglo-Saxon and Scandinavian-inspired designs. (p23) Was the brooch made in Waterford? It very probably was. The discovery during excavations of crucibles for melting precious metals and bone motif-pieces is tangible evidence that goldsmiths were active in the city. Motif-pieces were used by goldsmiths both as practice pieces and as moulds for casting decorative panels. One of the motif-pieces found in Waterford is of similar date to the kite brooch and another, the finest to survive in Waterford, dates from the late eleventh century and shows three patterns, one almost purely Scandinavian and two Hiberno-Norse, reflecting the blend of traditions or more correctly the extent to which the craftsmen based in the Hiberno-Norse towns were absorbed into the Irish metal-work tradition. (p25) Clearly, the Gaelic Irish and Viking traditions borrowed from each other. Although there is no evidence yet of signed pieces of metalwork from the Irish towns, it would be gratifying to think that the Hiberno-Norse craftsmen were held in the same high esteem as their Gaelic counterparts who signed their names to great works like the Lismore crosier. It was only from the time of the Renaissance that artists in mainland Europe signed their works.[23]

As the power of the Uí Briain, who had been so central to church reform movement and the development of new artistic trends, waned, so that of Cormac MacCarthaig rose. Between 1127 and 1134, he commissioned the finest example of Romanesque architecture in Ireland, Cormac's Chapel at St Patrick's Rock in Cashel. The influence of English and German Romanesque styles is very obvious in its architecture. The Scandinavian influence is also present particularly on the sarcophagus that lies within the chapel. It is dated to 1124 and is thought to be the tomb of Tadhg MacCarthaig brother of Cormac.[24] It is widely held that Malchus, first Bishop of Waterford and Archbishop of Cashel until 1135, greatly influenced this building.

The gradual assimilation of the Vikings meant that before the end of the eleventh century they were marrying into the Irish, speaking Norse-Irish and had become Christian. However, the Hiberno-Norse inhabitants of Ireland's first towns continued to play an important role in shaping the destiny of the island as they controlled the centres of international trade which continued to be conduits for new ideas. As the influence of the Scandinavian world was gradually eclipsed, Ireland's English, Welsh and continental trading partners filled the void. The archaeological record shows that for well over a century before the arrival of the Anglo-Normans their influence was becoming apparent in house styles, pottery and other everyday objects. Ireland was subconsciously being brought into the orbit of the Anglo-Norman world. Politics of course would play its part, as would religion, in the final sealing of these loose bonds and so when in 1165 Henry II of England wanted ships to attack the Welsh he borrowed them from Diarmait MacMurchada who supplied them from Dublin. A year later when Diarmait was exiled from Ireland by Ruaidrí Ua Conchobair, the last high-king of Ireland, he would naturally go to Henry II to draw in the favour and allow him recruit mercenaries to recover his kingdom.

It is ironic that the Vikings, founders of Ireland's first towns, with their expertise in naval matters and improved weapons technology, should turn out to act as catalysts for the development of a more centralised Ireland, making it possible for the Anglo-Normans to achieve a foothold over a major part of the island in the decades after 1170.

Kite brooch

The Waterford kite brooch is one of Ireland's finest pieces of late eleventh to early twelfth century secular metalwork, probably commissioned by a layperson and made locally. It is one of the finest of the fourteen kite-shaped brooches found to date in Ireland, most of which are intact, with a few fragmentary. Made of a hollow cast silver box and decorated with sumptuous gold filigree, impressed gold foil, amethyst-coloured *cabochon* (polished without being cut into facets) glass studs and niello (a black compound used in gold and silver work), it was made to close a cloak. It had a long pin on the back a short section of which remains together with the hinge to which it was attached. The brooch was secured by a chain or cord attached to a loose ring at the tip of the head and the free end wound round the protruding end of the pin. It was probably worn with the pin pointing at an oblique angle away from the wearer, either upwards or downwards. Long pins protruding could cause injury to passersby who could under ancient Irish law seek compensation for damage done. Irish law also stipulated that people had to wear brooches appropriate to their status. Similarly between the thirteenth and fifteenth centuries a series of sumptuary laws were enacted throughout Europe that formally restricted the wearing of certain types of clothes and jewellery.

It is a remarkable and well-preserved find from the excavations of Waterford city centre and bears testimony to the wealth and sophistication of the city's inhabitants. It was found in a pit in Peter Street having pre-sumably been lost. In this period secular metalwork was not as highly valued as church plate and much appears to have been melted down once it went out of fashion and the materials reused. To date this kite brooch is the sole really ornate piece of Irish jewellery to survive from the late eleventh to twelfth centuries. However it has many traits in common with contemporary ecclesiastical metalwork, e.g. St Patrick's bellshrine. In its use of low-relief ornament bordered by strips of niello it is also matched by the Lismore crozier group of reliquaries among other objects. Kite brooches are in the native Irish tradition with some English, continental European and Scandinavian influences and the Waterford brooch reflects the Hiberno-Norse town of Waterford. However the design of the kite brooch as a type has no single source. A lozenge-shaped dress fastener has many parallels in both early Christian and Byzantine models. The Virgin in the Virgin and Child page of the Book of Kells wears a lozenge-shaped cloak ornament on one shoulder.

New research is revealing the complexity of the arrangement of the tiny filigree pieces. The goldsmith appears to have selected the designs for the quadrants on the front of the brooch according to a simple numerical plan - a feature that is useful in reconstructing a picture of one of the quadrants where not all the pieces of filigree have survived. Mirror-imaging and other devices were employed by the smith to give the decoration in the front panels a strongly integrated quality. The choice of interlace patterns on the sides of the brooch may have been intended to echo the numerical theme of the front. The Waterford kite brooch weighs 20.6g.

DATE: c1090 A D
NUMBER: E434:3189:5/ WMT1999.0488
DIMENSIONS: brooch L 39 x W 27 x D 6
incomplete pin L 26.5
MATERIAL: gold, silver, niello, glass
PROVENANCE: Waterford excavations
FURTHER READING: Niamh Whitfield in Hurley & Scully 1997
Ó Floinn 1987
Brennan forthcoming

Ringed pin (A)

This pin is possibly the earliest pin recovered to date in Waterford. The polyhedral (faceted) head is socketed to accommodate the ring. Every facet of the head is decorated with an overall punched dot design, with a front panel divided into four diamonds, two of which are engraved in a cross-hatched motif. Ringed and plain stick pins were produced by hammer in great quantities. They were used to fasten cloaks throughout the Viking and medieval period with the point of the pin facing upwards, to avoid personal injury. They are attributed to the native Irish tradition and seem to have become very popular with the Vikings. In the main Waterford excavations alone, 232 plain stick pins were found. In one instance a cache of seventeen pins, of several varieties, was found rolled in a cloth, suggesting they were the property of either a tradesman or a pedlar. They are classified by the shape of the head, e.g. watch-winder, club, zoomorphic etc. The ringed pins are sometimes found with braided cord attached, to loop over the point as a precaution from loss. This ringed pin was found amongst crushed oyster and mussel shell in the humic back-fill of an early ditch, not far to the west of Reginald's tower. The ditch is associated with the enclosing of Dundory, the earliest fortified part of the city. A similar ringed pin was found at L'Anse aux Meadows, Newfoundland (Canada), settled temporarily by the Vikings in 1100.

Orla Scully

DATE: 10th/11th century
NUMBER: 99E0103:219:1 / WMT1999.0340
DIMENSIONS: overall L 99, ring 13 x 11, head 5 x 6.5 x 7
MATERIAL: copper alloy
PROVENANCE: archaeological excavations at Bailey's New Street
FURTHER READING: Fanning 1994
LOCATION: Reginald's Tower

Motif piece (B)

Motif pieces were primarily practice pieces by metalworkers or their apprentices in advance of casting. This almost complete motif piece, made from a longbone, is the most interesting of the four pieces found in the Waterford excavations because of its complex decorations: six, evenly-worked and deeply-carved animal interlaces, one geometric interlace and some unfinished designs. The same hand probably did all. This piece is a mixture of late eleventh/early twelfth century Hiberno-Norse and native Irish work, with strong south-east English Anglo-Scandinavian and native Scandinavian elements. The animal motifs are Irish-Viking and Scandinavian types, and are paralleled on motif pieces found in Viking Dublin and on the shrine of the Cathach, the bell shrines of St Patrick and St Seanan, the Clonmacnoise and Lismore croziers, and two Irish manu-scripts, all late eleventh/early twelfth century.

DATE: c1090 A D
NUMBER: E527:1614:4 / WMT1999.0151
DIMENSIONS: L 125 x W 26
MATERIAL: skeletal material
PROVENANCE: Waterford excavations
FURTHER READING: Uaininn O'Meadhra in Hurley & Scully 1997
                  O'Meadhra 1979 & 1987

Ring mould (C)

This mould for making three sizes of ring is expertly made: the two-pieces were laid together, wooden pegs inserted in the corner holes and bands put around the mould to stabilise it, stone pegs put in the central holes and the molten metal poured in through the three pouring grooves and the metal left to harden into D-shaped rings. When not in use wooden pegs were put in the central holes to prevent any rubbing. The finding of the mould suggests a degree of mass production because of its reusability. Other media, such as clay and shell could have been used only once. Three sizes (internal diameter 19, 16.5 and 15 mm) may indicate that the rings were cast in base metals. Unlike precious metals which can have pieces added, rings cast in base metals cannot be altered.

DATE: c1150 A D
NUMBER: E343:5394:111 / WMT1999.0161
DIMENSIONS: L 83 x W 75 x overall Th 42
MATERIAL: sandstone
PROVENANCE: Waterford excavations
FURTHER READING: Sarah McCutcheon & Jannes Helmholt in
                  Hurley & Scully 1997

Crucible (D)

This crucible, one of six imported from southeast Wiltshire in England, for melting metal, is further evidence of the presence of fine metalworkers in Waterford. The crucibles are all unglazed small, round or flat-bottom vessels with simple pulled spouts. Some crucibles had the remains of burnt metal attached. Pottery from Wiltshire found in Waterford dates from the late eleventh to the twelfth century, indicating a concentration of trade with that area of England almost a century before the Anglo-Norman invasion of 1170. From the thirteenth century on there is less found, reflecting increased trade with continental Europe, especially France and the Low Countries and also showing increased local production of pottery.

DATE: c1140 A D
NUMBER: E343:5404:1 / WMT1999.0013
DIMENSIONS: Dia 75
MATERIAL: pottery
PROVENANCE: Waterford excavations
FURTHER READING: Audrey Gahan & Clare McCutcheon in
                  Hurley & Scully 1997

Combs

These are the two most complete combs of the total of eighty-one found in the excavations, mostly twelfth and thirteenth century. All are of antler except three of horn, wood and bone. On the evidence of the excavations, the working of skeletal material, antler, bone and some horn, was a highly specialised craft with combs being the main product. 704 objects in all of skeletal material were excavated. Concentrations of waste antler prove the abundance of the raw material and production in Waterford. Antler combs were the work of expert craftspeople who with their skills and tools, could use the raw material to the full. Other objects such as the gaming pieces, which were probably made from spongy antler discarded as unworkable for combs, needed other tools. Antler was also used for musical instrument and crossbow parts. Both the use of specialised tools and the precise nature of the craft suggest a professional industry, not a domestic craft.

The antler is of red deer, native to Ireland in the Hiberno-Norse and medieval periods. As venison did not figure largely in the diet of Waterford in the twelfth century, the shed antler may have been collected in the hinterland and bartered with the urban craftspeople. However it may have been collected by the craftspeople themselves. The combs were assembled in the following way: rectangles of antler (later to be the teeth) were fashioned and laid side by side, then two pieces of antler were placed front and back, the length of all the parts, keeping the entire comb together when riveted. Finally the teeth were cut by saw.

Both these combs are mid-twelfth century, have very fine teeth, and are undecorated but highly polished. The top one is composed of sixteen separate pieces with eleven rivets, the other of eighteen with twelve rivets. The fine teeth suggest that lice were a problem for the inhabitants of the town. Quantities of twelfth century antler waste were found in the ditch that formed part of the town defences but outside the town wall itself. Waste antler was also found both in and close to houses in Peter Street suggesting that workshops were located there.

DATE:	c1150 A D
NUMBER:	E343:5375:34 / WMT1999.0056 &
	E343:5369:62 / WMT1999.0057
DIMENSIONS:	(top) L 211 x Th 8 x D 15
	& (bottom) L 203 mm x Th 8.5 x 14.5 D
MATERIAL:	antler
PROVENANCE:	Waterford excavations
FURTHER READING:	Maurice Hurley in Hurley & Scully 1997

Dog collar

This dog collar, an open-work band of copper alloy, is a very rare find from the city excavations. Backed by leather or velvet - attached to the metal through six small holes - it was an elaborate collar probably for a greyhound, the most popular dog in the hunting field. The missing section would have had the fastening, the leash ring and some sort of frontal ornament. The collar of that breed had the same value as a horse-saddle in early Welsh law. The dogs depicted on the Bayeux tapestry all wear collars. This may have been imported prior to the Anglo-Norman invasion, attesting to the wealth and sophistication of Waterford.

DATE:	12th century
NUMBER:	WMT1999.0498
DIMENSIONS:	Dia 122
MATERIAL:	copper alloy
PROVENANCE:	Waterford excavations
FURTHER READING:	H E J Le Patourel in Hurley & Scully 1997

Die (A)

The context in which this die was found makes it difficult to date. The numbers are shown by a dot-in-double-circle motif, regularly distributed. Dice, particularly in the twelfth to fourteenth centuries generally read 1 opposite 2, 3 opposite 4, 5 opposite 6, the arrangement here. This is different from Roman, early Christian and modern forms where opposite sides add up to seven. Comparable examples are known from Dublin and Cork and many from Winchester.

DATE: possibly 12th century
NUMBER: E343:2280:7 / WMT1999.0114
DIMENSIONS: 6.1 x 6.7
MATERIAL: skeletal material
PROVENANCE: Waterford excavations
FURTHER READING: M Hurley in Hurley & Scully 1997

Gaming piece (B)

The production of gaming pieces is probably a by-product of comb-making in Viking age Ireland. A central hole suggests that the piece was strung or stacked on a spike when not in use. It is decorated with three concentric circles with four dot-in-circle motifs and is polished. These disc pieces were sawn from antler shafts and were not produced on a lathe. Similar pieces have been found in several locations in Ireland and in Britain. Eleven antler gaming pieces in all and a die were found in Waterford. Objects like this help us to build up the picture of social life in a late Viking age town in Ireland.

DATE: c1150 A D
NUMBER: E527:377:6 / WMT1999.0109
DIMENSIONS: Dia 44 x Th 9
MATERIAL: antler
PROVENANCE: Waterford excavations
FURTHER READING: M Hurley in Hurley & Scully 1997

Piriform gaming piece (C)

This elegant piece, onion-shaped and tapering to a slim neck and head, was made on a lathe. Similar pieces are known from Viking settlements at Dublin, Cork and Jarlshof, Shetland.

DATE: c1180 A D
NUMBER: E434:3001:1 / WMT1999. 0107
DIMENSIONS: L 27.3 x max D 14.5 mm
MATERIAL: antler
PROVENANCE: Waterford excavations
FURTHER READING: M Hurley in Hurley & Scully 1997

Gaming piece (D)

This is probably a chess piece representing a knight and is an early indication of chess playing in Waterford. Round in section with a flat base, the top is rounded at the back, the front remains very straight. A small head is expertly carved on the front and the whole piece is further decorated with pairs of incised lines that cross as Xs on the sides. The piece is partly burned.

DATE: c1120 A D
NUMBER: E639:62:1 / WMT1999.0224
DIMENSIONS: L 38 x max D 19 mm
MATERIAL: yew
PROVENANCE: Waterford excavations
FURTHER READING: M Hurley & S McCutcheon in Hurley & Scully 1997

Kingpin (E)

This gaming piece now flat backed was originally carved in the round. The carving is of a face with ears and long beard; the lower half of the shaft is pared to peg into a gaming board.

DATE: c1120 A D
NUMBER: E639:62:34 / WMT1999.0221
DIMENSIONS: L 101
MATERIAL: yew
PROVENANCE: Waterford excavations
FURTHER READING: M Hurley & S McCutcheon in Hurley & Scully 1997

Mould (F)

This mould was found in 1996 in Belview on the north shore of the river Suir where the modern port of Waterford lies. It is carved to make two circular metal pieces possibly gaming counters, one highly decorated. A third circle is scratched on. It was probably lost from a ship.

DATE: possibly 12th / 13th century
NUMBER: WMT1999.1609
DIMENSIONS: L 950
MATERIAL: stone
PROVENANCE: found in river Suir

Hnefatafl gaming piece (G)

This dome-shaped gaming piece for the game of hnefatafl, one of five found in Waterford, was probably made on a lathe and is decorated with four sets of incised lines around the edge. This piece would have pegged into a gaming board similar to the one featured here. This type of gaming piece is a product of Viking cultural influence. Similar pieces have been found in Dublin.

DATE: c 1130 A D
NUMBER: E434:3087:1 / WMT1999. 0103
DIMENSIONS: L 30 x max D 36 mm, peg L 63 x D 7.5
MATERIAL: antler
PROVENANCE: Waterford excavations
FURTHER READING: M Hurley in Hurley & Scully 1997

Gaming board (H)

The undecorated board, a rare find, has a perforated wedge handle (for hanging) and a raised edge around a surface of seven holes by seven holes. It is similar to the Ballinderry, Co. Offaly gaming board although plainer and was probably used for the same game - hnefatafl - a common pastime in Viking times. Several of the gaming pieces found in Waterford could have pegged into this board.

DATE: c1150 A D
NUMBER: E527:1429:2 /WMT1999.0232
DIMENSIONS: overall L 165 x W 130
MATERIAL: oak
PROVENANCE: Waterford excavations
FURTHER READING: M Hurley & S McCutcheon in Hurley & Scully 1997

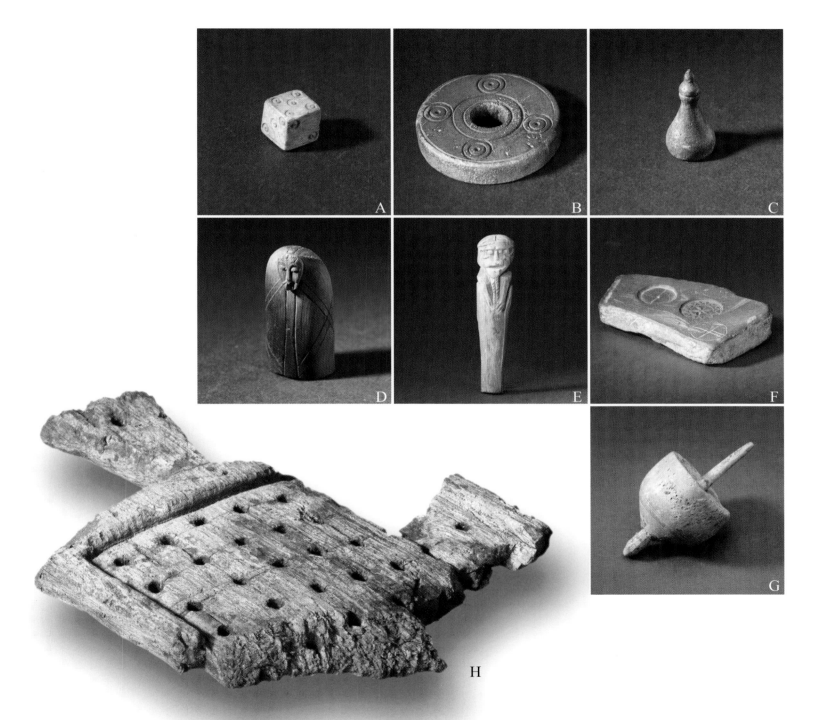

Relic of the True Cross

The relic, in the form of a double-armed or Archiepiscopal cross, consists of five pieces of wood, identified as cedar. It is held within a frame of sheet silver which shows evidence of repair. On the back, a Latin inscription in Lombardic capitals identifies the relic as the wood of the True Cross : + LIGNVM DE VERA [CR]UCE.

The exposed wood is plain except for a few silver nails which do not form a regular pattern. Small slivers have been removed from the base, no doubt to be used as relics in their own right. The relic is set in a hinged casing of silver and bronze in the form of a lancet window. This has a wooden core, hollowed in the front and lined with velvet to take the relic. The casing is fitted at the top with a loop and chain for suspension. The front is open and is now set with a piece of modern glass through which the relic can be viewed. Around the edge and along the base is a Latin inscription which reads ISTA PARTICULA LIGNI SACRATISSIME CRUCIS PERTINET AD ECCLESIAM CATHEDRALEM SANCTIS-SIME TRINITATIS WATERFORDIE IHS MARIE 1620. 'This piece of the wood of the Most Holy Cross belongs to the Cathedral Church of the Most Holy Trinity Waterford. Jesus Mary 1620.

The double-armed cross would originally have been set in an elaborate mounting, perhaps in the shape of a jewelled cross or a hinged rectangular jewelled plaque; the silver and bronze casing of 1620 is clearly a later replacement. The Lombardic inscription can be dated to the twelfth century and may thus lend some credence to the tradition that the relic was a gift to the Cathedral by Muirchertach Ua Briain, king of Munster who had received it around 1110 from Pope Paschal II. The Relic of the True Cross preserved at Holy Cross Abbey, county Tipperary has a similar history and is very close in shape and size. Relics of the True Cross were, however, usually acquired in the Holy Land and were brought to the West either as spoils of the Crusades or as gifts from the Byzantine emperors. We know that the portion of the True Cross enclosed in the Cross of Cong was part of a relic which was on circuit in Ireland in 1123 and perhaps the Waterford relic was part of this also. The Cathedral, established in 1096, would have been anxious to acquire relics and none would have been more important than that of the True Cross.

In the early eighteenth century, the Relic was entrusted to the Aylward family of Cross, county Waterford by Bishop Richard Pierse. In 1840 it passed into the hands of Joseph Murphy, a member of the Christian Brothers of Mount Sion, Waterford and was restored to Waterford Cathedral in the 1930s.

Raghnall Ó Floinn

DATE: 12th century, 1620 A D
NUMBER: WMT1999.1736
DIMENSIONS: relic L 127 x W 45, shrine L 220 x W 60
MATERIAL: cedar, silver, bronze, velvet, glass
PROVENANCE: The medieval Christ Church Cathedral Waterford
FURTHER READING: Power 1938
                      Olden 1993
                      Ó Floinn 1994

On loan from the Bishop of Waterford and Lismore

Archery material

The collection of excavated archery material dates from both Viking and Anglo-Norman times and is uniquely comprehensive. Archery was not practised by the Gaelic Irish at least for military purposes but was by the Vikings. A twelfth century account of the Battle of Clontarf talks of the Vikings' 'sharp, swift, barbed, murderous, poisoned arrows' and their 'polished, yellow-shining bows'. Archery, using both longbow and crossbow, was very important in the Anglo-Norman armies, vividly described by Gerald of Wales in his account of the invasion of Ireland. Archers comprised some eighty five per cent of the Anglo-Norman armies that came to Ireland and were undoubtedly significant in assaults such as Strongbow's on Waterford in 1170. The thirteenth century poem on the walling of New Ross states: 'the townspeople have plenty of good crossbow men and for hand bows plenty of good archers. Never in any town where I have been did I see so many good sheaves of arrows, so many crossbows hanging on the walls or so many bolts ready for use'. The poem further states that the town could muster 363 crossbowmen and 1200 other archers. In later centuries the Anglo-Irish government encouraged the development of a class of yeoman archers on the English model; this was generally ineffective outside the Pale, but probably had some impact in towns such as Waterford. Henry VII, in 1486-87 made a grant for the purchase of 200 bows, 400 sheaves of arrows (a sheaf contained twenty-four arrows) and 400 bowstrings for the defence of Waterford. A street in Waterford still called Shortcourse was the location of one of the medieval town's butts for archery practice.

One complete bow and six incomplete were found in Waterford, all of yew. The complete bow is one of the few surviving in Britain or Ireland and was probably made from a thirty-year-old tree. The nocks (notches where the string is attached at each end) on all the Waterford bows are cut into the stave rather than being separate pieces. The nocks of the complete bow are on opposite sides of the stave.

Some of the arrowheads are probably those that hit the defences of Waterford in the sieges of 1137 and 1170. Of the fifty iron arrowheads found, some are damaged where they impacted. The collection includes arrowheads of two main types: flat, broad triangular blades some of which are barbed for maximum injury when trying to extract them, and spike-like blades specifically designed to penetrate mail armour. The tanged spike-like blade arrowheads (called bodkin) are a Hiberno-Norse type and the socketed arrowheads were used both by the Hiberno-Norse and the Anglo-Normans. The bodkin arrowheads account for seventy per cent of the total and are proof of the use of body armour by the Hiberno-Norse. Five longer arrowheads, one illustrated here, belong to missiles fired by a crossbow or by larger ballistic machines. The arrowshaft, of yew, a very rare survival, was found with its arrowhead. The nut (the mechanism which controlled the string release) is evidence for the use of the crossbow; being of antler it is the most likely piece to survive. This is of typical medieval form and is almost identical to a thirteenth century one found in Winchester, England. The silk cord, found near one of the bows, may have been a bowstring. It is a tubular cord, very firm and strong, woven by tablet-weaving and is 1.177 m long. A thin string is better for long distance shooting but demands great mastery.

DATE:	bow:	c1220 A D
	arrowheads:	range from early 12th to early 13th century (one is 15th century)
	arrowshaft:	c1200 A D
	crossbow nut:	c1220 A D
	cord:	12th/13th century
NUMBER:	bow:	E406:2092:408 / WMT1999.0539
	arrowheads:	E343:5375:19 / WMT1999.0514
		E527:1339:14 / WMT1999.0515
		E434:3069:13 / WMT1999.0517
		E343:5374:61 / WMT1999.1578
		E527:1484:1 / WMT1999.1580
		E435:1161:32 / WMT1999.1676
		E435:1163:24 / WMT1999.1582
		E435:1113:17 / WMT1999.0513
		E435:1160:9 / WMT1999.1583
		E435:1160:8 / WMT1999.1584
		E343:5369:61 / WMT1999.1581
		E520:181:1 / WMT1999.0506
		E527:281:14 / WMT1999.0510
	shaft:	E343:5266:32 / WMT1999.0540
	crossbow nut:	E434:177:100 / WMT1999.0116
	cord:	E343:5368:285 / WMT1999. 1585
DIMENSIONS:	bow:	L 1258 x max W 24.5 x max Th 16.6 arrowheads: range from L 53 to 84; L of missile head 217
	shaft:	L 282 x D 9
	crossbow nut:	D 33.5 x Th 23 with a central perforation D 5
	cord:	L 1177
MATERIAL:		yew, iron, antler, silk
PROVENANCE:		Waterford excavations
FURTHER READING:		Andrew Halpin in Hurley & Scully 1997

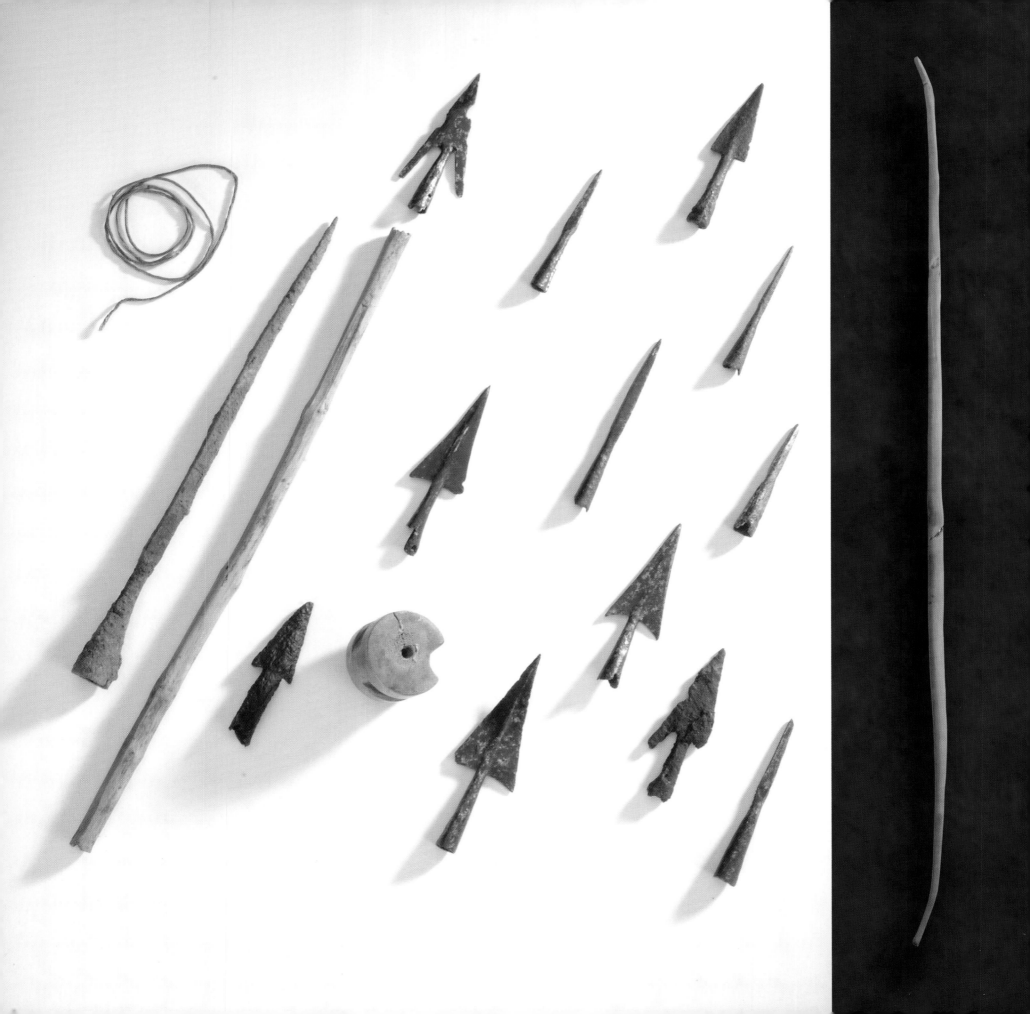

ANGLO-NORMAN
WATERFORD

As the influence of the Vikings waned and the descendants of those who had settled beyond their Scandinavian ancestral homelands were gradually assimilated into the local population, new forces began to exert themselves in Europe. In 1066 William the Conqueror, the French-speaking descendant of the Vikings who had settled in Northern France, invaded England and established his Anglo-Norman kingdom there. The conquest of England marked the beginning of two centuries of unprecedented European expansion. To the south the Muslims were forced back by a combination of crusading armies and Italian naval power. East of the Elbe there emerged a constellation of new states extending almost up to the Urals, while the Baltic became the northern counterpart of the Mediterranean under the impact of German colonisation and its attendant urban development. Spain, Portugal and the 'Celtic fringe' represented the western extreme of this centrifugal movement of European trade and colonisation.

Ireland's involvement in this great outward expansion began with the fall of Waterford to the Anglo-Normans in 1170. Their arrival heralded a century of extraordinary economic, institutional, intellectual and political enterprise. About two thirds of Ireland became part of the Angevin Empire which brought it closer not just to England but also to France. This empire was a federation of feudal lordships owing allegiance to a common lord (the king of England) who exercised varying degrees of control over an area extending from Antrim to the Pyrenees. Thus John governed England as king, Normandy as duke, Anjou as count and Ireland as lord - *Dominus Hiberniae*.

In Ireland, as elsewhere within this Empire, the aristocracy provided the initial mainstay of the colony, but what gave it permanence was the subsidiary influx of tenants and townsmen who responded - as they did elsewhere in Europe - to the opportunities of the frontier. Without them the widespread network of manors, towns and villages - so characteristic of the new Europe -

could never have been established or would ever have flourished.[1] Waterford was now part of a mini-common market, its primary function to export the rich harvest of the hinterland and the import of luxuries and necessities such as wine, salt and iron.

The city's economic success was built upon the introduction of the feudal system which revolutionised Irish agriculture. Within decades of the invasion vast surpluses were being produced on the manors and exported through ports such as Waterford, the revenues in turn paying for imports. Of course Waterford also had a number of geographical advantages, being the closest port to continental Europe and convenient to Bristol, one of the most important ports in medieval England. A 1339 Italian map shows many ports along Ireland's coast but only one harbour and river system - Waterford harbour with the Suir and Barrow, is indicated by a large flag.[2] The three rivers that flow into Waterford harbour, the Barrow, Nore and Suir, drain a fifth of the landmass of Ireland and, in an era when transport by water was the only cost-effective option, they acted as highways linking the city to its hinterland.

Nature's bounty was not enough to make the port a success however; it also required institutional infrastructure and personnel with knowledge, drive and ambition to push it forward. King Henry II (1154-1189) laid the solid foundations for much of the governmental infrastructural arrangements by making Waterford part of the royal demesne, in other words, it was owned by the king and not one of his vassals. Though always fearful of creating new power bases within their dominions, medieval kings in general were supporters of towns. They granted charters which effectively transferred control of the internal affairs of the city to a ruling oligarchy of wealthy merchants.[3] In some ways these charters were instruments of deregulation, placing the administration of the town in the hands of the merchants who would keep trade and commerce on the top of the agenda, thus reducing central government interference. There were of course ample checks and balances built into the system to ensure the king did not lose control and that he benefited financially from the process.

The 1215 charter of King John (1199-1216), the oldest charter to survive, saw elected representatives of the merchant class gain control of the city courts. (p63) The 1232 charter of King Henry III (1216-1272) gave the city the right to pay the rents due to the king as a fixed sum of one hundred marks, the second highest rent paid by an Irish city and proof of Waterford's standing within the Irish urban hierarchy.[4] (p65) This charter excluded central government rent collectors from the city and passed on the responsibility initially to the city officials and by 1272 to an elected mayor. The right to elect a mayor marks a high-point in the development of medieval civic government and the survival of the office to the present is a testament to the success of the institution. By the end of the thirteenth century the mayor was personally responsible for the debts of the city for which he accounted yearly at the Exchequer.[5] The payment was recorded on receipt rolls and, as an independent check, on a tallystick. (p47)

Besides giving Waterford the governmental structures to encourage trade, the Angevin kings also created monopolies to ensure the prosperity of their port cities. Waterford's claim that all foreign ships entering Waterford harbour must dock at Waterford and not at the newly-established port of New Ross (established by William Marshall, Strongbow's son-in-law in about 1210) was upheld by successive monarchs. Marshall also built the Hook lighthouse, the oldest in the British Isles to guide ships safely to his port. Yet by law only ships from the lordship of Leinster could unload at New Ross. The monopoly led to much tension, a legal dispute which lasted over four hundred years and the compilation of the Great Charter Roll.[6] (p59) The monarch also limited the import of wine to specific ports, Waterford being among the lucky few to be designated, and in 1232 the king conferred on the city the added bonus of having to pay only half the tax required of other ports. The customs

returns on wine which survive for much of the mid-thirteenth century consistently show Waterford asIreland's largest importer of wine.[7] A by-product of the trade was the importation of beautiful wine jugs gracing many a thirteenth century Waterford table and providing a tangible link to the city's position as the medieval wine capital of Ireland. (p49, 51, 53)

The king could encourage international trade in other ways: in 1204 King John allowed Waterford to hold an annual fair during the first eight days of August, his grandson Edward I later extending the period by a further eight days. The grant of an annual fair was a special privilege intended to attract foreign merchants as those who travelled to and from them were under the king's pro-tection. By the terms of Waterford's thirteenth century Borough Customs, the mayor presided over the fair, wit-nessed agreements and reimbursed out of local funds any foreign merchant defaulted by a local.[8] The Borough Customs were given even greater status by Edward I when in 1285 he decreed that the Statute of Merchants was to be applicable in Ireland. Under the statute, special seals were used to certify contracts and a central government official was appointed to oversee the process. However, not all attempts by the king to create a single market within his empire were appreciated locally. In 1280 Edward intro-duced regulations standardising the weights and measures used in both Ireland and England. In 1300 a government official was sent from England to assess the measures in use. The mayor of Waterford at that time, Ralph de Hampton, together with the mayors of the chief cities of Ireland, presented the official on his arrival with gifts in the hope that 'he would not charge them falsely with hav-ing improper measures'. The official took the gifts and then proceeded to fine the mayors for using incorrect weights in breach of the 1280 regulation.[9]

The availability of an accepted currency was a pre-requisite for the promotion of international trade and provided an opportunity for extending this concept of a common market within the king's dominions. King John established a mint, probably in Reginald's Tower, in 1195-6. In 1204 when he established the fair in Waterford he also undertook a major reform of Anglo-Irish coinage and re-opened the Dublin mint. By this time the Waterford mint had been closed, however in 1210 he re-established the mint in Waterford. (p47) It was incumbent on the keeper of the mint to protect the value of the coin by ensuring that it was the correct weight. Coins were valued, not on their face value, but on their bullion content. Because the weight of the coin was critical, coin balances were used to verify the weight. A very rare coin balance dating from the twelfth century, found during the city centre excavations, is a potent link with John's initiatives. (p47) So popular was John's coinage on the continent that a whole generation later they were subject to imitation in Germany, an area well outside the king's control.[10] This is perhaps the highest tribute that could be paid to the quality of the coins. In 1281 Edward I re-opened the mints in Dublin and Waterford. The keeper of the Waterford mint was Mayor Roger de Lom. The metallic content and weight of these coins were equivalent to coins issued in England. The Waterford mint closed in 1282 but reopened in 1294, the keeper almost certainly Roger the Goldsmith, a local official.[11] (p47)

Royal patronage and bureaucratic refinements certainly helped Waterford but in the end the king depended on the merchant class to deliver. Finding markets for the produce of the hinterland was facilitated by the influx of merchants from both within and without the king's dominions. Merchant traders and craftsmen from Wales, England, France, the Low Countries and Italy settled in Waterford. In time a new merchant oligarchy emerged as each merchant brought with him an intimate knowledge of and contact with his own town or area of origin. This access to overseas markets generated the wealth to purchase, perhaps for the first time in Irish history, consistently large amounts of foreign goods. We know the names of many of the leading late thirteenth century Waterford merchants. They include Englishmen like Roger de Lom from Bristol, Ralph de Hampton and

Jordan de Bristol, all mayors, and Nicholas de Portsmouth, a customs collector. Frenchmen also rose to prominence - Eymar de Godar, described as a merchant of Gascony, was four times mayor of Waterford. Richard de Barry, an official for many years, was finally elected mayor late in life in 1319. Italians such as Servasius Copale, a customs official working on behalf of the city, also feature. Most of these individuals were newly arrived in Waterford showing that well over a century after the conquest of Ireland the 'Anglo-Norman tiger' was still attracting enterprising merchants from abroad.[12]

Medieval monarchs promoted towns and trade because they provided much needed revenue through taxation and in particular the merchant class and their activities could provide ready cash as opposed to payment in kind such as knight's service or other military aid. In 1275 Edward I introduced the Great New Custom, a tax on the export of wool and hides, used to service huge loans he had received from Italian bankers to finance his wars against the Scots.[13] Edward was the first monarch to engage in winter campaigns, an expensive business that in the end almost led to the bankruptcy of the Irish Lordship. The collection of the Great New Custom was supervised by locally elected officials and a representative of the Italian bankers who had bank-rolled Edward's extravagant wars. As most of the Italian tax collectors came from Lombardy in Northern Italy they were referred to locally as 'Lombards', an attribution which in time became a surname. Between 1371 and 1569 twelve men by the name of Lombard were mayors of Waterford and one of the great figures of the Counter-Reformation movement was the Waterford-born Peter Lombard (1554-1625), Archbishop of Armagh. The family name is still preserved in Lombard's Marsh and Lombard's Street in Waterford.[14]

The importance of Waterford's wool and hide trade is attested to in the documents of the period which record the Great New Custom. The figures show that by 1290 Waterford and New Ross were neck and neck in terms of quantities exported. However their combined exports were greater than Dublin and the other eight ports in the colony put together. At this time the revenue generated for the king from the Great New Custom was equivalent to one fifth of the total revenues of the colony.[15] The popularity of the wool trade was revealed in the city centre excavations when numerous examples of the tools associated with the trade were uncovered. One of the most interesting pieces unearthed is a thirteenth century lead seal matrix probably the property of an artisan, very likely a weaver. It has what appears to be an abbreviation of the name Gavin Comerford emblazoned on it and was possibly used by the weaver when making agreements with a merchant. (p45) In 1448 Waterford had a mayor by the name of Comerford and indeed the family was involved in the government of the city until the end of the middle ages.

Taxing trade helped the king raise revenue for the defence of the realm and on a local level this included the defence of the city itself. Both kings Henry III and Edward I made murage grants to the city specifically for the building and repair of its defences. Such grants allowed the authorities to collect specific taxes on a named range of goods entering the city; the revenue collected was used to enclose the city with walls and towers. By the end of the thirteenth century Waterford was, like most cities in Europe, surrounded by walls. The quays and harbour were defended by the city's own ships built by order of King Henry III for 'the defence of the realm'. One ship was requested in 1222 and a further two in 1241. Did the three ships on the city arms originate here? The Waterford ships were probably among the twenty three ships carrying nearly six hundred horses from Waterford to Milford Haven for the war against the Welsh in June 1256.[16]

The middle ages was also an age of faith - all the charters begin with the king's name preceded by the words *Deo gratia* - by the grace of God, King of England, Lord of Ireland - but an even more potent reminder of this is to be found in the streets of Waterford. The ruins of the twelfth and thirteenth century churches and monasteries evoke the spirit of this great age of devotion. King John endowed and founded the Leper Hospital of St Stephen in the late twelfth century as well as the Benedictine Priory of St John the Evangelist, originally outside but enclosed by the town wall at the end of the middle ages. He also endowed Christ Church Cathedral, paving the way for the construction of the magnificent gothic structure begun about 1210, the same year he visited the city.[17] In 1226 his son Henry III gave permission to build the Dominican Priory on a vacant site, close to Arundel Square, where stood formerly an ancient tower presumably part of the Hiberno-Norse defences.[18] Henry also gave an annual allowance to buy tunics to the Franciscans of Waterford. The arrival of the Franciscans and Dominicans in the city within a few years of the founding of the orders illustrates that Waterford was very much part of the new religious movements sweeping Europe in the thirteenth century. The two new orders were essentially urban, the intellectual Dominicans educating the sons of the merchant class while the Franciscans ministered to the needs of the poor urban dwellers.

All of these churches were repositories of great art treasures: paintings, plate, reliquaries, bells, statues and vestments. At the time of the Reformation while many of these local church treasures were destroyed, some survived, either because they were well hidden or preserved in the safety of the almshouse established in part of the dissolved Francisan Friary. (p125) Other religious treasures have been found by archaeologists including a decorated ecclesiastical knife, translucent amber prayer beads and badges brought back as souvenirs by pilgrims. (p55, 57) Trade encouraged people to go on pilgrimage; it also encouraged sculpture and fine stonework in churches. There is plenty of evidence in the churches of Waterford, notably the cathedral, of the import of Dundry stone, from near Bristol, for such work. This stone was used as ballast in ships on their return voyage, having embarked from Waterford earlier loaded with the agricultural produce of the south-east.

Much evidence remains today in the streets of Waterford, its churches and defences, as well as in the city's museum, to suggest that the thirteenth century was a golden age. Symbolically it is best represented in the archaeological record by the ring brooch, probably the oldest gold ring brooch in Europe. (p43) The gold stirrup ring and the meticulous detail on the belt mount are reminiscent of thirteenth century fashion accessories, linking the wearer to the concept of courtly love. They suggest an affluent society with an eye for the finer things in life.

Unfortunately for Waterford the sophisticated system of both local and central government developed by the Anglo-Normans during the thirteenth century was a contributory factor in the decline of the Anglo-Norman Lordship. Edward burdened the colony with heavy taxation which he spent on provisions then transported to Scotland in merchants' ships arrested for that purpose.[19] Developed and organised cities like Waterford were central to this exploitation because much of the work of provisioning the army was carried out by locally elected officials. For a time, no doubt, the king's demands saw prices rise and individual fortunes made. But eventually it disrupted trade and because the revenue was diverted away from the Dublin administration it was unable to react effectively when the Gaelic princes began to re-assert themselves.[20]

When Edward I died in 1307 he had defeated the Scots but at the price of leaving the Irish colony vulnerable. Edward I was succeeded by his son, Edward II (1307-1327), whose reign was plagued by court intrigue and civil war. Robert Bruce, King of Scotland, won major victories against the English and his brother Edward Bruce invaded Ireland winning the support of many of the Gaelic princes and several Anglo-Norman lords. Although the Bruce invasion failed to re-instate the Gaelic princes, it was nonetheless a major boost to them as they continued to make gains at the expense of the Anglo-Normans. The

problems of the colony were compounded when the Anglo-Normans married into and allied with ruling Gaelic families. Gradually during the fourteenth century the descendants of the Anglo-Normans became 'more Irish then the Irish themselves'. Waterford city tried not to become embroiled in the complex series of alliances and feuds that usually involved a mixture of both Gaelic Irish and Anglo-Norman interests.

The Bruce invasion of 1315 had highlighted the vulnerability of the Dublin administration. Lack of finance led to a change of emphasis in the government of the Lordship, as central government began to rely more and more on the local magnates to keep the peace. In theory this was a good idea because the magnates were powerful locally and it was in their best interests to keep law and order. However, rivalry between Anglo-Norman families, their gradual gaelicisation and their military and marriage alliances with the Gaelic princes all combined to ensure that they could not be relied upon. Peace existed when it suited the local lords and wars were fought not to protect the king's territory but because they promoted local political ambitions. In east county Waterford the Power family of Dunhill, the principal Anglo-Norman authority during the fourteenth century became involved in all manner of disputes and alliances which were to have disastrous consequences for Waterford city. The late 1320s saw the Munster area plunged into political and economic turmoil reflected in the following lines penned by an anonymous contemporary poet:
'Young men of Waterford learn how to fight for your ploughshares are being carried off. Burnish your weapons that have long been unused, and defend yourself against the Powers who are patrolling the roads.'[21]

The accession of Edward III (1327-1377) saw little improvement and in fact the Powers destroyed the countryside around the city in 1345. Four years later a more deadly enemy appeared, the Black Death, killing at least a third of Waterford's population. The sharp decline in population all across Europe as a result of the plague saw a corresponding fall in the demand for imported goods; this was particularly catastrophic for Waterford which was so dependent on its overseas markets. However the resilient merchant class went out and sought fresh opportunities, establishing branches of their export business in English ports, from where it would be easier to find markets in Europe. In 1368 the city was again attacked by the Powers, this time allied to a Gaelic family, the O'Driscolls of Baltimore, county Cork. John Malpas, a merchant with extensive trading interests in Bristol was Waterford's mayor at the time. The situation called for more than business acumen; however the central government was unable to help and the unfortunate Malpas was killed in the ensuing battle along with 'twenty six of the better men as well as eighty men of England, Coventry, Bristol, Dartmouth and other ports'.[22] Six weeks later the enemy was back at the gates of the city but this time the city was victorious.

The 1370s saw no respite for the city. Against a background of contracting markets, declining trade and government inability to enforce the king's peace, the equally hard-pressed burgesses of New Ross had their lord demand an enquiry into the hotly-contested monopoly claimed by Waterford over all ships entering Waterford harbour. Times were extremely tough and the city pulled out all the stops in its efforts to have the monopoly confirmed by the king. To this end it assembled one of the great treasures of the fourteenth century, the Great Charter Roll, a compilation of charters and other documents dating from 1215, together with seventeen illustrations of kings of England and governors of Ireland. (p61, 79) The roll illustrates vividly how the citizens of Waterford viewed themselves - very much linked to the English crown. As merchants engaged in overseas trade it would be surprising if they perceived themselves any differently; they traded with territories controlled by the crown, they used crown courts to gain redress if debtors defaulted, they expected the king to provide them with protection on the seas from piracy and of course, as subjects of the king, they were exempt from taxes paid by foreign merchants.

Many also received licences from the king to operate out of London and Bristol.[23] The city had colonies of English merchants and its inhabitants were now probably speaking a form of Hiberno-English. Waterford was gradually becoming a loyal outpost in a colony where the territory in which the king's writ was obeyed was continuously contracting. Despite the valiant show of loyalty to the crown and the crown's acceptance of Waterford's monopoly, times were extremely difficult. Waterford's Golden Age had well and truly come to an end.

Ring brooch

'To show off her neck, she closed the top of her shift with an exquisitely worked and finely made gold brooch; she placed it rather low so that an opening, one finger wide, gave a glimpse of her breasts, white as snow on the branches, this made her look even lovelier'.

- Jean Renart, *The Romance of the Rose* or *Guillaume de Dole*, thirteenth century

Dating possibly from as early as 1220 this sumptuous ring brooch is of great historical interest as one of the earliest, if not the earliest, surviving medieval ring brooches. Ring brooches were among the commonest jewels of the middle ages before the fifteenth century and survive in some numbers in England, France, Scotland and Ireland. This beautifully crafted brooch, consisting of a ring with a hinged pin, was used to close a cloak or the slit at the neck of a dress.

In the middle ages both men and women wore jewellery - ring brooches were worn and given as love tokens by both. Interestingly the only known example of a ring brooch illustrated on an Irish manuscript is to be found on the figure of John Darcy, Justiciar of Ireland (1324-1327) in the Great Charter Roll of Waterford. (p75) The giving of jewellery to a bride on betrothal and marriage was an established custom in western Europe in the middle ages. A French poem dated 1184 includes the lines 'my bride shall wear a brooch - a witness to her modesty and a proof that hers will be a chaste bed. It will shut up her breast and thrust back any intruder'. The very fine quality of this brooch probably means it belonged to a person of high standing in society and is evidence of a wealthy, sophisticated society in thirteenth century Waterford. In the thirteenth, fourteenth and fifteenth centuries a series of sumptuary laws were enacted throughout Europe formally restricting the wearing of clothing and jewellery. This legislation attempted to preserve the hierarchy of feudal society by preventing members of the lower orders from dressing above their station so that any stranger should be able to tell merely by looking at one's dress to what rank in society one belonged. It is interesting in the Waterford context that such laws were often specifically aimed at the increasingly wealthy urban merchants, who, with their greater spending power, occasionally 'behaved like aristocratic consumers' in displaying and storing their wealth by buying plate and jewels.

Archaeologist Orla Scully found the brooch in pristine condition in layers of ash and charcoal, associated with industrial hearths, in Bakehouse Lane in the Waterford city centre excavations. It is decorated with finely corded rims soldered to the outer and inner edges; on it are set four simple tubular collets filled with two blue and two green glass stones, almost certainly thought by the wearer and perhaps by the jeweller to be precious stones. Between the collets is filigree scroll-work applied in relief, formed by thin metal walls inset with a corded wire. The curling ends and significant points of the scroll-work are set with tiny balls of gold. The back is plain.

Unfortunately it is not known where the brooch was made though we do know that goldsmiths were resident in thirteenth century Waterford. Roger Goldsmith was a bailiff during the 1280s and goldsmiths were employed in the mints established in the city in 1195, 1210, 1281 and 1294. Some specialists suggest that the brooch was an import and certainly we know from court cases that merchants did bring jewellery with them to Ireland possibly for resale. Money, jewels, gold, silver and cloth were taken from a house of Lawrence de Marreys in Waterford in 1295, the chest in which they were stored belonging to a Flemish merchant. Whatever the origins of this brooch it is a wonderful reminder of that great age when courtly love and chivalry were the order of the day. The ring brooch was among the commonest jewels of the middle ages and was made of all qualities - from gold and silver to base metals - and often bore an inscription such as a protective formula or the name of the owner. Four definite and seven more possible ring brooches, all made of copper alloy, were also found in the Waterford excavations. They were often sold by travelling pedlars as evidenced by a thirteenth century French poem - the *Dit du Mercier* - where a pedlar offers to women gathered around him 'little brooches of gilt brass and of silvered latten [a brass alloy] and so fond are folk of latten that often it is valued as silver'.

DATE:	c1220 A D
NUMBER:	E435:1013:3 / WMT1999.0489
DIMENSIONS:	brooch Dia 26.5, pin L 20
MATERIAL:	gold, glass
PROVENANCE:	Waterford excavations
FURTHER READING:	Ronald Lightbown in Hurley & Scully 1997
	Deevy 1998
	Terry & Durling 1993

Stirrup ring (A)

This gold ring is another example of the very fine jewellery found in the Waterford excavations, in a house in Peter Street, one of the principal streets of the Viking and Anglo-Norman town. Rings of this type are called stirrup rings and were common in medieval times. This ring is set with a blue stone, probably a sapphire. Wearers believed that stones had magical properties to protect them from sickness and harm. Numerous medieval lapidaries (texts on gemstones) were written in the thirteenth century and deal mainly with the virtues of gems. Medieval sources specifically state that stones to be worn as charms were to be mounted in finger-rings, bracelets or pendants. There was also great symbolic importance attributed to gold, the incorruptible metal, for ties of marriage, affection and positions of trust. In the middle ages if a person owned only one object of gold it would probably be a finger-ring.

DATE:	c1190 A D
NUMBER:	E520:57:5 / WMT1999.0490
DIMENSIONS:	Int Dia 19
MATERIAL:	gold, sapphire
PROVENANCE:	Waterford excavations
FURTHER READING:	Ronald Lightbown in Hurley & Scully 1997
	Deevy 1998

Child's ring-brooch (B)

A typical child's ring-brooch, popular in the thirteenth and fourteenth centuries, this is a common type made in copper alloy, for either a child or poorer person, while the gold ring-brooch in the Waterford collection is the deluxe end of the market. The thirteenth century pedlar in an anonymous French poem also offers 'little brooches of gilt brass, pewter brooches for children'. The oblong head on the pin indicates a late thirteenth century date. Such brooches were not just decorative but were used as dress fasteners at the neck.

DATE:	c1250 A D
NUMBER:	E435:228:B118:1 / WMT1999.0493
DIMENSIONS:	Ext Dia 20
MATERIAL:	copper alloy
PROVENANCE:	Waterford excavations
FURTHER READING:	Ronald Lightbown in Hurley & Scully 1997
	Deevy 1998

Seal matrix (C)

This matrix consists of a circular seal die on the face of a pierced handle that was probably hung from a belt by the owner, possibly a merchant or artisan of some standing in the community. A central design of a bird is surrounded by an inscription in capital letters. The letters are reversed so that they would read properly when the seal is used. The inscription reads Sigullum Gafin Qu which can be interpreted as the Seal of Gafin (first name, maybe Gavin) Qu (an abbreviation of a family name), possibly Quemerford. Comerford was a known Waterford merchant family in the fourteenth century. Every merchant would carry around his own seal die to seal documents when he made transactions.

Orla Scully

DATE:	13th/14th century
NUMBER:	98E0447:46:11 / WMT1999.1684
DIMENSIONS:	overall L 22.5, Dia of seal die 18.5
MATERIAL:	lead
PROVENANCE:	archaeological excavations of Deanery garden in 1988
FURTHER READING:	Armstrong 1913
	Harvey & McGuinness 1996

Belt mount (D)

From the twelfth century until the early seventeenth century belts or girdles were worn by both men and women. The belts were often strengthened and decorated with metal mounts. Some of the best Irish illustrations of medieval belts or girdles are to be found on the images of the kings in the Great Charter Roll of Waterford. (pxxx) From the belt medieval people hung much that we today keep in pockets or handbags: a purse, a personal table-knife, a paternoster (rosary beads). This copper mount is beautifully engraved with the figure of a lady holding something in her arms. The image may be that of Saint Margaret holding the head of the dragon, that according to medieval tradition, she had slain. Such an image would express the chivalric gallantry of the man, possibly a knight, who wore the belt. Gifts of jewellery and belts, like the one to which this mount was originally attached, played an important part in the highly ritualised *l'amour courtois* (courtly love) and is another connection with the age of chivalry.

DATE:	c1250 A D
NUMBER:	E435:504:43 / WMT1999.0494
DIMENSIONS:	L 50.5 x W 9.5 x Th 1
MATERIAL:	copper
PROVENANCE:	Waterford excavations
FURTHER READING:	Ronald Lightbown in Hurley & Scully 1997

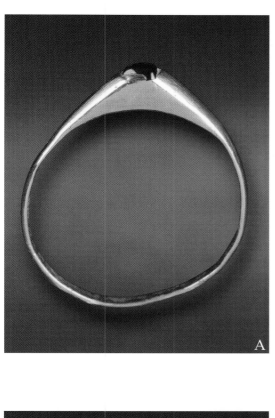

A

C

B

C

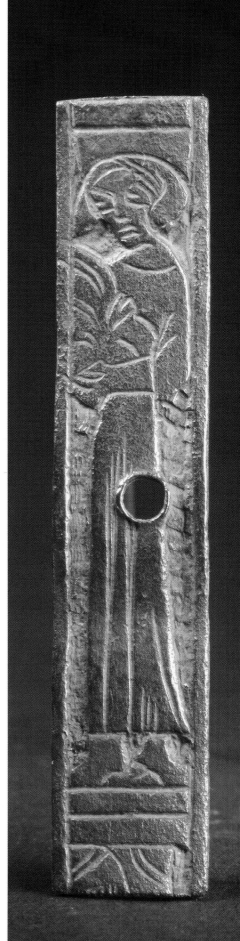

D

Coin balance (A)

This complete fold-up coin balance is a very rare find from the excavations, reminding us of the importance of commerce in Waterford in the late twelfth century. It was used to ensure that a silver penny was the proper weight. 240 pennies weighed or should weigh a pound weight of silver, hence 240 old pence in the pre-decimal (pre-1972) £1. Made of two arms and a shaft all of yew wood, with an iron pin, the horizontal arm pivots through a slot in the vertical arm and folds up into the vertical. A coin of correct or excess weight would tip up the balance and slide off. When used in a mint, the moneyer would clip the excess silver so the coin was the correct weight. A coin without the proper amount of silver would not be heavy enough to lift the arm of the balance and would not fall off. Also, although the balance appears to weigh coin against a fixed weight, one can quickly learn how much a coin is underweight by the position at which it will finally tip the scales. Only officials of the mint were allowed to use such balances but although denounced by the church as a sin, they were probably used illegally by merchants who kept a perfect coin against which to check that other pennies they received were not clipped. Coin-clipping was a well-documented crime in the middle ages for which there was a severe punishment. Edward I unjustly accused the Jews of England of coin-clipping in 1290. Having extracted confessions from some of them he expelled all Jews living in the kingdom, confiscating their property. There were mints established in Waterford by John as both prince and king, by Edward I and Edward IV, probably in Reginald's Tower. Coins from all these mints are represented in the display on commerce in Reginald's Tower today and an original Waterford Prince John halfpenny, the coin owner would have used, is placed on one of the arms of the balance.

DATE:	c1170 A D
NUMBER:	E527:1207:1 / WMT1999.0217
DIMENSIONS:	L 101
MATERIAL:	yew/iron
PROVENANCE:	Waterford excavations
FURTHER READING:	Maurice Hurley & Sarah McCutcheon in Hurley & Scully 1997 O'Sullivan 1961 McEneaney (ed) 1995
LOCATION:	Reginald's Tower

Money-box (B)

This lovely object is one of two early thirteenth century money-boxes found in the excavations of Waterford city centre. It is of Waterford ware which probably began production in that same century. Jugs, dripping/baking dishes, an ointment jar and unglazed cooking pots were found of the same ware; little bits of mica and quartz crystals in the clay are visible on the surface. The glaze is lead with varying amounts of copper, giving a green to black range of colours. This object has a lustrous deep purple-black sheen and was made on a potter's wheel. Although complete, it consists of two pieces, probably broken to get the coins out. Similar glazed wares were found in Jerpointchurch townland, Co. Kilkenny. A range of pottery made in Waterford today has been inspired by this ware.

DATE:	c1220 A D
NUMBER:	E527:1079:1 / WMT1999.0055
DIMENSIONS:	Dia 85
MATERIAL:	pottery
PROVENANCE:	Waterford excavations
FURTHER READING:	Audrey Gahan & Clare McCutcheon in Hurley & Scully 1997
LOCATION:	Reginald's Tower

Coin (C)

This is a Waterford King John silver penny with the king's head on one side encircled by the legend IOHANNES REX and on the other side - within a triangle - the starfish shaped sun and a crescent moon, surrounded by the words ROBERD ON DIVE. Waterford and Dublin were the two most important Irish centres for minting in John's reign.

DATE:	1210 A D
DIMENSIONS:	Dia 22
MATERIAL:	silver
FURTHER READING:	O'Sullivan 1961 Michael Kenny in Hurley & Scully 1997
LOCATION:	Reginald's Tower

Coin (D)

Stephen de Fulbourn, bishop of Waterford and governor of Ireland, used his influence as governor to secure a mint for Waterford, probably in Reginald's Tower, in 1281. This is a coin from that mint, an Edward I silver penny with the king's head on one side and a cross on the other surrounded by the words CIVITAS WATERFORD (the city of Waterford).

DATE:	1281 A D
DIMENSIONS:	Dia 23
MATERIAL:	silver
FURTHER READING:	O'Sullivan 1961 Michael Kenny in Hurley & Scully 1997
LOCATION:	Reginald's Tower

Both coins on loan from the National Museum of Ireland

Tallystick (E)

A tallystick was used to keep an account of a payment. The record of payment was made by scoring the wood across with notches, the stick was then split in two along its length so that the two parties to the transaction held matching halves, hence the expression 'does it tally?' When the mayor of Waterford made the city's annual payment to the royal exchequer in Dublin, it was recorded on the receipt rolls of the Irish exchequer and on a receipt which was taken back to Waterford. As a further precaution against fraud, one half of a tallystick was also brought to Waterford while the other half was enrolled with the receipt roll in Dublin. This was to guarantee security against unscrupulous practice by officials on both sides. Throughout the late thirteenth century writs were sent by the royal exchequer to the mayor of Waterford asking that he bring his rolls and tallies to Dublin when the accounts were being audited. It would be nice to think that this tallystick came from the Dublin exchequer.

DATE:	c1260 A D
NUMBER:	E343:5324:2 / WMT1999.0231
DIMENSIONS:	L c240
MATERIAL:	yew
PROVENANCE:	Waterford excavations
FURTHER READING:	Maurice Hurley & Sarah McCutcheon in Hurley & Scully 1997 McEneaney (ed) 1995
LOCATION:	Reginald's Tower

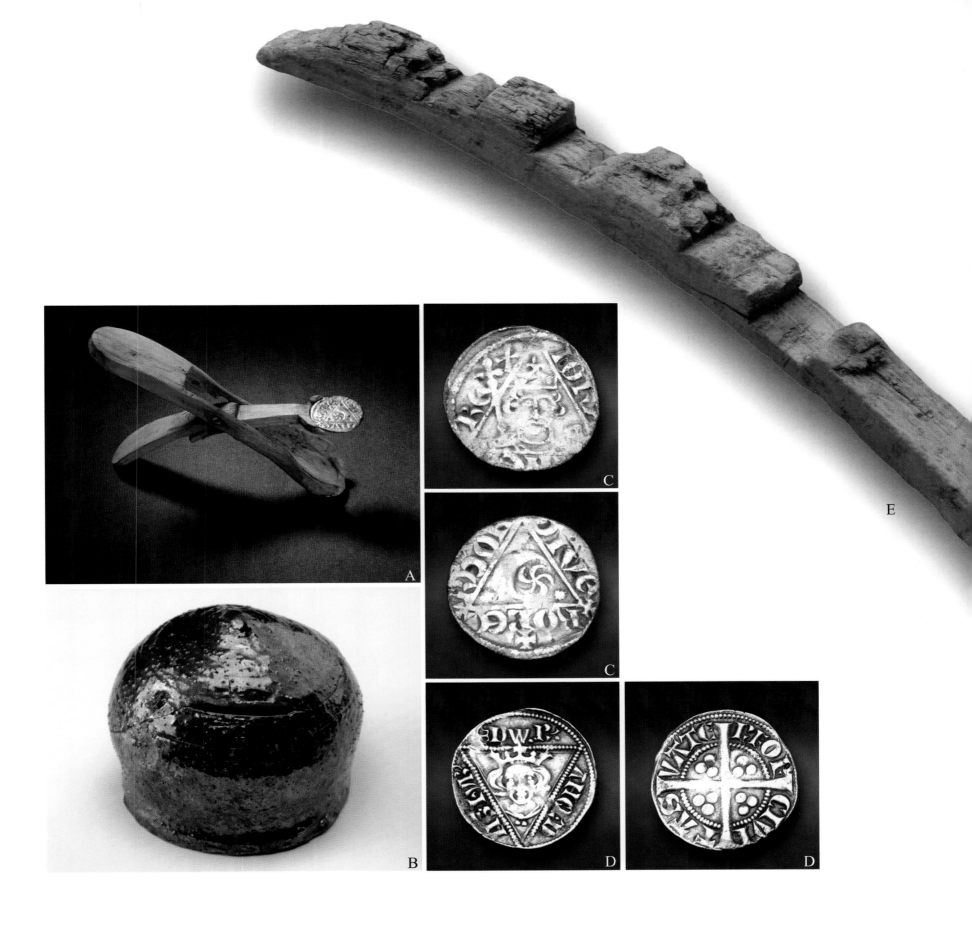

A

B

C

C

D

D

E

French wine jugs

The pottery here dates from the late twelfth and thirteenth centuries and is all French. Wares from south-west France represent the largest group of continental pottery found in the Waterford city excavations, reflecting the strong links with the wine-producing region of Bordeaux. These Ireland-southwest France trade routes were boosted by the marriage of Eleanor of Aquitaine to Henry II in 1152 and the subsequent loss of Normandy by their son in 1204. Wine was probably the commonest drink in twelfth and thirteenth century Waterford. In the twelfth century the Anglo-Norman historian Gerald of Wales remarked of Ireland that 'imported wines, conveyed in the ordinary commercial way, are so abundant that you would scarcely notice that the vine was neither cultivated nor gave its fruit there'.

In 1232 King Henry III granted the city of Waterford a charter and one of its provisions was that the city pay only half the tax or prise of wine. This prise was usually two casks of wine from every ship docking at the port, one cask taken from before and one from behind the mast. In 1292 an English ship called the Alice, out of Harwich, was arrested in New Ross, its crime being that as a foreign ship it had not docked in Waterford where it would have been forced to pay the king's tax, the prise of wine. Waterford was also a major centre for the provisioning of King Edward I's army in Scotland. Huge amounts of wine were imported for this purpose with local and national taxes paying for the wine and local officials carrying out much of the work of purveying and transporting it to Scotland. At one stage in the war against the Scots part of Edward's army threatened to mutiny, one of their grievances being that red wine had been promised but instead the troops received white wine dyed red with berries! Another of Waterford's links with south-west France is one of Waterford's most famous early fourteenth century mayors, Eymar de Godar, a merchant from Gascony. The records show that he was an extremely wealthy individual who served as mayor four times between 1304 and 1313 and was still involved in the government of the city until 1336.

The majority of vessels found in Waterford are wine jugs and many are almost complete and were made in Saintonge near Bordeaux, an area owned by the English king throughout the thirteenth century. All the jugs illustrated here are Saintonge. The barrel costrel was unglazed to keep its contents - probably wine - cool while being carried on a journey or pilgrimage. Two are green-glazed, one is squat and the other is a fine example of the tall type with parrot-beak spout and applied strips. The decorated jug represents the prestige end of the pottery market and is representative of several such jugs found during the Waterford excavations, its style of decoration is called sgraffito and shows a fox-and-cockerel motif. It was found in the stone-lined cesspit of a house in Peter Street along with other unusual finds namely Flemish highly decorated ware, a German jug, imported glass, an amber paternoster and walnut and fig seeds.

Costrel

DATE:	c1270 A D
NUMBER:	E406:2010 / WMT1999.0048
DIMENSIONS:	L 230
MATERIAL:	pottery
PROVENANCE:	Waterford excavations
FURTHER READING:	Audrey Gahan & Clare McCutcheon in Hurley & Scully 1997
	Lydon 1972
	McEneaney (ed) 1995
	McEneaney in *Decies* 13

Jug

DATE:	c1300 A D
NUMBER:	E406:1214 / WMT1999.0040
DIMENSIONS:	H 180
MATERIAL:	pottery
PROVENANCE:	Waterford excavations
FURTHER READING:	Audrey Gahan & Clare McCutcheon in Hurley & Scully 1997
	Lydon 1972
	McEneaney (ed) 1995
	McEneaney in *Decies* 13

Tall Jug

DATE:	c1250 A D
NUMBER:	E520:97:5 / WMT1999.0033
DIMENSIONS:	H 305
MATERIAL:	pottery
PROVENANCE:	Waterford excavations
FURTHER READING:	Audrey Gahan & Clare McCutcheon in Hurley & Scully 1997
	Lydon 1972
	McEneaney (ed) 1995
	McEneaney in *Decies* 13

Sgraffito Jug

DATE:	c1270 A D
NUMBER:	E434:529:8 / WMT1999.0047
DIMENSIONS:	H 260
MATERIAL:	pottery
PROVENANCE:	Waterford excavations
FURTHER READING:	Audrey Gahan & Clare McCutcheon in Hurley & Scully 1997
	Lydon 1972
	McEneaney (ed) 1995
	McEneaney in *Decies* 13

Bruges wine jugs

These two jugs are examples of Flemish highly decorated ware made near Bruges in modern day Belgium. Archaeologists working in Waterford found the largest collection of such pottery outside Bruges itself. The dominance of Waterford in the import of wine throughout the thirteenth century is reflected in these and other wine jugs being found in the city. The importation of wine jugs is interpreted as a by-product of the wine trade. The jugs did not come filled with wine but were imported for domestic use along with linen, fine cloth and other luxuries. We know that Flemish merchants were active in Waterford in the thirteenth century. The city had extensive trading links with the Low Countries, wool and hides being the main export from Ireland. The complete jug, left, has bands of roller stamping and a thumbed base, while the incomplete jug has moulded impressed raspberry motifs. Both have a very glossy green glaze over a brick red fabric and would have probably belonged to wealthier citizens.

DATE: c1220 A D
NUMBER: E406:2088:54 / WMT1999.0051
DIMENSIONS: H 350
MATERIAL: pottery
PROVENANCE: Waterford excavations
FURTHER READING: Audrey Gahan & Clare McCutcheon in Hurley
                                          & Scully 1997

DATE: c1220 A D
NUMBER: E434:114:24 / WMT1999.0052
DIMENSIONS: H 170
MATERIAL: pottery
PROVENANCE: Waterford excavations
FURTHER READING: Audrey Gahan & Clare McCutcheon
                                          in Hurley & Scully 1997

Waterford jug

The production of pottery in Waterford city began in the thirteenth century to cater for an expanding population - previous to that all Waterford's pottery was brought in from further afield or from other countries. The black jug here is an example of the first pottery we know of that was made in Waterford and is the same ware as the money box (p47), with a deep lustrous purple to black glaze on the outside. The Waterford ware is characterised by mica and quartz crystals visible on the surface. The complete jug has six thumb marks around the base but is otherwise undecorated. The fabric is not as fine as the French ware, obvious even in the photograph here, indicating the level of development of pottery in the two places.

DATE: c1290 A D
NUMBER: E421:1007:24 / WMT1999.0054
DIMENSIONS: H 184
MATERIAL: pottery
PROVENANCE: Waterford excavations
FURTHER READING: Audrey Gahan & Clare McCutcheon
                          in Hurley & Scully 1997

German jar

Pottery from continental Europe other than France represents only one per cent of the total medieval pottery assemblage from Waterford city. The small amount of German ware includes this unique unglazed proto-stoneware jar. This ware was produced at many centres in Germany, the most famous being Siegburg. The vessel is wheel-thrown, has a tapered body, a thumbed base and may originally have had a lid. It seems not to have had a handle or spout. This may be regarded as an exotic find as it was found in a stone-lined cesspit in association with other exotic imported wares including Saintonge polychrome, sgraffito and Flemish highly decorated wares. The presence there also of imported glass, an amber paternoster and the remains of walnut and fig would suggest that this pit was associated with a person of some wealth. This piece of pottery dates from the early to mid-thirteenth century and is older than the other wares found with it, suggesting the vessel may have had strong personal associations and was held for many years before being discarded.

DATE: c1220 A D
NUMBER: E406:2092:158 / WMT1999.0049
DIMENSIONS: H 215
MATERIAL: pottery
PROVENANCE: Waterford excavations
FURTHER READING: Audrey Gahan & Clare McCutcheon
                          in Hurley & Scully 1997

English jug

Some sixty percent of the pottery found in excavations was of English or Welsh origin. By mid to late twelfth century the bulk of the pottery found in Waterford was coming from England. This late medieval jug was made in Redcliffe near Bristol. Redcliffe pottery was produced from the later thirteenth century and represents a continuity of ceramic links with that general area going back to the eleventh century, indicative of Waterford's trade with Bristol. The greeny-yellow glaze is on the outside only, appearing brown on the applied strips. Jugs are the most common vessel form present. These jugs typically have bridge spouts, strap handles and like this one, a flat base that is also frilled. This jug is undecorated other than with concentric lines, it has a small spout and is almost complete. Waterford had strong links with Bristol even before the Anglo-Norman invasion and following that invasion many of the settlers in Waterford would have come from the Bristol region. In 1306 Waterford's mayor was Jordan of Bristol and we know from an account of a siege of the city in 1368 that a number of Bristol merchants were killed suggesting that the city may have contained a small colony of Bristol merchants. In the 1390s, in an attempt to secure new markets, many Waterford merchants established themselves in Bristol. Indeed so successful were these merchants that Bristol had an Irish (of Anglo-Norman origin) mayor in 1393. So many Irish settled in Bristol in the century after the Black Death (1349) that by 1439 the mayor of Bristol was prohibiting anyone of Irish birth from becoming a member of the city council.

DATE: c1260 A D
NUMBER: E527:638:20 / WMT1999.0028
DIMENSIONS: H 223
MATERIAL: pottery
PROVENANCE: Waterford excavations
FURTHER READING: Audrey Gahan & Clare McCutcheon
                          in Hurley & Scully 1997

Paternosters

Two paternosters, the medieval equivalent of the rosary beads, of light amber beads and used for telling prayers, were found in the Waterford city centre excavations. Cistercians in the eleventh and twelfth centuries allowed laybrothers and sisters to recite the pater noster (the Our Father prayer) instead of the 150 psalms and lessons that the monks recited. The beads helped with counting. The large beads are the marker beads, designed more for the fingers than for the eye. One paternoster is complete, consisting of seventy-four small flattened circular form beads and nine large shaped ones. The other paternoster is incomplete and consists of six beads of various types, slightly superior to the beads of the complete paternoster though all are elegantly crafted.

Paternosters were usually worn hung from the girdle (belt) or round the neck and were long for women and short for men, sometimes only a few beads. Amber is fossilised resin from the shores of the Baltic and there is every reason to believe that these beads were crafted in Waterford. It is known that it was a specialised craft in Paris as early as the 1260s. These two paternosters and one other found in Cork are not only the earliest medieval amber paternosters but are also the only ones yet discovered in Europe.

DATE: c1250 A D
NUMBER: E406:2060:2 / WMT1999.1737 & 1738
DIMENSIONS: L 248 & 73
MATERIAL: amber
PROVENANCE: Waterford excavations
FURTHER READING: Ronald Lightbown in Hurley & Scully 1997

Parchment pricker

This lovely object is redolent of the sophisticated literate society in Waterford in the thirteenth century. Made of ivory on a lathe it is one of two parchment prickers or styli found in St Peter's church which were used by scribes to score several sheets of vellum at the same time, thus making it easier to write horizontally. This one is in perfect condition and even has the original iron point intact.

DATE: c1250 A D
NUMBER: E343:355:1 / WMT1999.0145
DIMENSIONS: L 92, spherical head D 7, tapering shaft L 79, metal point L 3 x D 1
MATERIAL: ivory, iron
PROVENANCE: Waterford excavations
FURTHER READING: Maurice Hurley & Sarah McCutcheon in Hurley & Scully 1997

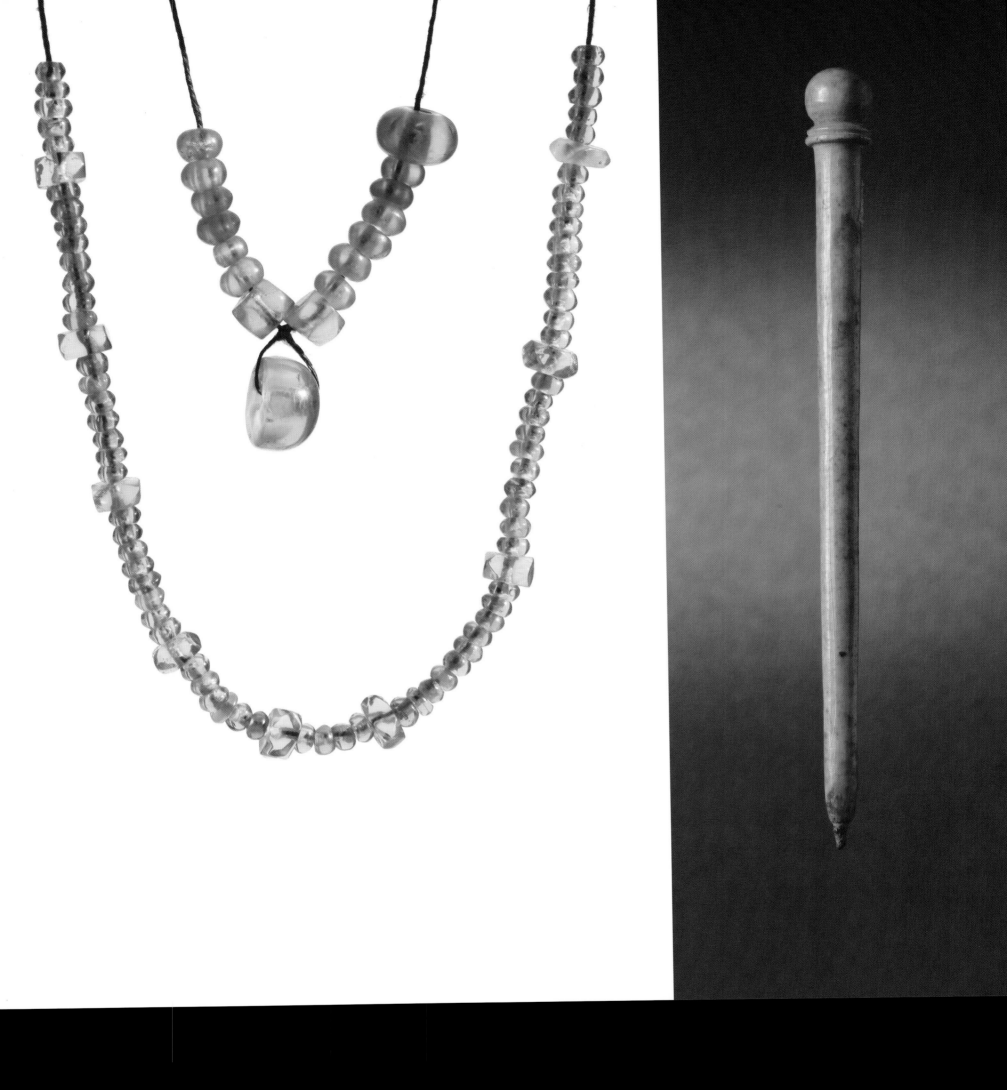

Pilgrim badge of St John the Baptist

Of circular openwork form, this badge shows a man's face with a full beard, no ears and a band of hatching across the forehead, suggesting a tonsure (a monk's haircut). This is undoubtedly St John the Baptist whose face only is often depicted - remember that Salomé was presented with the Baptist's head on a plate. Three almost identical badges have been found in England. All celebrate the famous relic of the Baptist's head that was brought to the Cathedral of Amiens, France in 1206 after the Sack of Constantinople, starting a major and long-lasting pilgrimage. The organisers of that pilgrimage only ever claimed to possess the front part of St John's head, hence the effort on all four badges to show the absence of the cranium by foreshortening the forehead in various ways. The face on this badge is surrounded by a slender circular frame, the spaces on either side of the face being bridged by short bars also hatched. The badge had originally four rings around the rim, one of which survives, for attachment to the pilgrim's clothes. The idea of wearing a pilgrim badge was to alert everyone to the fact that you were on pilgrimage and therefore carried no great wealth. It was hoped that this would deter would-be thieves.

DATE: c1230 A D
NUMBER: E527:262:16 / WMT1999.0501
DIMENSIONS: Dia 28
MATERIAL: tin-lead alloy
PROVENANCE: Waterford excavations
FURTHER READING: Brian Spencer in Hurley & Scully 1997

Pilgrim badge of an Unknown Saint

Found in the fill of a thirteenth century pit, two figures are depicted on the front of this square pilgrim badge acting out, as many other pilgrim signs do, the final moments in the life of a saint. Both figures are dressed in belted, knee-length tunics and stand on either side of a tree. The right-hand figure, who may be wearing a coif (head-covering), has his arms stretched out in front, as if bound at the wrists to the tree-trunk and evidently awaits his impending martyrdom. The left-hand figure brandishes a billhook with which he has lopped some branches from the tree, reducing it to a simple, still leafy, T-shaped cross, the implement of the martyr's death. The inscription translates 'the seal (or sign) of John, crucified by the Jews at P'. The lettering suggests a date after 1350. No saint corresponding to these details has been identified nor has any similar badge been found among European pilgrim badges. This negative evidence suggests that 'John of P' may have been a devotional figure of somewhat obscure and mainly local or short-lived significance. If so the badge would not be the first to provide the evidence of a popular, unofficial cult. On the other hand it should be noted that several major pilgrim centres are now represented by one or two surviving pilgrim souvenirs. The solid rectangular form was one favoured by French pilgrim sites particularly during this period. It may be therefore that the shrine lay on or near one of the four traditional through-routes across France on the way to the sanctuary of St James of Compostella in north-west Spain. The badge was cast in a two-piece mould and would originally have had rings at the corners by which it could be stitched to the pilgrim's hat or knapsack and worn as a souvenir and a talisman.

Sadly this badge may be associated with a belief in thirteenth and fourteenth century Europe that the small Jewish communities scattered throughout the continent needed the blood of a Christian boy to celebrate Passover. There was of course no substance to these rumours that were often spread by unscrupulous individuals in order to incite the mob to attack these small communities so as to destroy all records of debts owed to the Jews. If a Christian boy was found dead close to the feast of Passover then the Jews were often accused of his murder. The boy then became a Christian martyr; the medieval St Julian of Norwich is a case in point. The belief that the Jews performed such ritual murders persisted in Russia until 1917.

DATE: 13th century
NUMBER: E527:748:1 / WMT1999.0500
DIMENSIONS: 40 square
MATERIAL: tin-lead alloy
PROVENANCE: Waterford excavations
FURTHER READING: Brian Spencer in Hurley & Scully 1997

Inscribed knife

This is a twelfth century iron knife, consisting today of a blade and a handle-tang or core; the handle was of wood, bone, horn or other perishable material and is gone. All parts of the knife - blade, hilt band and end cap (except the tang) - contain copper-alloy plates containing decoration and texts. This was no ordinary domestic knife (it is bigger than the average domestic knife found in Waterford) but probably had a religious function. It is similar to a late twelfth/early thirteenth century knife found in Winchester (there, only the blade survives which has copper alloy plates on the back, it is decorated in similar style but is not inscribed) and to another more elaborate late ninth/early tenth century knife from Sittingbourne in England. The Latin inscription in capitals probably reads: '+ what is cut with this sharp edge, may it be filled with the powerful love of Christ'. The knife was possibly used to cut the blessed but unconsecrated bread after mass for distribution to the poor.

DATE: 12th century
NUMBER: E527:1475:2 / WMT1999.0499
DIMENSIONS: overall L 260, blade L 128
MATERIAL: iron, copper-alloy
PROVENANCE: Waterford excavations
FURTHER READING: Elizabeth Okasha in Hurley & Scully 1997

The Great Charter Roll

Waterford's Great Charter Roll, four metres in length, consists of fifteen documents and seventeen illustrations on vellum. Compiled c1373 it is one of the great treasures of medieval Ireland. The top of the roll has a view of Waterford c1370 and is the earliest extant view of an Irish city. Five kings of England are featured - Henry II, John, Henry III, Edward I and Edward III, who appears twice. The images of Edward III are among the few contemporary images of the king to survive. The illustrations of the mayors of Dublin, Waterford, Cork and Limerick are the earliest in Ireland, while the image of Henry de Londres, Archbishop of Dublin and Justiciar of Ireland is the earliest Irish illustration of an Anglo-Norman bishop or of a justiciar, the king's representative in Ireland. Six other justiciars and a judge are illustrated, all of whom held office in Ireland between 1213 and 1372.

The roll was compiled as a 'book of evidence' and brought to the Chancery in London to support Waterford's claim to have a monopoly forcing all ships entering Waterford harbour, except those of the lordship of Leinster, to unload at Waterford and not New Ross. There are two interesting facets to the story of the roll - one the chronology of the dispute between Waterford and New Ross and the second to discover why the mayor and council went to so much trouble to illuminate the roll. After all enrolled documents were common in the middle ages but attaching so many illustrations was unheard of in fourteenth century England or Ireland. We will begin with why the roll was illuminated and what purpose did these illuminations serve.

Art and Diplomacy in Medieval Waterford

As a group the seventeen late fourteenth century illustrations are extremely important in providing an insight into costume in Ireland at a time in our history when we have almost no visual evidence in terms of painting or sculpture. There is nothing similar to the roll in either Britain or Ireland. Its creation is unique in that it was not devised as a public document intending to appeal to an illiterate populace, as was most religious art of this period. Neither can we classify it

DATE:	1373 A D
NUMBER:	WMT1999.1594
DIMENSIONS:	overall L 3950
MATERIAL:	vellum
PROVENANCE:	historic municipal collection
FURTHER READING:	McEneaney (ed) 1995
	Fletcher 1994
	Walton 1992

The Walled City of Waterford c1373

While this is a typical fourteenth century view of a walled city it is nonetheless distinctly Waterford, showing the city from the east with St John's river (a tributary of the river Suir) flowing below the whitewashed town walls. Both Reginald's Tower and the roof of Christ Church Cathedral are discernible. It is interesting that the image shows three ships anchored in the river, for in 1241 the city had, by order of King Henry III, built three ships for its protection and to this day three ships are emblazoned on the arms of the city. On the riverbank we find rabbits, animals introduced into Ireland by the Anglo-Normans to provide winter protein. Every aspect of the image reinforces the Anglo-Norman identity of the city.

DIMENSIONS: L 550 x W 290

along with chronicles of the time where illuminations served to elevate important or historic events or personages. Stylistically the roll's illustrations (which vary in size, some almost as large as an A4 page) bear no relation to those found on contemporary royal charters, where illustrations of the king are merely encompassed in the capital letter of the opening sentence.

Why create the roll?
To appreciate the unusual nature of the illuminations we must understand the rationale behind the document as a whole. The roll was not conceived as a work of art, it was created by city officials to assist in presenting Waterford's case in an enquiry held in London during the 1370s regarding the monopoly that Waterford claimed over the port of New Ross. The documents, dating from 3 July 1215 to 11 May 1372, all relate in some way to the dispute between these two ports and are of varying shape and size with the illustrations attached. Consequently the roll is irregular in shape, no attempt is made to standardise the documents with the result that the right hand side is very uneven - the roll varies in width from 29 to 71 cm. The unevenness of the roll is a result of the compilers using original documents because these would carry more weight at the Chancery.

There can be little doubt that the roll was taken to London and presented like a Book of Evidence to bolster Waterford's case. Proof that the roll was reduced to a manageable size for transportation was found during conservation when a number of fold marks became obvious. The outer skins were folded inwards, reducing the width to 29 cm corresponding to the width of the top illustration. As was the practice in the middle ages its length was reduced to a manageable package simply by rolling. Thus the 'Book of Evidence' was reduced to a small cylinder-shaped package that could be conveniently conveyed to London.

Why Illustrate the Roll? - Subliminal messages
When put end to end the city's charters and other documents relating to the dispute measured almost three and a half metres; however within these documents there was no actual royal charter (until that granted by Edward III in 1356) that stated clearly the monopoly claimed by the city on ships

KING HENRY II (1154-1189)
Although there is no caption attached to this illustration it is almost certain that it represents King Henry II as he was the first English king to impose his rule on Ireland when he landed in Waterford in 1171. Because of its position near the top of the roll it is in very poor condition. The armoured figure stands in a cinquefoil arch which was grey in colour though almost all of it is now gone. The king is dressed in a red surcoat with a knightly belt around his hips. His arms are protected with rarebraces and gauntlets on his hands. The king holds a fleur-de-lys sceptre in his left hand and a large battle-axe in his right. His legs are armed with cuisses and greaves and his feet, which are armed in articulated sabatons, stand on a grassy green mound.

DIMENSIONS: L 320 x W 200

entering the harbour. The best that Waterford could produce were documents proving that in the past English kings and their justiciars upheld Waterford's monopoly. As their case rested on legal precedence rather than on clear and unambiguous right enunciated in a royal charter, greater status had to be conferred on these documents. This was achieved by adding the illuminated panels. By illustrating all of the English kings since the Anglo-Norman invasion (Edward II was once on the roll but his portrait was removed at some point in history), Waterford's officials were linking their claim, as the premier port, to the arrival of the Anglo-Norman kings in Ireland. Continuity, legitimacy and genealogy were inseparable in the medieval mind. Indeed the notion of continuity, particularly genealogical continuity, was almost a medieval obsession. Edward III himself, in what was probably one of the most important pieces of artistic patronage of his reign, had his family members represented in St Stephen's Chapel in Westminster between 1355 and 1363. This obsession with genealogy and continuity as the basis of legitimacy was not lost on Waterford's well-travelled ruling and merchant class, the group that had most to lose if New Ross won its case.

By illustrating the justiciars together with the kings, such was the power of the visual that it performed the unspoken task of providing a royal seal of approval for the justiciars' actions. The illustrations were also an *aide memoire* for Waterford's lawyers; particularly the illustrations of the justiciars who enforced Waterford's monopoly by having arrested foreign ships that bypassed the port. It is easy to visualise Waterford's lawyers unrolling the four-metre-long, magnificently illustrated roll before the officials at the Chancery. Its sheer length, together with the richness of the illustrations, must not only have intimidated the lawyers for New Ross but must also have helped to sway the Chancery officials who eventually settled in Waterford's favour.

The top illustration differs from the others in that it shows the walled city. In the general treatment of perspective and attempts to create distance by situating rows of houses on top of each other, this view is not dissimilar to contemporary English and French illustrations. The motivation for its inclusion may reflect the mayor's and council's desire to send

KING JOHN (1199-1216)

Situated below the illustration of Henry II is an illustration of King John as identified by the inscription on the parapet of the canopy. This is one of the finest drawings on the roll. He is positioned next to his charter of 1215. John is dressed in a cote hardie with a scalloped edge and long thin sleeves which reach to the knuckles. He also wears a grey (originally gold) coronet and knightly girdle. The king stands, legs apart, over the edge of the frame. The figure holds a hawk on a gauntlet in his right hand, the legs of which are firmly attached to his glove. He also holds a heron leg as a lure for the hawk. Hawking was considered to be a sport of the nobility in the late medieval era. The king's hair is fashionably cut into a bobbed chin-length style and the v-shaped beard was typical of the time. It should be remembered with all the illustrations that the illustrator dressed the figures in contemporary fashion. Medieval artists had no appreciation that historical personages would have dressed or appeared any differently from themselves.

DIMENSIONS: L 390 x W 200

a broader political message to the king. In about 1373, when William Lombard was mayor and the roll compiled, a petition was sent to the king, ostensibly seeking a reduction in rents owed to him by the city, but in reality informing him of their case against New Ross then pending at the Chancery. Using words on parchment the officials recited a litany of disasters which had befallen the city: military attacks, loss of ships at sea, decline in trade and finally 'the cost of having to defend the King's rights by a plea between their city and the town of New Ross which is pending at the King's Chancery'. The petition goes on to turn the screw by stating that 'Waterford, no more than seven acres within its walls is like a little castle... and if the said lands of Ireland should be gained by your enemies it could be better regained by means of our city'. The top illustration on the roll was performing the same function as the petition, except this time the city was using paint on parchment to get the message across. The image of the walled city was a reminder to the king that he needed the support and loyalty of the city as much as it needed him. The message was reinforced by placing above the city, almost floating over it, an image of the king accepting the key of the city gates from the mayor and the mayor in turn accepting from the king a sword. The keys were a symbolic recognition by the city that Waterford was part of the royal demesne and that the city belonged to the king who could come and go as he pleased. The sword represented both the mayor's obligations as chief justice within the city to administer royal justice and also his duty to defend the city on the king's behalf in times of war. The message conveyed by the illustration was as clear as that in the written petition of c1373 quoted above. If the king favoured Waterford and not New Ross, then the mayor and citizens would protect the king's interests in Ireland and at some future date possibly facilitate the re-conquest of the colony by offering the royal walled city of Waterford as a bridgehead.

English influence on Irish Art

The style of the sixteen figures illustrated fits very comfortably into the late fourteenth century English school of illumination, though it is difficult to make direct parallels. Waterford in the 1370s was culturally very much an English city; we know that there were colonies of English merchants

KING HENRY III (1216-1272)

The king is identified by the caption on the canopy. The king wears a long fawn-coloured mantle with elaborately scalloped and dagged edges. Underneath he wears a cote hardie, the chest of which is visibly padded; it buttons down the centre. He holds a large fleur-de-lys sceptre in his right hand and gestures perhaps towards the adjacent charter which is the 1232 charter of Henry III. The king has a full beard. He also holds a long sword hanging from his dark grey (originally gold) coloured knightly belt. Henry was the longest reigning medieval English monarch.

DIMENSIONS: L 285 x W 200

living there, eighty of whom were slain in a battle defending it in 1368. The leading citizens were also very aware of contemporary fashions in art and clothing in both England and France, as shown by the illustrations of Edward III who is depicted in what was sophisticated fashion at the time the roll was compiled. This awareness is to be expected as many of the leading merchants such as William Lombard, five times mayor of Waterford (1371-1373, 1377-1379 and 1384-1385) and the only mayor mentioned in the roll, spent much of his time in England. Indeed he received royal letters of protection allowing him to carry out business there and later had the monarch's approval to act as agent for French merchants in Ireland.

Two Ports one Harbour
The Dispute between Waterford and New Ross
One of the most protracted legal disputes in Irish history must surely be that which involved the citizens of Waterford and the burgesses of New Ross. It lasted from 1215 until 1518 when it was finally settled, not in a court of law but when the burgesses of New Ross suffered a crushing military defeat at the hands of the citizens of Waterford. The story of the dispute is beyond doubt one of the great stories of medieval economic rivalry and is worth recounting in some detail as it is central to the compilation of the Great Charter Roll.

Waterford's location, its fine natural harbour and inland navigable rivers, its proximity to Bristol and to the ports of France gave it a distinct advantage over other Irish ports. That was of course until William Marshal decided to build a new port to service his lordship of Leinster on a green-field site, *Pons Novus* or, as we know it today, New Ross.

The story of New Ross really begins in 1204 when King John of England lost Normandy to King Philip Augustus of France. Marshal tried to retain a foothold in Normandy by performing feudal submission to King Philip Augustus. His dual loyalty so antagonised King John of England that Marshal was forced to go into exile in Ireland. Marshal was one of the most powerful magnates in Ireland, having secured the lordship of Leinster by marrying Isabel de Clare, Strongbow's heiress. The two great ports servicing Leinster

KING EDWARD I (1272-1307)

The style of canopy under which the king stands is the same as in the illustrations of King John and Henry III. The illustration is attached to a writ of Lord Edward, a title he held from 1254 until he became king in 1272. The figure depicted is very young so it may have been the intention to show the young Lord Edward before he became king. The king stands with a dog at his feet, symbol of loyalty and faithfulness. He wears a scalloped shoulder cape which closes at the right shoulder, underneath is a blue cote hardie. Under the cote hardie is a gipon that stretches to the knuckles and is fashionably buttoned from elbow to wrist. He wears a standard knightly belt with a long dagger attached. He also wears a coronet and an ornamental collar all coloured in distinctive grey, originally gold. His face is very long, its length accentuated by his pointed beard and is highlighted with touches of faded vermillion that is characteristic of the treatment of the other kings. Edward's reign marked a golden age for the city of Waterford as during his lifetime a sophisticated system of local government was introduced. Ironically the more advanced this system was, the easier it was for the king to exploit the Irish lordship to finance his extravagant wars. Following the illustration of Edward I is the remains of another illustration, presumed to be that of Edward II (1307-1327) the deposed King of England.

DIMENSIONS: L 300 x W 200

were Dublin and Waterford, both royal ports since Strongbow submitted them to King Henry II in 1170. (p61) For Marshal it was unacceptable that the merchants of Waterford and Dublin should make huge profits, not only from the export of the agricultural produce of his lordship of Leinster, but also from the importation of luxuries and necessities required by the lordship's inhabitants. With the loss of his lands in France it was to be expected that Marshal should set about deriving the greatest possible economic benefit from his lordship. Firstly he introduced the new techniques of the European agricultural revolution, removing the native Irish from the land and replacing them with peasants from England and Wales who were more versed in the new agricultural methodologies. With the land now producing huge surpluses, he put in place the second phase of his strategy - the foundation in c1210 of a deep water port in New Ross and the construction of the Hook lighthouse at the entrance to Waterford harbour to guide ships safely to his port. For the first time in history Waterford port shared its harbour with a rival. The two ports, Waterford and New Ross, would spend the next three hundred years vying with each other for the lion's share of the trade that used this gateway to the south-east.

By the time the port of New Ross was becoming established in 1215 Marshal was an ally of King John, even witnessing the charter granted by the king to Waterford in July 1215 - a copy of this charter is contained in the Great Charter Roll. The first mention of tension between the two ports appears in August 1215 when King John ordered that 'ships could land at New Ross provided no injury should thereby result to the city of Waterford'. As an ally of a king who was now facing civil war in England Marshal was no doubt able to extract some concessions. The king's order implies that the men of Waterford had been attempting to prohibit ships from bypassing the port of Waterford and secondly that an inquiry would be held to determine if the king's port of Waterford suffered by ships landing at New Ross.

We do not know if an inquiry into the economic impact of New Ross on Waterford was ever undertaken but if it was it is very likely that its findings were quashed, for on his deathbed in 1216 King John appointed Marshal as guardian of the young King Henry III. (p65) William was now the

KING EDWARD III ON HORSEBACK (1327-1377)

Edward III, positioned under a pointed arch, rides a white horse that rears up on its hind legs. The horse is decorated with red braiding. Red, being one of the most expensive colours to produce during the middle ages, was always associated with royalty. The king is fully armoured wearing an uncoloured surcoat over a scalloped hauberk. The armour is high-waisted as was the fashion of the time. The king is fully bearded with delicately drawn features, dotted eyes and slightly toned face. He holds a shield that has the three lions of the English crown quartered with the French fleur-de-lys representing his claim to the French throne. He holds a large sword as if in battle, Edward of course being the great warrior king who launched the Hundred Years War (1337-1453) with France.

DIMENSIONS: L 300 x W 200

most powerful man in England and in January 1219 the justiciar (governor) of Ireland was ordered to allow ships to 'ply through the lands of Marshal, the king's guardian'. Marshal died the following May and interestingly in August, with the reins of government now firmly in the hands of Henry III, a new enquiry was held to ascertain whether or not ships could touch at New Ross without hindrance to Waterford. On 6 November the king ordered that 'ships shall, as they used to, diverge at the port of Waterford', the reason being 'because the city of Waterford would be injured if ships and merchandise were allowed to touch at New Ross'. Clearly the king was not going to allow his port of Waterford go into decline just to make Marshal's heirs rich.

In 1222 Justiciar Henry de Londres (p73) was ordered 'not to permit any ships with merchandise to touch at the port of New Ross except those who were wont to touch there in the time of King John before the war between him and his English barons'. In 1227 what appears to have been the policy adopted by the king of England for the remainder of the middle ages came into force. William Marshal (junior) was granted a licence 'so that his ships with merchandise could freely go to his port of New Ross, remain there and depart while other ships from Ireland and foreign parts would ply at Waterford'. Though figures for the volume of trade in this period are scarce, a reference to the mayor of London purchasing 1000 crannocks of wheat from Marshal in 1224 suggests that his lordship of Leinster was booming.

Writs sent by the king to the Irish justiciar in 1230 and again in 1236 ordered that 'all ships except those from the Earl Marshal's lands shall touch at Waterford and not New Ross'. The 1236 writ continued 'those who go to New Ross contrary to the king's command do so under pain of forfeiture'. These writs from the king suggest that Waterford in fact was being bypassed and that the city's merchant oligarchy had been continuously making representations to the monarch.

For thirty years between 1236 and 1266 the sources are silent concerning the dispute. However this does not imply that the residents of both towns were in that period living in peaceful co-existence, for the complaints which surfaced in 1266 revealed an explosive situation. Waterford city sent a depu-

KING EDWARD III ENTHRONED (1327-1377)

Edward III, like all the figures on the roll, is surrounded by an architectural canopy as was the fashion in English illuminations of the period where figures do not tend to appear in isolation. Similar treatment of figures is to be found in the brass of Sir Hugh Hastings c1347 from Esling, Norfolk. The canopy style is also to be found in stained glass from the mid-fourteenth century. A most interesting example is a window in Ely Cathedral where two rows of cusped niches contain small figures of soldiers wearing long surcoats over chain mail and standing in a variety of lively poses. The arch surrounding Edward is particularly ornate, having a slight ogee arch ending in three cusps. The outer edges of the arch end in turrets complete with a parapet and slated roof. The king sits awkwardly with legs crossed on a large wooden throne very similar in style to the bishop's chair in Hereford Cathedral which is of Norman origin. Like the bishop's chair the throne appears to be made of spindles worked on a lathe. The king wears a gold knightly belt that became fashionable between 1360 and 1370 and was very popular in courtly circles. In about 1370 the belt or girdle hung very low about the hips, so low in fact that a series of small hooks had to be attached to keep it in place.

DIMENSIONS: L 280 x W 200

tation to the king to complain about the malpractices of the burgesses of New Ross 'who were not only bypassing the port of Waterford but were, by force of arms, diverting trade to their own port'. The king sent a writ to the justiciar David de Barry (p75) calling on him to conduct an enquiry. The justiciar appointed a judge, Alexander de Nottingham, to preside over the enquiry that was held in Waterford on 6 December 1266. The proceedings revealed that 'some forty ships had been arrested by the men of New Ross and forced to land at that port to the detriment of the king and the city of Waterford'. It goes on to state that two men were killed trying to prevent the men of New Ross diverting ships. The written testimony of this enquiry with the names of the witnesses, or jurors as they were known, is preserved in the charter roll and placed alongside it is an image of Judge Alexander De Nottingham 1265-1270. (p75)

In 1267 Edward, Lord of Ireland, son of King Henry III issued a general proclamation 'to all merchants and masters of ships who were not of the land of William Marshal's heirs and who come to Ireland with merchandise' warning that if they 'bypass Waterford in favour of New Ross they would have their merchandise forfeit to the king'. The justiciar of Ireland at the time of the proclamation was still David de Barry. Edward's threat was not an idle one, as in 1275 Justiciar Geoffrey de Geneville, also featured on the roll (p75), ordered the sheriff of Dublin to go to New Ross and 'take as forfeit to the king all ships with their wares and merchandise that had landed contrary to the king's lawful prohibitions'.

The proclamation was reissued in 1277 under the justiciarship of Robert de Ufford (p75) and again in 1291. In 1292 the sheriff of Dublin was sent to New Ross to arrest a ship called the Alice, out of Harwich in England, which was carrying 137 hogsheads of wine. Ships importing wine and landing at New Ross were particularly frowned on by the authorities as there was no mechanism at that port to collect the king's tax on wine known as the prise of wine. Therefore the king was at the loss of the revenue that would normally be collected at Waterford.

The arrest of the ship antagonised the men of New Ross and,

HENRY DE LONDRES, ARCHBISHOP OF DUBLIN 1213-1228 AND JUSTICIAR 1221-1224

The archbishop stands in full canonical dress under a canopy with an ogee arch that ends in cusps. The dark brown background seems to obscure the red foliage outlining the figure. Grey is used to colour the edges of the mitre, of the light blue chasuble and also the crozier (originally gold). The chasuble is decorated with red, beneath which he wears the dalmata reaching just below the knees and fawn in colour. Beneath this again is a pink alb. The drapery falls in hook folds across the middle of the chasuble and there is a great sense of movement in the flowing robes. The hands are finely covered in ecclesiastical gloves and he holds in his left hand a crozier in the shape of a cross and a sudarium or napkin. The image may have been taken from an effigy that was once in Christ Church Cathedral, Dublin.

DIMENSIONS: L 280 x D 200

tiring of the power and influence of Waterford, they appealed to their lord to petition the king to investigate Waterford's monopoly. As Leinster had been divided among five co-heiresses in 1247 the burgesses of New Ross tried to rally the support of the lords of the three lordships bordering New Ross - Kilkenny, Wexford and Carlow. The burgesses claimed that any injury to the town of New Ross was an injury to the ancient rights and liberties of the old lordship of Leinster, part of which the three lords now held. The enquiry was held in Dublin in 1292 and found in favour of Waterford. During the enquiry the Lord of New Ross tried to discredit Waterford's claim by arguing that its monopoly was of relatively recent origin - from the time of Robert de Ufford's justiciarship (1267-1270).

Exactly ten years later in 1302 another enquiry was held - this time the lord of New Ross claimed that Stephen Fulbourn, justiciar from 1281-1288, was the author of Waterford's monopoly. This was a good try because Stephen had also been bishop of Waterford and therefore likely to favour the port. Realising that the loss of revenue to the king was a factor that would influence the decision of this second enquiry, both the lord and burgesses of New Ross were by 1302 now willing to allow the collection of royal taxes such as the prise of wine within their own port. Although the results of the enquiry do not survive, it is obvious that the status quo was maintained as Waterford's monopoly was still proving contentious in 1339 when the next enquiry was held. This time it appears that the king faltered and the case had to go to an appeal which in the end Waterford won.

In 1356 King Edward III issued a new charter to the city which stated clearly that all ships entering the harbour must unload at Waterford. This charter is referred to in a writ sent to William of Windsor, the king's lieutenant in Ireland in 1371. (p77) This is the last document on the Charter Roll, it states that 'all ships entering Waterford Harbour should proceed to the city and not elsewhere'.

The fact that a copy of this writ is on the roll proves that the roll was not compiled until after 137I. Yet we know from the petition sent to Edward III in c1372/3 that the citizens were defending their rights against New Ross at the royal

ALEXANDER DE NOTTINGHAM, JUDGE (1265-70)

Alexander de Nottingham stands in an archway with slated turrets. The caption identifying him is badly stained. He wears a dark blue mantle which opens to reveal a green houppelande and matching shoes. The mantle is edged in red and underneath the wide sleeves one can see the tight green sleeves of the houppelande. There is also a shoulder cape and hood with liripipe which stretches down the judge's back. He also wears a simple coif which had been fashionable from the thirteenth century. Alexander's face is the standard skin colour, his hair is yellow and he has a distinctive forked beard.

DIMENSIONS: L 220 x W 160

DAVID DE BARRY, JUSTICIAR (1266-1267)

David de Barry wears a fawn buttoned mantle with large black buttons (originally gold). The mantle has scalloped edges at the sleeves which end at the elbow revealing a blue gipon which ends in a dark grey band at the wrist (originally gold). There is a long hood with liripipe in pale blue matching the gipon. The shoes are fawn like the mantle and are embroidered with black stripes. He has a blue beard and hair. The background was ornamented in red foliage but this has been painted over with dark brown pigment.

DIMENSIONS: L 280 x D 180

ROBERT D'UFFORD, JUSTICIAR (1267-70 & 1276-1281)

Robert d'Ufford stands in a trefoiled arch with foliated sprandrels. The parapet is badly stained making it difficult to read the inscription. The justiciar stands with feet stretching over the architectural frame with large fawn embroidered shoes. He wears a long blue mantle and it is one of the few illustrations where colour is used in modulated tones to create volume. The folds of the voluminous mantle are highlighted in white. Underneath he wears a fawn houppelande. His arms are wrapped in the mantle which opens at the right side and is held together with a brooch. Robert d'Ufford wears a matching fawn hood. Underneath a magnificent high crown hat the face is flesh coloured and bearded in a bluish grey colour.

DIMENSIONS: L 280 x W 180

GEOFFREY DE GENEVILLE, JUSTICIAR (1273-1276)

The justiciar is set in a canopy with slated turrets. He wears a parti-coloured outfit of red and fawn. No distinction is made between the hose, shoes, gipon or possibly the shoulder cape. He wears a broad brimmed hat with a large parti-coloured feather springing from a gold brooch (now grey in colour). He stands with his right hand resting on his knightly belt that was originally gold.

DIMENSIONS: L 250 x W 170

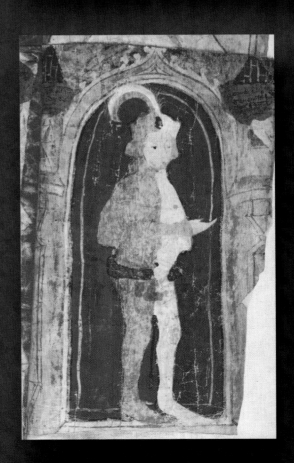

Chancery. Clearly, despite Edward's charter of 1356 and the various writs sent upholding Waterford's monopoly, the men of New Ross were still hopeful of a change of heart by the king or a successful challenge to Waterford's monopoly. It looks very likely that the roll was compiled by the mayor and council to prove the legitimacy of their case and settle once and for all the dispute with New Ross. The enquiry at the Chancery seems to have dragged on until Edward's death in 1377. During the last few years of his reign the king was very inactive and so perhaps no decision was taken. Finally Edward's successor Richard II came down on the side of Waterford. In fact he even took up the city's earlier offer to use the walled town and port as a bridgehead to land troops when he arrived at Waterford in 1394 at the head of the largest armada ever to sail into an Irish port.

Almost eighty years later another aspect of Waterford's monopoly was being hotly contested and seven folios of the Great Parchment Book are given over to this dispute. In 1472 the mayor of Waterford demanded that his counterpart, the reeve of New Ross, attend court with his attorneys to prove under what law they could force Waterford ships to pay taxes to New Ross. The account informs us that 'sundry citizens of Waterford who load boats at Thomastown, Inistioc and St Molyng' were arrested as they travelled to Waterford. Apparently the New Ross authorities had impounded a Waterford ship as it passed the port because it had failed to pay a tax known as the cocket. The dispute became very complicated but essentially Waterford claimed that its citizens were free of tax on the three rivers from the entrance of the harbour up to Inistioge on the Nore, St Mullins on the Barrow and Carrick on the Suir. New Ross lost this case but a hundred years later in 1574 when the city received a new charter from Queen Elizabeth, the charter included a recitation of Waterford's admiralty rights on the three rivers.

It could be said that the dispute per se finally came to a conclusion in 1518 when, according to a jury empanelled at New Ross, 'thirty-four of the leading citizens of Waterford, accompanied by many Spaniards, Frenchmen, Bretons and Irish.... came riotously with a fleet of boats in piratical or warlike fashion, variously armed, to wit, with surcoats, coats

JOHN WOGAN, JUSTICIAR (1295-1301 & 1305 -1308)

The Justiciar wears an unusually ornate houppelande which is gathered at his waist with a grey (originally gold) beaded belt. Across his shoulders is a hood in vermillion which extends with long liripipe which he holds in his left hand. The other end of the hood is edged in grey (originally gold). The embroidered shoes are very long extending to the edge of the picture frame. Wogan's chest visibly projects as the top of his houppelande is liberally padded. The figure is surrounded by a dark blue background with a white outline of the rounded arch.

DIMENSIONS: L 250 x W 150

JOHN DARCY, JUSTICIAR (1322-1333)

He stands in a trefoiled arch against a dark blue background with foliage outlining his figure. He wears a ceremonial garb which is parti-coloured in blue and yellow. He is dressed in a houppelande which reaches to his ankles revealing embroidered shoes of similar colour. The shoulder cape opening at the right shoulder is held in place by a large round brooch (see ring brooch p43) and also matches the houppelande, as does the ornate hat. A knightly belt sits on his hips and he holds a long sword attached to it. John Darcy was the longest serving justiciar of the fourteenth century.

DIMENSIONS: L 265 x W 200

JOHN MORICE, JUSTICIAR (1346)

He stands in a trefoiled arch filled with faded vermillion, wearing a long blue mantle with matching hood with liripipe hanging down. The mantle opens to reveal a pair of yellow hose and yellow embroidered shoes. The sleeves are decorated in grey possibly originally gold colour. He also wears a knightly belt but not down on the hips as was the fashion. He holds a dagger in his right hand. The artist used shading to pick out highlights and shadows around the edge of the figure. The face and hands are also given distinctive flesh tone. The vermillion background has a foliated decoration.

DIMENSIONS: L 280 x W 200

WILLIAM OF WINDSOR, LORD LIEUTENANT OF IRELAND (1369-1372) GOVERNOR AND KEEPER OF IRELAND (1374-1376)

This illustration is in poor condition and may have been added to by later generations. The red houppelande hangs in folds but is very blotchy with black staining obscuring the waist and parts of the skirt. He wears a hat that has gold decoration. The face is almost completely obscure.

DIMENSIONS: L 290 x W 200

of mail, helmets, shields, spears, swords, lances, crossbows, darts, bows, arrows, broadaxes and bombards or cannon and assaulted their town'. They inflicted one hundred pounds worth of damage before being bought off by 'the gift of a silver gilt mace'. There was only one casualty, a Bristol man, who was slain by a bombard or cannon and afterwards thrown off a ship into the sea and drowned.

The mace taken from New Ross is still a prized item in the civic regalia of Waterford and is displayed in the museum. (p139) Centuries of litigation tend to make cities careful about their muniments and it is fascinating to contemplate the scribes and lawyers in 1372 going to the city treasury to search for the relevant documents to include in the roll. Some of the documents on the roll were almost a hundred and fifty years old when the roll was compiled. The power of the written word was very important to a city where rights and privileges could mean the difference between success and failure, poverty and prosperity. It was this respect for the written word that has ensured the survival for us today of two wonderful treasures - the Great Charter Roll and the Great Parchment Book wherein are preserved details of the dispute.

The author would like to acknowledge Annie Fletcher's 'A Study of the Great Charter Roll of Waterford', Moderatorship Thesis, for the descriptions of the illuminated panels.

THE MAYORS OF DUBLIN, WATERFORD, CORK AND LIMERICK c1373

These are the mayors of the Irish royal cities and their order reflects the hierarchy that prevailed in the middle ages. In the Rolls of the medieval Irish Parliament, Waterford always takes second place to Dublin in listing of the cities. Dublin received the right to elect a mayor in 1229. The cities of Waterford, Cork and Limerick all had mayors prior to Edward I becoming king in 1272. It is very likely that Waterford and perhaps the other cities received this right from Edward when he was lord of Ireland from 1254 to 1272. These are the earliest images of Irish mayors.

DIMENSIONS: L 280 x W 200

LATE MEDIEVAL
WATERFORD

The outbreak of the Hundred Years War between France and England (1340-1453) added to Waterford's woes as it disrupted trade and saw piracy flourish. The cumulative effect of these calamities in the European context was the ending of the medieval expansionist era and the shrinking of the sphere of Anglo-Norman influence in Ireland, mirrored elsewhere in the abandonment of colonies in the Holy Land and the ending of German colonial expansion in Eastern Europe. The mayor and citizens of Waterford were aware of the declining fortunes of the colony when they wrote to King Edward III in c1373 pledging that 'if all the said lands of Ireland should be gained by your enemies which God forbid, it would be regained better and more quickly by your said city [Waterford] than by any other city throughout our said lands of Ireland'.[1]

King Edward III did not take up the offer to use Waterford as a bridgehead for a major expedition to Ireland. However his successor Richard II (1377-99) did; in an attempt to curb the power of the McMurroughs of Wicklow who were organising raiding parties as far north as Dublin and as far south as Wexford, he sailed for Waterford in 1394, arriving at the head of the largest fleet, over five hundred ships, ever to sail into an Irish port. He probably stayed at Greyfriars as we know he took the submissions of Gaelic princes there. Edward also witnessed the installation of the first bishop of the united dioceses of Waterford and Lismore in Christ Church Cathedral.[2] Despite early successes the long-term objective of the mission was not achieved and Richard was back in Waterford in 1399. However, shortly after landing, news came of the arrival in England of the king's exiled cousin Henry Bolingbroke. Richard was forced to return home only to be deposed by Bolingbroke who became King Henry IV.

In an attempt to improve the government of the lordship Richard's reign witnessed a transfer of some central government functions to the local administration. In 1381 John, son of William Lombard (the only Waterford mayor mentioned in the Great Charter Roll) was ordered to elect a sheriff for county Waterford and was himself appointed sub-sheriff.[3] In 1395, the year Richard returned to England following his expedition to Ireland, Lombard was again called upon to elect a sheriff, not only for county Waterford but also for counties Wexford, Tipperary and Kilkenny.[4] It would be gratifying to think that Richard was a king who favoured decentralisation and saw the city of Waterford as the administrative centre for the south-east region. The reality was however that this was a rearguard action: the king's administration was simply recognising that the Dublin government did not have the resources necessary to carry out its functions effectively. In the long run Waterford was left to its own devices, as unrest within the colony saw its links with central government gradually decline. In 1413, the last year of Henry IV's reign, the city received a charter stating that the mayor 'could not be harassed by the king's ministers in Ireland or the liberty of the city taken into the king's hands without special mandate under the great seal of England.'[5]

That same year Mayor Simon Wicken decided to teach a lesson to the O'Driscolls of Baltimore who had been harassing the city, along with the Powers of Dunhill, since 1368 when the then mayor was killed in a battle. We must assume that these attacks were part of their attempts to extract black rent from the city in return for allowing fishermen from Waterford fish for herring off the coast of county Cork, regarded by the O'Driscolls as theirs. We know that herring was being exported to London from Waterford at this time and that this trade was lucrative. Mayor Wicken gained entry to the O'Driscoll stronghold at Baltimore on Christmas Eve when he said he had come with a ship laden with wine (the black rent). The O'Driscoll leaders were then taken prisoner and ordered 'come with me to Waterford to sing and make merry'. We can assume that the O'Driscolls were released on payment of a ransom.[6] This was however a pyrrhic victory, for the attacks on Waterford continued in 1430, 1442, 1448 and 1461. The practice of paying black rents to the O'Driscolls must also have continued, for in 1450 the Irish parliament enacted that 'no persons from Waterford, Wexford, Youghal, Cork or Kinsale shall fish at Baltimore or sell them victuals or arms'. The act went on to articulate the reason for the ban: 'Finian O'Driscoll is an Irish enemy and has slain the king's subjects'. [7]

The fifteenth century Irish parliament made feeble efforts to maintain, even at a basic level, the concept of 'one war one peace' which existed during the heyday of the Anglo-Norman colony, when only the Dublin government could make war and agree peace terms. The reality was that the mayor of Waterford had been conducting peace terms with the Powers of county Waterford from as early as 1345 and from 1447 the city was empowered by the Dublin administration to make war.[8] The 1461 attack on the city saw a combined Power and O'Driscoll armada assemble at Tramore in county Waterford against which the mayor led an army, capturing their leaders and three of their galleys. The mayoral election took place within weeks of the attack. Clearly the perks of office did not outweigh the risks for nobody was willing to accept the post. The city's Great Parchment Book records various pieces of local legislation enacted to cajole, induce or otherwise force freemen to accept the mayoralty.[9] (p129) As the city faced its crisis of government the English monarchy was also in turmoil as King Henry VI was ousted by the Yorkist Edward IV. Appraised of the problems in Waterford, the new king issued Waterford a charter cancelling the city's debts. The charter includes the provision that 'the mayor, bailiffs and citizens should have a sword with an adjoined scabbard to be borne before the mayor.' (p87) A mace was also given, another attempt to add prestige to the office of mayor and maintain a close relationship with what was probably the most loyal city in Ireland. (p139)

Yet despite all the disturbances and battles on both sides of the Irish Sea there was an economic upturn in England. Edward encouraged trade, especially the wool trade and he was the first solvent monarch at his death since 1189. There was a corresponding growth in the Irish wool trade during these years, with London as the distribution centre.

By 1486 a guild of wool manufacturers had been established in Waterford, a development that reflects a growing stability in the hinterland where sheep rearing flourished.[10] Today we can still see the signs of this prosperity in the now ruined monasteries, the traditional providers of wool. Many of these still show the signs of late fifteenth century rebuilding or enlargement and the most obvious sign of this wealth was the addition of a bell tower, something of a luxury. These symbols of prosperity can also be seen in churches of the urban-based orders. Their wealth is a reflection of that of their congregation, the wealthy citizens no doubt financing the addition of bell towers to the Franciscan and Dominican churches in the late fifteenth century. In 1999 a large bronze bell was discovered during building works close to the Dominican Church of St Saviour and a large wooden tongue, perhaps from a funeral bell, had been found under its bell tower in 1916. (p109) The most popular woollen product exported was a shawl-like garment sold in England and on the continent and although not all of them were made in Waterford they were nonetheless known abroad as 'Waterford Rugs'.[11] Such was the importance of this trade in manufactured woollens to Ireland that in 1522 the Irish parliament banned the export of raw wool altogether.[12]

Clearly something of a *modus operandi* had been reached between the citizens of Waterford and the Irish and Anglo-Irish of the hinterland. It happened in spite of ethnic and cultural differences, simply because cities like Waterford provided the facilities to exchange agricultural produce for luxuries and imported necessities. The fourteenth and fifteenth century wars in which the city had been embroiled were not wars of conquest but attempts to extract protection money and it would be safe to assume that many of the disputes arose when the city refused to pay up or when extra money was demanded. By the end of the middle ages the Irish were being integrated into urban life: they could now be citizens and apprentices and the Irish language was permissible in the city courts. The increasing stability of the countryside is reflected in the acceptance by Irish chiefs like Florence McCarthy and

Cormac McTeg of English law and custom in a ceremony in 1488 presided over by Mayor James Rice who represented the king.[13] The most obvious sign of an economic upturn was the decision of the Irish parliament, meeting in Waterford, to establish a mint in Reginald's Tower for the first time in almost two hundred years. The coins were struck with an image of the king's head on the obverse and on the reverse the words *Civitas Waterford.* (p89)

In the late fifteenth century the trade guilds, producing woollen cloth and leather goods, appear to have been the mainstay of the city. Naturally there were still some merchant princes who managed the city's imports and exports. James Rice, eleven times mayor, stands out head and shoulders above the rest. James was not a power-crazed megalomaniac; he had the city council pass several laws to try to spread the responsibility of the mayoralty to others. When those failed he had a law passed prohibiting a mayor from holding office two years in succession.[14] His munificence epitomises the new-found wealth of late fifteenth century Waterford. He was particularly generous to the church and to John Collyn, Dean of Christ Church Cathedral who founded the chantry chapel of St Saviour and a hostel for the poor men of the city, known as the Good Men's House, built near the cathedral. Rice endowed the foundation with 6 houses and gardens, 3 shops, 2 gardens and rents to the value of thirty shillings and other tenements of unspecified value. A basement of one of the six houses bequeathed to the dean in July 1468 has been identified as the upper deanery undercroft in Cathedral Square.[15]

Rice's cadaver tomb, one of the grandest and earliest extant examples of a fully developed Irish 'apostle tomb', is in Christ Church Cathedral. When sculpted in 1480 he had it housed in a special chantry chapel built on the side of the medieval cathedral and dedicated to St Catherine and St James. Twice he went on pilgrimage to the tomb of St James of Compostella in Spain.[16] Among the items mentioned in Dean Collyn's 1481 will was a boat shaped silver cup willed to James Rice. This oldest surviving

Waterford will shows the wealth of the late fifteenth century church; among the many items mentioned is a set of green velvet vestments that Collyn bequeathed to the dean and chapter. The green cloth-of-gold dalmatic, c1460, is almost certainly from this set. (p107)[17]

The rent roll of the cathedral, compiled at Collyn's instigation in 1483, shows exactly the amount of property owned by the cathedral and is therefore a vivid reminder of the great wealth that the church had accumulated. (p111) The set of four cloth-of-gold benediction copes, also belonging to the medieval cathedral and dating from c1480-1500, are other symbols of its great wealth and the patronage the church enjoyed from merchants like James Rice. (p90, 91) It is interesting that despite this apparent wealth, some time around 1480 the churches and monasteries in the Waterford area decided to make null and void all grants and leases of the lands they owned. We can only presume that over time inflation had made the rents ridiculously low and so the churches were trying to restructure their assets by re-leasing the land at higher rents. Rice was mayor when the issue came to a head in 1481 and this time he took a strong stand against the churches. In what was obviously an attempt by the city council to prevent the churches nullifying the leases, it prohibited anyone in the city from taking a lease on land which the churches had recovered from another citizen. A land-grabbing freeman would lose the franchise of the city whilst a guilty foreigner was to be exiled and abjured out of the city and suburbs forever.[18] This action appears to be an early example of what became known as 'boycotting' as practised by Parnell in the late nineteenth century. Clearly, as elsewhere in Europe, there was tension between the civil and church authorities. Two years later in 1483 the city council passed a law prohibiting the breaking of glass in church windows and if children were found to have committed the crime their parents were held responsible.[19] Was this an indication that the standing of the church in the eyes of some of the faithful had been diminished?

James Rice was bailiff (deputy mayor) in 1487 when the

lord deputy, the Earl of Kildare, threatened to hang both him and the mayor 'at their door posts' if they did not accept the pretender to the throne of King Henry VII, Lambert Simnel. The earl had the pretender crowned king of England in Christ Church Cathedral in Dublin and expected Waterford to follow suit, which it refused to do. The whole affair soon came to nothing but it provided Waterford with an opportunity to display its loyalty and the king with an opportunity to thank the city. Henry gave Waterford a new charter, on display in the museum, and a grant for the purchase of two hundred bows, four hundred sheaves of arrows and four hundred bow strings.[20] An even greater threat came in 1495 when the supporters of another pretender, Perkin Warbeck, laid siege to the city. This was the first artillery siege of an Irish city and a cannon probably from one of Warbeck's ships, was dredged from the river Suir in 1901.[21] (p113)

Waterford was now on the crest of a wave, the most favoured city in Ireland; the people of Dublin and Cork had embraced the pretenders as had the lord deputy. Waterford alone stood firm and the pride felt by the city after the Simnel debacle was beautifully captured in a poem of three hundred lines, *The Mayor of Waterford's Letter*, recited by James Rice when the king's agent, Sir Richard Edgecom, visited Waterford on his way from Cork to Dublin to receive the submissions of Simnel's rebel supporters.[22] It was as a mark of gratitude for the city's loyalty and defence of the king against the pretenders that the city is believed to have received its motto *Urbs Intacta Manet Waterfordia*, 'the city of Waterford remains untaken'.

Bearing sword and mace of King Edward IV

Edward came to the throne in 1461 having ousted the Lancastrian, King Henry VI, in the dynastic civil wars later called the Wars of the Roses. In 1461 Waterford had its own crisis - the city council had to enact special legislation in order to persuade members of the merchant oligarchy to 'accept the office of mayor and not absent themselves from the mayoral elections'. Recent attacks on the city by the Powers and the O'Driscolls had shown that the office of mayor had few perks, especially as the mayor was expected to lead the city's army against the enemy when under attack.

It is clear from surviving documents that Edward was made aware of the crisis when the mayor requested that part of the farm of the city, rent owed to the king, be given to the city fathers for the repair of fortifications. Being a new and not altogether secure king, Edward decided to court the support of Waterford. Not only did he reduce the rent owed to him, as requested, he also issued Waterford with a new charter in 1461. In this charter he decreed that the city should have 'a sword with an adjoined scabbard, to be borne before the mayor by a sergeant within the city and when the occasion arises to be borne before the king' i.e. in the event of a visit from the monarch. The king's generosity included the gift of a mace, also to be carried before the mayor. Although this is the earliest known reference to a civic sword, it is clear from the illustration at the top of the Great Charter Roll that the Waterford authorities were at least familiar with the idea of a ceremonial sword.

Edward's sword obviously helped to raise the status of the mayoralty, for in 1481 medieval Waterford's most famous mayor, James Rice, together with his friend, John Collyn, dean of Christ Church Cathedral, initiated a new civic ceremony. The details of the ceremony are recorded in both the Great Parchment Book and Dean Collyn's Register of the Chantry of St Saviour's. This new ceremony would be performed each year on 'the Monday after the feast of the Exaltation of the Holy Cross when all the council shall attend at the chapel of Jesus beside the Trinity Church [Christ Church Cathedral] and there to hear Mass of the Holy Ghost solemnly said and sung with due observance'. Following the mass 'all of the council shall proceed from the chapel to the Guildhall with the sword bearer holding aloft the civic sword and when there to elect and choose a mayor and bailiffs for the year next following'. Any councillor who failed to attend the mass was to be fined ten pounds. Mayor James Rice was of course a very religious man who had twice made the pilgrimage to the tomb of St James in Compostella in Spain. He endowed both the cathedral and Dean Collyn's almshouse for poor men of the city with large amounts of property. He was also very much a supporter of Waterford's strong links with the English monarchy and all things English. There can be little doubt that the ceremony he initiated in Waterford in 1481 was a direct copy of that begun in London in 1406. The man elected mayor of London that year was none other than the celebrated Dick Whittington!

Edward IV's bearing sword is one of the oldest items of the civic regalia preserved in the museum. Fortunately both sword and scabbard survived, although the black velvet of the scabbard is a relatively modern replacement. The mace shown in the illustration is believed to be that given to the city by the king. For discussion of the mace see p139. The sword has a steel blade and a silver hilt. The hexagonal pommel is of steel, as is the guard. The top of the scabbard is decorated with a crest-like motif, while the finial has a silver guard.

DATE:	1461 A D
NUMBER:	WMT1999.1595
DIMENSIONS:	sword overall L 1100 x max W 320
	blade L 888; handle L 153; pommel L 59 x W 55
	scabbard L 889 x W 47, silver finial L 94, motif L 40
MATERIAL:	silver, steel, leather, velvet
PROVENANCE:	historic municipal collection
FURTHER READING:	McEneaney (ed) 1995
	Byrne forthcoming
	Gilbert 1885
	MacNiocaill 1966

Coins of King Edward IV

By the time Edward IV came to the throne in 1461 there was an acute shortage of coin in Ireland. Most of what existed were old or cut down. Such poor coinage was not difficult to copy, so the Gaelic Irish of Meath and Louth produced counterfeits. These forgeries, sometimes called O'Reilly money, were condemned by the Anglo-Irish parliament. It was against this background that the Irish Parliament met in Waterford in 1463, where it was decided to open a mint in 'Reginald's Tower alias Dundory'. There the keeper of the mint began striking groats (four pence coins), half groats (two pence coins) and pennies. The groats illustrated are of two types. The first are called 'Titled crown coinage', where both the crown and title of the monarch appear. This coin was made in 1463/5. The second type, known as 'Light coinage', was produced after 1464, as in that year the king, anxious to keep some control over the Irish coinage, ordered that 'only dies made in the Tower of London could be used in any mint'. On this coin the king's head appears and below his neck, the letter G can be seen, standing for Germyn Lynch, the keeper of the mint.

Germyn Lynch was a most interesting character. Born in Galway, as early as 1441 his name is found in the records of the Worshipful Company of Goldsmiths, London. Five years later he is recorded as having been admitted to the freedom and the liberty of the goldsmiths of London to exercise the craft as a freeman. In 1457 he appears before the mayor of London to show letters patent, obtained from the king, exempting him from various civic duties. This suggests that Lynch found the performing of his civic duties something of an imposition, and so he used his wealth and influence to have the king grant him the exemption. A real entrepreneur, he was by 1459 involved in the Icelandic fishery, no doubt making good profits for the sale of fish in the ever growing and prosperous London market.

In February 1461 he was appointed keeper of the Irish mint for life, suggesting very good connections in court circles. However within a month of his appointment, his patron, King Henry VI, was deposed. For most rising stars this would have been calamitous but not for Lynch, whose appointment was approved by the new king, Edward IV, in August 1461. His position was not recognised in Ireland until the end of 1463, by which time he was minting in Dublin and Waterford.

Germyn Lynch was a skilled moneyer (the person in charge of the mint) and he would have manufactured the dies for the Irish coins. The cylindrical dies, made of steel on a blacksmith's forge, hold the design of the coin. The coin design was created on the smooth end of the die, using a hammer and a limited range of punches to make the letters and decorations. The punches could be in the shape of wedges, straight lines, crescents or points. Two dies are needed to strike a coin. The lower die, called the pile, holds the design of the obverse side of the coin, the upper die, called the trussel, holds the design of the reverse side of the coin. To strike a coin, the spike at one end of the lower die is secured in a wooden block. Then a circular piece of silver, known as the blank, is placed on the lower die and the upper die is positioned over it. The upper die is then struck with a hammer, thus producing the coin.

The job of preparing the blanks was more complicated than the less prestigious job of actually striking the coins and this was reflected in remuneration. In the time of King Edward I the person who made the coin blanks was paid two and a half pence per pound weight, while the hammerman or coin striker was paid only a halfpenny per pound weight. The blanks were made by melting down silver to form an ingot that was then flattened and discs cut from the flattened sheet. Both the weight and fineness of the blanks had to be carefully controlled. Coin balances could be used to determine the correct weight of the blank or coin. (p47)

The office of mint master was a lucrative one and the method of remuneration undoubtedly appealed to the goldsmith-businessman. Of the 120 fourpenny silver pieces, or groats to the pound troy, the master was allowed five of these for himself. However, a skilled operator like Lynch could, and did, considerably increase his profits. In 1472 while working in Drogheda as undermaster of the mint, he was found to be making underweight coins - literally making too much money! He was getting an extra three coins from every ounce of silver. Under normal circumstances this was a major crime, as it caused devaluation of the currency, and as such disrupted trade. In earlier periods the penalty for having clipped a coin, removing a piece of silver from its edge, was to have your hand chopped off and displayed in the mint. The penalty for debasing coins, mixing copper with silver or producing light-weight coins, was castration, before being hung drawn and quartered. Lynch was however pardoned and re-appointed the following year as master. Five times in all he was dismissed from his post but the first four times he was re-appointed. On the fifth and final dismissal in 1483, when he was well over sixty years of age, he was not re-instated for in that year his patron King Edward IV died. The mint in Waterford closed for a time after Edward's death but was re-opened by his successor Richard III (1483-1485).

Germyn Lynch does not appear in the records after his final dismissal but the records of the preceding four decades show him as a man of many talents. He was master of a ship called the Michael that transported herring, salmon and hides to Bristol, returning to Ireland with salt, honey, alum, cloth and wine. He also took parties of pilgrims to the shrine of St James in Compostella in Spain, one of the most popular pilgrim sites in Europe. Five hundred years later his name is still mentioned in Reginald's Tower by the guides as they point out to visitors the very coins that were struck under his stewardship in that same building.

Titled crown coinage groat

DATE:	c1463 A D
NUMBER:	WMT1999.1606
DIMENSIONS:	Dia 230
MATERIAL:	silver
FURTHER READING:	Michael Kenny in Hurley & Scully 1997 & Dolley 1969
LOCATION:	Reginald's Tower

Light coinage groat

DATE:	c1470 A D
NUMBER:	WMT1999.6248
DIMENSIONS:	Dia 230
MATERIAL:	silver
FURTHER READING:	Michael Kenny in Hurley & Scully 1997 & Dolley 1969
LOCATION:	Reginald's Tower

Both on loan from the National Museum of Ireland

The Magi Cope

The Waterford collection of fifteenth century Benediction copes and High Mass vestments afford a rare insight into the richness of liturgical practice in late medieval Ireland. It is the only set of pre-reformation High Mass vestments to survive in Ireland and the superb quality of the fabric, Italian cloth of gold, and the artistic mastery of the decorated panels, the work of Flemish artists and embroiderers, make it a collection of national importance. The vestments show that Waterford, at the close of the middle ages, was a cosmopolitan city connected to the great art centres of Europe. They are a product of an artistic world that produced the renaissance though Ireland, because of political and religious conflict, would never experience the glories of that great movement. Consequently the history of the vestments reflects the turbulent history of the city.

As early as 1481 the vestments are mentioned in the will of John Collyn, dean of Christ Church Cathedral, where he bequeathed them to his successor and to the chapter of the cathedral. They remained the property of the Cathedral after the establishment of the Church of Ireland. In 1577 David Cleere, dean of Christ Church, placed the silver plate and vestments in the custody of the staunchly catholic corporation in a pledge for £400, possibly in an attempt to keep them in catholic hands. Two years later Dean Cleere was the person who led the opposition to Marmaduke Middleton, the bishop who almost single-handedly tried to impose protestantism on his diocese. One suspects that the commitment to the reformed church by some Irish churchmen was less than wholehearted. Then in 1637, as a result of a royal edict demanding the 'proper and decorous performance of Divine Service', Mayor Richard Butler became involved in a protracted argument with Thomas Wentworth, the king's lord deputy in Ireland. Wentworth demanded the return of 'certain copes and vestments belonging to the Dean and Chapter of Christ Church'. The mayor acquiesced. The letter, signed by Wentworth, survives, and is displayed beside the vestments in the museum.

The greatest threat to their survival came from the Cromwellians. Oliver Cromwell unsuccessfully laid siege to the city in November 1649. However, it fell to his son-in-law,

The orphreys
The meeting of Joachim and Anna at the Golden Gate

The embroidered panels on the orphreys have New Testament scenes representing the birth and childhood of Christ. Artists skilled in miniature painting and familiar with the rich contemporary sources drew the scenes. Each panel measures 460 x 240 mm. This is the first panel and is the first scene in the cycle. It shows Joachim and Anna meeting at the Golden Gate as told in the Apocryphal Gospel. Near the massive gilded pillars of the city gate with its medieval portcullis the elderly couple are seen rejoicing at the angel's message. Anna will have a daughter and 'she shall be made the mother of eternal blessings'.

Ireton, in August 1650. The respite between the two sieges provided an opportunity for the church authorities to hide their treasures in the cathedral vaults. The subterfuge was only partly successful: a woman informed the city's Cromwellian governor, Colonel Sadlers, who found one of the vaults and sold twelve hundred weight of brass ornaments at nine pence per pound. The cathedral's silver plate or vestments were not found - an enquiry held in 1661 tells us that 'not finding silver plate they arrested several priests in their mass houses and in Irishmen's houses where there was a great store of plate, chalices, rings, and rich copes as rich as ever seen in Spain.' The cathedral's own vestments were so well hidden that they escaped detection and the secret of their hiding place so well kept that all who knew of their existence died before they could be safely recovered. The vestments lay hidden for 125 years and were accidentally discovered when John Roberts demolished the medieval cathedral in 1774. On their discovery the protestant bishop, Chenevix, in a goodwill gesture to the catholic community, generously presented them to the catholic dean, Dr Hussey, later bishop of Waterford and first president of Maynooth. They have remained the property of the catholic bishop of Waterford and Lismore ever since. Canon Power, the diocesan historian, recounts the finding of the vestments in 1774 and their return to the catholic church. He comments on the crude repairs to the vestments. The cleaning and conservation undertaken in recent years has made these good in the case of the Magi Cope and the Dalmatic, and the opulence of crimson, emerald and gold now shine out again, as they did when first made.

It is fascinating to speculate on the circumstances of the cathedral acquiring these vestments. Were they a royal gift? Were they the commission of a wealthy patron such as James Rice? Whatever about their origin, it is not difficult to imagine these vestments being worn by the bishop and clergy at the high points of the year, for example on Christmas Day, Good Friday or Easter Sunday, in the cathedral. Remember that this was a time when the division of the sacred and the secular had not yet happened, nor had the reformation, the seamless garment had not yet been rent. Imagine the effects on the faithful in the great candle-lit cathedral when the bishop raised the monstrance at Benediction, the splendour

The Presentation of the Blessed Virgin

The second scene, the Presentation of the Blessed Virgin, again follows the Apocryphal Gospels and the stage directions of the mystery plays. Joachim and Anna are before the temple - a little church with gothic windows. Joachim has the head covering, cloak and white beard required and Anna is represented in the style of an 'old respectable matron' in both her clothing and headdress. Close by, Mary, a child of about three years in a long dress with a gilded halo and long hair down her back, ascends a long flight of steps. These are the fifteen symbolic steps of the temple which led to the altar of burnt offering and as the Apocrypha tells us, the Blessed Virgin 'went up all the steps one after the other without the help of any one leading her or lifting her, in such a manner that in this respect at least you would think she had already attained full age.' Thus would the medieval writer impress on us the maturity and wisdom even as a child of the future Mother of God. We know that the mystery play of the Presentation of the Blessed Virgin Mary was performed at Avignon, France, in 1385.

of the Magi Cope falling in folds around him.

The copes are really a set - the arrangement of the embroideries follows the great cycles of the Old and New Testaments, going from Creation, through the life of Christ to the Last Day and Salvation of Souls. Thus the first cope is the red Creation Cope, showing the Mystery of the Incarnation as the central theme, and the six panels showing the Fall of Lucifer, the Birth of Eve, the Fall of Adam and Eve, the Crucifixion and finally the Resurrection and Redemption of Souls. As the Golden Legend has it, Adam and all the just souls are led 'into the glorious grace of paradise'. The second is the Magi Cope, featured here. The third is the green Passion or Crucifixion Cope, with the Crucifixion on the hood. This cope, once again resplendent, having been conserved, is on display in the National Museum of Ireland. The other embroidered scenes are the Agony in the Garden, the Arrest of Christ and His healing Malchus's ear, Christ before Herod, the Scourging at the Pillar, the Crowning of Thorns and the Carrying of the Cross. The final cope is the green Annunciation Cope. While belonging to the same suite, it is slightly different from the others in terms of the brocade and the embroidery. The scenes are: Joachim's Vision, Joachim and Anna at the Golden Gate, the Presentation of the Blessed Virgin, a symbolic representation of the Conception, the Visit to Elizabeth and the Birth of St John the Baptist and the Marriage of Mary and Joseph. The final scene in this cycle, the Annunciation, is on the hood.

The high mass vestments consist of a chasuble, dalmatic and tunicle, all of green velvet brocades on cloth-of-gold ground. The chasuble is the 'Roman' type with straight back and fiddle-shaped front. The back depicts Our Lady of Sorrows, with angels to the sides and pairs of apostles below. The front orphreys show saints. The orphreys of the dalmatic (p107) and tunicle also illustrate single saints and apostles. Two stoles and two maniples make up the set. The high mass vestments are undoubtedly those mentioned in Dean Collyn's will of 1481.

The semi-circular Magi Cope, the one featured here, is one of the finest pieces in the collection. The Magi are depicted on the hood, hence the name. Four full widths of the fifty-

The Annunciation

The third panel is the Annunciation. Mary, as the legendary gospel continues, is in her chamber. The gothic windows with diamond panels, the bed with embroidered hangings and cushions are as we see them in fifteenth century illustrations. She kneels beside a low stool, upon which rests a book, the Book of Wisdom. Light surrounds her fair head and the blue and gold mantle falls about her feet in widespread gothic folds. The archangel Gabriel, with wings of blue red green and gold, alights before her. In his hands are a sceptre and scroll bearing from heaven the message of the Annunciation. On the tiled floor rests the vase of lilies, symbol of purity, so dear to contemporary Flemish painters.

eight cm wide velvet and two pieced ends were required, making the cope almost one and a half metres high and maximum two metres wide. It is made of brocaded velvet on cloth-of-gold ground with pomegranate design in red silk pile and tiny gold loops coming through the pile. The crimson velvet pile is of two heights and has a large asymmetrical pattern composed of undulating stems, leaves and stylised pomegranates. The pomegranate symbolises fertility or in the Christian context, spreading the message of Christ. Most specialists agree that the velvet came off a Florentine loom about 1480, when the Medici princes, great patrons of all the arts, including textiles, ruled the city. Textiles were not regarded as a lesser art. The cloth of the cope was probably woven by men.

The Flemish workshops of Brussels, Bruges and Ghent were great centres of embroidery in the fifteenth century. The magnificent embroidery on the hood and orphreys (decorated panels on the front of the cope) is worked with silver-gilt metal thread and coloured silks and split, brick and stem stitches, couched work (the surface covered with threads and these secured by stitches forming a pattern, a technique perfected in Flanders) and the *or nué* (shaded gold) technique on linen fabric. The scenes are framed by ogive arches, typical of the late fifteenth century: these are worked in gold thread laid over string and parchment padding, with blue silk spandrels. The embroideries are even more remarkable for their period by the unusually large number of figures and details in each panel. All of these represent specific people and details from the Old and New Testaments, from medieval tradition, drama and literature including the Apocryphal Gospels, The Golden Legend and *The Meditations on the Life of Jesus Christ,* by the Franciscan Thomas de Caulibus, and the mystery plays. The faces of the figures are Flemish, as are the details of architecture, of dress and armour.

The author is indebted to the late Catriona MacLeod

DATE: c1480 A D
NUMBER: WMT1999.0005
DIMENSIONS: H 1410 x max W 2000
MATERIAL: linen, silk, gilt-silver metal, paper
PROVENANCE: the medieval Christ Church Cathedral
FURTHER READING: MacLeod 1952

On loan from the Bishop of Waterford and Lismore
Conserved with generous assistance from the Heritage Council and Waterford City Council

The Nativity

The fourth panel, the Nativity, is especially rich in design and in the variety of stitches and shades of bright silk. From the gothic arcades above, God the Father, accompanied by angels, contemplates the scene where the shepherds have assembled, and with Mary, adore the infant. (In the early liturgical office, a choir boy, representing an angel, had his place in the gallery overlooking the altar. From there he announced to the shepherds just before mass began, the birth of the Saviour.) Close by are St Joseph with a lantern to represent night and the ever-present ox and ass thus fulfilling the prophecy of Isaiah: 'the ox knoweth his owner and the ass his Master's crib'. Another detail popular in contemporary painting is the single pillar prominently shown. This is the pillar referred to in *The Meditations* against which Mary braced herself when the hour of midnight came.

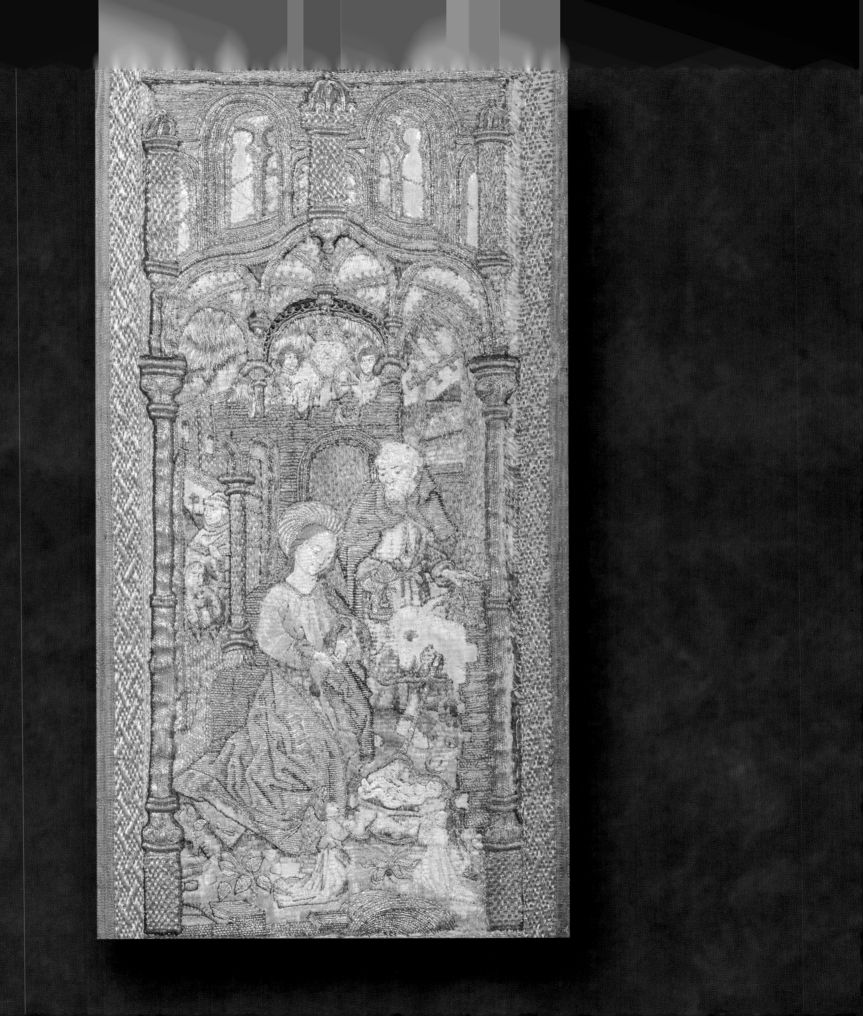

The Circumcision

The fifth panel, the Circumcision, shows the infant with St Joseph, the officiating high priest vested as a medieval bishop, the acolyte and serving women in late fifteenth century dress. The young woman, so prominently shown and fashionably gowned, and whose hair is stuffed into the gold net caul, is almost certainly the Hebrew woman, who according to the Apocrypha, assisted at the birth and circumcision and whose withered hand the Christ child cured. Thus would medieval faith outdo the Gospel and attribute miracles to Christ from his infancy.

Jesus among the Doctors

Jesus among the Doctors is the final panel. This scene, which in the gospel serves as a transition between the childhood and manhood of Jesus and between His private and public life, was added at a certain moment to the liturgical drama of the Nativity. It served as a link between the two cycles of Christmas and Easter, that is between the drama of the Nativity and that of the Passion.

There are altogether nine figures in this panel, but the grouping is so skilfully arranged that there is no sense of overcrowding. The child sits meekly amid the doctors, whose learned faces and varying expressions of gravity, pomp and astonishment have all the meticulous realism of a Jan van Eyck painting. Most of them wear the ever favourite chaperon, some have the hood back on the shoulders, others wear it pulled over the head or twisted with one end hanging down in the fashionable mode of the late fifteenth century. One has spectacles, whose great round frames remind us of the donor in van Eyck's 'Madonna and Child with Canon van der Paele', painted in 1439. In the background the humble, grateful expressions of Joseph and Mary complete this panel as a collective portrait in silk.

The Hood

The hood, perhaps the most spectacular part of the cope, depicts three scenes: the visit of the Magi in the centre, with the arrival of the Queen of Sheba at the court of king Solomon on the left, and Abraham's visit to Melchizedek on the right. These two Old Testament scenes prefigured the homage of kings to the infant Jesus. This is the central theme. The Adoration of the Magi became a very popular theme for artists in all media from the mid-fifteenth century. This type of pictorial representation with events from the life of Christ illustrated by parallel scenes from the Old Testament goes right back to the medieval teaching of the gospels. It was an art form used in sculpture, illuminations, enamels and textiles. Many artists drew inspiration from the Golden Legend and the Apocryphal Gospels, sometimes following them very closely. In the fifteenth century, with the invention of printing, the triple statement of a gospel theme became elaborated in the *Biblia Pauperum.* This book, because of its woodblock illustrations, was known as 'The Bible of the Poor', and had a widespread circulation, becoming the most popular book of the day, especially in Germany and the Netherlands. Its influence on contemporary art and the production of the mystery plays cannot be overlooked; in it the artists found their theology and Christian symbolism presented in pictorial form. For the first time artists had in their workshops and ready to hand a framework of ideas which each might express according to his craft in wood, paint, enamel, stained glass, tapestry or embroidery. The Visit of the Magi is almost certainly inspired by a page from a fifteenth century Flemish copy of the *Biblia Pauperum.*

In the centre Mary sits with Jesus on her lap. The traditional open hut with raftered roof, is familiar to us through Rogier Van der Weyden and his school, artists who followed the texts closely, as well as the directions of the mystery plays. The wood paling made by Joseph 'a master carpenter', shepherds gazing over it and singing angels above, are all here - all are described in *The Meditations* and brought on to the stage in the mystery play of the Incarnation. About Mary are grouped Joseph and the Three Kings, Gaspar, Melchior and Balthasar, who as the Golden Legend relates, 'made strict inquiry of the Jews, saying 'where is the king who has been born to you for we have seen his star in the east and have come to worship him'. The large embroidered star, now much worn, is still visible on the raftered roof.

The three kings are dressed as medieval princes in rich oriental silks. Young Balthasar, fresh-cheeked and curly-haired, has a blue silk mantle and pink tunic fringed with gold. His long hose are yellow and short bootees green, with scarlet overshoes. His sword with fifteenth century quillons hangs before him in a green velvet scabbard. Each king bears a golden chalice in his hand, a symbol that goes back to the eleventh century rubric which prescribed a chalice for each of the three canons who then represented the kings. Just before the offertory they marched in by the great door right up to the choir where they prostrated themselves and gave their gifts. 'Gold' said the first king, 'to signify that He is king.' 'Incense to justify that he is God' said the second, 'Balm to justify that He must die' said the third. The kings are depicted as a young man, a middle-aged man and an old man and not as from India (Gaspar), Persia (Melchior) and Arabia or India (Balthasar), commonly seen in paintings from the later

fifteenth century onwards, where one king is often an African. Another idea came from the English monk Bede, who suggested that they came from Africa, Asia and Europe.

The Queen of Sheba's homage to Solomon is shown left. The young king is crowned with a gothic crown and bears a sceptre in his right hand. Through his open mantle of crimson, lined with fur, appears a green silk stomacher edged with gold. The wealthy queen, who as the Golden Legend tells 'came from far countries to see him with much people and riches and camels charged with aromatics and gold infinite', kneels before him. The bodice of her blue and gold high-waisted gown is cut to a low v-shape at the back and fastens in front with a great gold ornament. It has the regulation deep cuffs and tight undersleeves of the period. Her hair is gathered back from a typically Flemish face into a stiff heart-shaped headdress with finely worked red and gold net cauls, and at the back a long white floating veil. One attendant maiden also wears the heart-shaped hat, but without veil, and the other shows the black silk frontlet of the contemporary steeple headdress. All three offer gifts to the king - 'the queen gave to the king one hundred and twenty besants of gold, many aromatics and precious gems ... seeing his wisdom and goodness she blessed him.'

The homage of Melchizedek and his servants to Abraham and the offering of gifts make another parallel with the Magi visit. Here Abraham, in royal robes and fur tippet, crowned and bearing a sceptre, is shown as a king. Melchizedek and his servants whom Genesis describes as 'well-appointed' are here definitely armed. They have chainmail shirts under silk doublets and sleeveless leather gipons. One soldier has a salade helmet with sliding vizor. Melchizedek as king of Salem, wears a circlet crown - he has an oval shield and on the feet of his long leather boots glint shining rowel spurs. All these details of dress and armour date about 1470.

The closeness of the parallel with the Magi lies in the king of Salem's discernment of Abraham as the Lord's chosen leader, as against the blindness of the wicked kings of Sodom, Gomorrah, Adama and Bala. 'Melchizedek bringing forth bread and wine for he was the priest of the most high God, blessed Abraham' and he said 'Blessed be Abraham by the most high God who created heaven and earth. And blessed be the most high God by whose protection the enemies are in thy hands.'

Dalmatic

One of the most important pieces from the set of Waterford vestments is the dalmatic. Almost certainly among the green velvet vestments specifically mentioned in the will of Dean Collyn in 1481, the T-shaped dalmatic is one of the six pieces of the high mass vestments.

A dalmatic was worn by bishops and deacons. The dalmatic is T-shaped with open sleeves and sides. This dalmatic is made from green silk velvet, with an asymmetrical pattern of plant ornament and is decorated by embroidered bands called orphreys. The velvet is weft patterned, voided and cut; the voided areas are covered by gilt-silver metal threads and locally by massed gilt-silver loops. Twelve pieces of this velvet are used to make the dalmatic, but the most impressive section of the pattern is reserved for the back of the vestment, being more in view than the front. The red silk tape outlining the orphrey bands is original; the pale orange tape is a later addition. On either side of the neck there are cords with rich tassels. There are large fragments of the original brown twill lining

There are two sets of orphrey bands on the back and front, two on each sleeve and one on the front and the back neck. Apart from those on the neck, each orphrey depicts a single saint standing beneath an architectural canopy. Each figure holds their symbol, for example St James the Less holds a fuller's club; the mitred St Gregory the Great holds a book; St Agnes a cross; St Dorothy a casket; St Lawrence a miniature gridiron; St Matthew an axe and St Jude an oar. The arrangement of holy figures most likely followed a plan familiar at the time. The figures are embroidered on separate pieces of shaped linen fabric, appliquéd to a space in the embroidered background. The robes of the figures were embroidered first using a technique called 'shaded gold' or *or nué* which consists of couching two parallel gilt-silver metal threads with polychrome silk threads. The couched stitches are worked closely to achieve recession or depth of colour and more open to create highlight and pale colours. When complete, the skin, hair and facial features were embroidered using fine silk threads in subtle shades and a limited number of stitches (split, stem, laid threads, satin stitches).

The skin was worked in encroaching satin stitch (face worked directly onto the linen ground whereas hands were worked over the metal threads). The stitching on the faces imitates the brushstrokes of painting. For example, dark shadows under the eyes (on the upper figure, back proper left) are made by laid stitches at various angles over the skin stitches. The effect is stunning, even though the two threads appear to be of the same colour. The background is worked through two layers of tabby woven linen. Parts of the background (twisted columns and architectural mouldings above the canopy) and the border are worked in relief. As for the neck orphreys, the details including the angel's heads (back neck) were stitched over the *or nué* embroidery. A layer of paper and two types of lozenge patterned linen fabric back the orphrey bands.

Clíodna Devitt

DATE: c1460 A D
NUMBER: WMT2002.0100
DIMENSIONS: overall L 2240 x max W 1365
MATERIAL: Silk and linen, gilt-silver metal, paper
PROVENANCE: The medieval Christ Church Cathedral Waterford
                   Velvet possibly Florentine; embroidery, paper, linen fabric, probably
                   Flemish; Tassel and cord unknown; Assembly probably Flanders
FURTHER READING: MacLeod 1952

On loan from the Bishop of Waterford & Lismore
Conservation generously assisted by the Heritage Council

Bells

The larger bronze bell is a very fine fifteenth century tower bell recovered in 1999 in Conduit Lane in Waterford from a site close to the ruins of the Dominican priory of St Saviour's, known as Blackfriars. The Dominicians were commonly known as black friars because of their black habit; the black gown of academics today comes from them. The prosperity of the fifteenth century saw many monasteries, including the Waterford Dominicans, building belltowers mostly over the crossing of the church. This bell more than likely is the bell of St Saviour's in Waterford. In 1235 Henry III granted the city authorities permission to give to the Dominicans a piece of ground within the old city. This site had become available after King John re-fortified the city, moving the line of the defences to the south-west, thus leaving an old tower from the now redundant fortifications derelict within the city bounds. On this site, Arundel Square today, the Dominicans built one of their first houses in Ireland. During the 1260s a monk known as Geoffrey of Waterford lived there, a scholar of Greek, Arabic and Latin and highly regarded as a wine expert. He died in Paris about 1300. The Dominicans were very much an intellectual order of preachers who organised schools to educate the sons of the merchant class.

DATE: 15th century
NUMBER: WMT2002.0094
DIMENSIONS: H 420, Dia 340
MATERIAL: bronze
PROVENANCE: municipal collection since 1999
FURTHER READING: Fenning 1990

                     Langrishe in *JRSAI* 1881

Bell tongue

This wooden tongue belonged to the bell used in Blackfriars Dominican priory in Waterford. It was found on 12 August 1916, 'four feet under' the floor of the fifteenth century tower. This is very probably the tongue of the bronze bell recovered in 1999.

DATE: possibly 15th century
NUMBER: WMT1999.1903
DIMENSIONS: H 120, Dia 105
MATERIAL: wood, metal
PROVENANCE: historic municipal collection since 1916
FURTHER READING: Langrishe in *JRSAI* 1881

Handbell

The small bronze handbell is decorated with columnar figures with swags between and birds and a monkey below and is inscribed ME FECIT IOHANNIES A FINE A° 1549 - Johannies A Fine made me in 1549 - in Roman capitals around the base. Johannies A Fine was an alias of Jan van den Eynde, a bronze founder at Malines in Belgium. The design of the bell, however, shows southern European influence. The bell was probably commissioned for the private chapel of the Earl of Tyrone at Curraghmore, county Waterford. When that was demolished the bell was presented together with other articles of church furniture to the old church of Portlaw. When the present church was built in 1856 the bell was kept in the parish priest's house; it was used as a mass bell in the private oratory for over half a century. It was loaned to the museum of St Patrick's College, Maynooth, by Bishop Kinnane in 1939 and was included in a

Tóstal exhibition there in 1955. It is in perfect condition and the clapper survives. A similar bell, inscribed ME FECIT IOHANNES A FINE A° 1548, is in the Vleeshuis, Amsterdam.

DATE: 1549 A D
NUMBER: WMT1999.1763
DIMENSIONS: H 100, Dia of base 80
MATERIAL: bronze
PROVENANCE: the Earl of Tyrone, county Waterford
FURTHER READING: Tóstal catalogue 1955

                     Smekens, n d

On loan from the Bishop of Waterford & Lismore

Rent roll - 1483

In medieval Ireland the church was one of the principal property owners. In each diocese the income derived from its property was used for the upkeep of the cathedral and payment of its clergy, and the responsibility for its administration lay with the dean and chapter. The dean also controlled the day-to-day running of the cathedral and was thus a priest of considerable importance, second only to the bishop, from whom he was to a certain extent independent. The chapter (from the Latin word *capitulum*) consisted of a number of priests of whom the most important were the precentor, the chancellor and the treasurer, responsible respectively for choral services, secretarial administration and finance.

In 1483 the dean of Waterford Cathedral was John Collyn, who played a leading role in the life of the city and collaborated closely with the mayor, James Rice. In that year he and his colleagues compiled a rental of all their property in the diocese, consisting of house property within the city and lands in the rural part of the diocese (roughly the areas between the present Tramore road and Waterford harbour, and west of the city as far as Kilmeaden). The rental is followed by several documents relating to the cathedral, the organization of its services, and the functions of the vicars choral and the chantry of St Saviour's. This document was obviously of crucial importance in determining exactly which property was held by the dean and chapter, not only at the time but in centuries to come; hence its careful preservation in the cathedral archives.

The document consists of a long roll of parchment, measuring 250 x 22 cm. It is in good condition and most of the text is remarkably clear and legible. The flap of the roll is formed by a fragment of manuscript containing Latin proverbs in verse. The rental itself shows what an impressive amount of house property in Waterford was owned by the church. From it we learn the names of a number of leading citizens of the time and the terms under which they held their property. Their location can often be traced on today's city map, evidence of the remarkable continuity of Waterford's streetscape down the centuries.

On the back of the roll is written in English a list dated 1585 of tithes and possessions of the cathedral which had hitherto been held in common by the members of the chapter, but which were now shared out among them. It is signed by the dean, "chanter" (precentor), chancellor and treasurer: David Clere, Patrick White, John Quoayne and Thomas Sherloke.

When the property of the church was taken over by the government in 1871, the rent roll fortunately remained in Waterford and thus escaped the fate that befell most records of the church of Ireland when the Public Record Office was blown up in 1922. Today this unique record of medieval Waterford is on loan to Waterford Treasures.

Julian Walton

DATE: 1483 A D
NUMBER: WMT1999.1740
DIMENSIONS: L 2500 x W 220
MATERIAL: parchment
PROVENANCE: The medieval Christ Church Cathedral Waterford
FURTHER READING: Irish Manuscripts Commission forthcoming

On loan from the Dean, Chapter & Select Vestry of Christ Church Cathedral

Cannon

This wrought iron gun was found in the river Suir in 1901 during routine dredging by the dredger, the Port Láirge. It is the oldest cannon or bombard extant in Ireland. The remains consist of the barrel and swivel only, with some fragments of the original chamber holder. The gun is of typical stave and hoop construction, built in the same way as a timber barrel, hence the expression - the barrel of a gun. An interesting feature of the gun is that the staves from which the barrel is constructed have been turned around the muzzle hoop. While there are only fragments of the original chamber holder and its appendages remaining, that which does survive shows that this ironwork was about 30 mm thick. The detachable chamber for holding the powder charge is missing, as is usual with these guns. When first installed on the ship, two chambers were always supplied so that a spare is readily available in the event of a chamber being damaged. The chamber was wedged into the gun before it was discharged and the gunner would direct the fire using a long tiller or arm that projected from the rear of the gun but is now also missing.

It is almost certain that this gun was mounted on the rail of a ship and that it fired stone as opposed to iron balls. It has a striking resemblance to the bombards or cannon mounted on the rail of the Niña, Christopher Columbus's favourite ship. The cannon dates to c1490 and is believed to be from a ship sunk by fire from Reginald's Tower in a siege of the city in 1495.

Given its age and the location of its discovery it is interesting to speculate that this gun could be from the Warbeck siege, the first artillery siege of an Irish city. Perkin Warbeck was a pretender to the throne of King Henry VII. According to the Waterford account of the siege 'Warbeck's ships drew into Lombard's Wear, on the Suir and put down soldiers there. The citizens replied by sending a retinue of their own men to attack what they presumed were Rodigue de Lalaing's men [Warbeck's Flemish allies]. The Flemish were defeated, some were killed outright and some taken prisoner. The prisoners were brought to the city, taken to the market place and beheaded. Thereafter their heads were put on public display'. The town gunners got their ships in their sights and 'two of Warbeck's ships were bulged or drowned with ordinance shot out of Dundore [Reginald's Tower]'.

DATE: c1495 A D
NUMBER: WMT1999.1744
DIMENSIONS: L 819, int Dia of muzzle 78 - 'Smith Type SW I-6'
MATERIAL: wrought iron
PROVENANCE: historic municipal collection since 1901
FURTHER READING: Smith 1988
                             Lyon in *National Geographic* 1986
                             Arthurson 1994

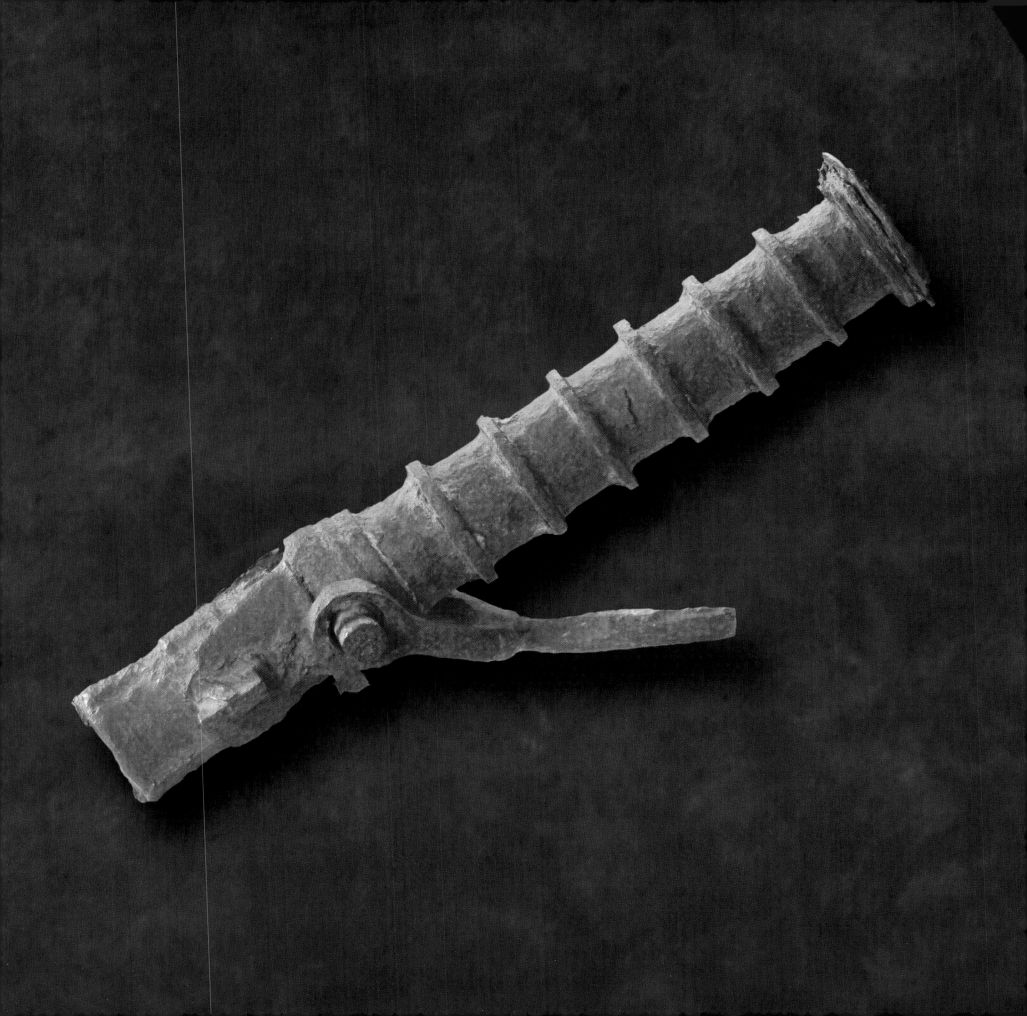

SIXTEENTH
CENTURY

WATERFORD

As the sixteenth century dawned, the citizens of Waterford had every reason to be optimistic. In backing King Henry VII (1485-1509) they had made the right choice: not only was he more secure on his throne but he had a son to succeed him, the dashing renaissance prince who would become King Henry VIII. The turmoil of the reformation in mainland Europe appeared remote as Henry VIII (1509-1547) had by 1521 made peace with France and the Pope had conferred on him the title 'Defender of the Faith'. Adding to the city's good fortune was the fact that it had a friend at court, William Wyse.

In 1492 John Wyse, son of Maurice a former mayor of Waterford, was appointed one of the principal Irish judges with the title Chief Baron of the Exchequer. Also elected bailiff of Waterford in 1496, he used his influential position to further his family and sent his son William to England to be brought up at the royal court. The young William soon worked his way up the ladder of promotion so successfully that by 1520 he was one of the eight pages chosen to accompany King Henry VIII during his celebrated meeting with the king of France at the 'Field of Cloth of Gold', where the two kingdoms agreed a peace. It is at this famous gathering that Henry is said to have met Anne Boleyn for the first time. Henry's desire for a male heir and Anne's refusal to accommodate him until he divorced Catherine of Aragon was to change the course of English and Irish history. But all of this was in the future.

William Wyse was to become a great friend of Henry VIII, who showered him with many gifts and honours, including making him Constable of Limerick Castle and Receiver of the Customs of Bristol, one of the wealthiest ports in England. He was granted the manor of Chapelizod, near Dublin, for the annual rent of one red rose. His native city was not neglected and Henry granted Waterford three charters. His charter of 1510, on display in the museum, has the earliest known representation of the city's coat of arms as three galleys or barges.[1] Wyse returned to Waterford in 1528; five years later he was elected mayor and played a significant part in the suppression of the

Silken Thomas rebellion. Wyse provided a secure base at Waterford for the landing of troops and supplies to crush the revolt. In 1535 Wyse was no longer mayor but acted as emissary of the city to the royal court at Greenwich. However, his loyalty was not forgotten and in February 1536 Thomas Cromwell, Cardinal Wolsey's successor, arranged for him to be thanked for helping to suppress the rebellion. Wyse returned to Waterford in triumph with a letter from the king and a gift of 'a bearing sword to be borne before the mayor from time to time within our said city'.[2] (p121) Wyse returned to the royal court and was sent back to Waterford again in April with a letter, a gift and a promise that the city's privileges would not be interfered with at the next parliament. The gift was 'a cap of maintenance to be borne at times thought fit before our mayor.' The cap of red velvet embroidered with marguerites and Tudor roses is one of the oldest caps of maintenance in Western Europe and the only item of clothing from Henry's wardrobe to survive. (p123)

The rebellion of Silken Thomas coincided with the English reformation that was brought on in part by Henry's divorce of Catherine of Aragon. The subsequent break with Rome was to set in motion the dissolution of the monasteries in both England and Ireland. Wyse was well placed to cash in on the subsequent social and religious upheaval. He sent his son Henry, no doubt named in deference to the king, to his friend Thomas Cromwell with a gift of a 'leish of falcons' and a request that he be given the dissolved Benedictine abbey of St John. Wyse promised to remove the monks and pledged his own lands as security if he failed in this task. The king agreed, the family became the Wyses of the Manor of St John and until the end of the nineteenth century continued to play a role as one of the leading catholic families in national and local politics.[3]

The Wyses were not exceptional in their eagerness to expel the monks. As the monasteries in Waterford and elsewhere in Ireland were dissolved and their inhabitants ejected, the Gaelic Irish, the Old English gentry and the wealthier merchants, pious catholics all, had no scruples about accepting monastic grants from the king. In Waterford the Walsh family were granted Greyfriars, the dissolved Franciscan friary. The Walshes were one of the most powerful families in the merchant oligarchy which ruled Waterford. In 1556 a member of the Walsh family was both dean of Christ Church Cathedral and bishop of Waterford and Lismore and his relatives Henry, Peter and James were mayors and bailiffs. In 1544 the Walshes received a charter from King Henry to convert the old friary church into an almshouse, the Holy Ghost Hospital that exists to this day.[4] The Walsh family, like the majority of the merchant class, favoured moderate reform and accepted the Act of Supremacy, recognising Henry as head of the church. Yet they still respected the old traditions and housed in the almshouse a collection of medieval statues that once adorned the churches of Waterford. The statues are the single largest collection of medieval statuary in Ireland. (p125) It was in front of these statues that the inmates of the hospital prayed, every night for over four hundred years, for the soul of the hospital's benefactor, Henry VIII.

The short reign of Henry's son Edward VI (1547-1553) saw protestant ideas from Europe gain hold in England and consolidate the reformation there. His reforms, however, had little impact on Ireland. He granted Waterford two new charters, in 1548 (on display in the museum) and in 1549 (in the archive). His successor and half sister, Mary (1553-1558), an ardent catholic suppressed protestantism and restored the old religion, creating two hundred and eighty three martyrs and earning the nickname 'Bloody Mary'. She married Philip of Spain and they granted Waterford a charter in 1556, (on display in the museum). She also began a new phase in the Tudor re-conquest of Ireland with the plantation of Laois and Offaly. Her links with staunchly catholic Spain would impact on trade and give the Spanish crown a heightened interest in England and the spread of protestantism there.

Elizabeth I (1558-1603) dominated Irish history in the second half of the sixteenth century. When she came to the throne, royal power in Ireland did not extend much beyond the Pale (an area about thirty miles wide running north from Dublin to Drogheda) and the larger towns. By the end of her reign great tracts of land had been devastated and Gaelic power had been crushed forever. Elizabethan conquerors sought to impose their brand of state protestantism on a country which was coming more and more under the influence of the counter-reformation catholicism of mainland Europe and especially Spain.

Waterford's traditional loyalty lay with the crown yet through their trading contacts with France and Spain, the greatest catholic powers in Europe, the merchant class had developed a strong loyalty to Rome. This loyalty, reinforced by the counter-reformation ideas carried back to Waterford by priests trained in Spain and France, made it impossible for them to acquiesce to the doctrinal changes which acceptance of Elizabeth's reformed church would require. Waterford was the most English of Irish cities and while the leading merchants had been willing to accept Henry VIII's reforms they, unlike their English counterparts, would not accept Elizabeth's established church.[5] Waterford received a charter from the queen in 1574, only four years after she had been excommunicated by the pope, bestowing extra privileges upon the city. This charter, beautifully decorated in a renaissance style, showed for the first time the arms of the city as three lions passant, the royal arms above the three galleys, a symbolic representation of the political philosophy of the queen that her authority would be absolute throughout her dominions. (p127) Yet the ruling merchant oligarchy failed to realise that there was no room for small cities which behaved at times like independent city states.

Why the city should now be so staunch in its loyalty to Rome may be explained by the fact that Waterford's wealth and overseas trade had brought the leading citizens into contact with renaissance humanist ideas. These ideas were disseminated in a school founded by Peter White of Waterford and believed to have been maintained by the

Waterford municipality from 1560 to at least 1649. White was a fellow of Oriel College, Oxford and both he and John Flahy of Waterford have been described as 'trojan horses' of the counter-reformation. In this way the renaissance in its northern form came into Ireland by way of Oxford, Cambridge and Louvain. From the school in Waterford the sons of the leading families went on to the seminaries of Spain and France. Consequently the experience in Ireland at the edge of Europe differed from that elsewhere. In Europe the reformation preceded the counter-reformation; in England they synchronized, but in Ireland the counter-reformation was established before the reformation made any real headway.[6] The impact of the reformation was only felt in Waterford with the appointment of Marmaduke Middleton as bishop in 1579, a zealot who tried almost single-handedly to impose protestantism on his diocese. Opposition to him was led by his own dean David Cleere, Mayor Patrick Dobbyn and Sir Patrick Walsh, a former mayor and cousin of the late Bishop Walsh.[7]

It was Dean Cleere who in 1577, possibly anticipating the arrival of a zealot such as Middleton, placed the cathedral's plate and vestments in the custody of the corporation in pledge for four hundred pounds - no doubt as a means of keeping them in catholic hands. (p90, 107) Marmaduke Middleton's dubious character made him, from the viewpoint of the establishment, a most unsuitable character to promote the reformation and the corporation tried unsuccessfully to have him removed. Against this background the city tried to remain loyal but its trade with Spain made some of Elizabeth's officials suspicious of them. Such suspicion would appear to be unfounded however as throughout the period, particularly after the Spanish Armada 1588, the mayors continued to question merchants returning from the peninsula for information on Spanish military and naval activities. The mayors would forward any relevant intelligence to the government. Elizabeth's lord deputy wrote that the mayors of Waterford 'are the best advisers of foreign news of any city in Ireland and yet they still send their sons to

Spain in large numbers to train for the catholic priesthood and harboured priests in their houses when they returned home'.[8]

The city also attended to military matters, making more secure the blockhouse at Passage East to protect the harbour. St Patrick's fort or citadel was begun under Captain Yorke as an additional defensive structure outside the walls overlooking the river Suir; however it was not finished during Elizabeth's reign.[9] A map dated to c1590, and possibly drawn by Yorke, shows a part of the city's stone-built defences running from Reginald's Tower in the north-east as far the Watch Tower in the south-east. A second set of earthen-work defences constructed during Elizabeth's reign are also shown, as is the blockhouse built in front of Reginald's Tower to accommodate large cannon. (p131)

The *Great Parchment Book* details Waterford's involvement in the Nine Years War (1593-1603), the rebellion of the northern Gaelic lords which eventually spread to the whole of Ireland. Under the leadership of Hugh O'Neill, attempts were made to enlist the support of the Old English (catholics of Anglo-Norman origin) in a bid to create an autonomous catholic Ireland. The long anticipated involvement of the Spanish finally materialised with their arrival at Kinsale in December 1601. However, following their defeat they left on 2 January 1603 taking with them the hopes of an independent catholic Ireland. O'Neill submitted at Mellifont on 30 March 1603, unaware that Elizabeth had died six days earlier. During the war Waterford was a base for landing government troops to quash the rebellion. Details of the troops, names of generals, colonels and captains who landed at Waterford are preserved in the *Great Parchment Book* as are details of the supply of arms to the towns of the south-east. There is even an account of a soldier from Duncannon fort being stopped and searched as part of the normal security at one of the city gates. On being found to be secretly carrying twenty six pounds of gunpowder to supply the rebels, he was summarily 'hanged at the market cross of this Cittie by course of martial law'.[10]

In 1598 Sir Henry Norreys commanded two thousand soldiers who had landed at Waterford from England and were fed and billeted in the city for seven weeks prior to marching westwards to besiege Cahir. More soldiers billeted in the city at the end of the war are recorded as being responsible for spreading the plague that struck the city. The *Great Parchment Book* tells that 'undercover of darkness they were raiding the house of the dead to steal their clothes and their goods'. The city council's successful measures to stop the pilfering and thereby contain the plague are also recorded in the *Great Parchment Book* and make fascinating reading, as do the figures for those who died of plague: two thousand two hundred and fifty-six in the year ending September 1604 with a weekly figure of one hundred and sixteen deaths during the previous August.[11] These figures are probably the earliest and most detailed accounts of the ravages of plague in an Irish city and are a unique record.

Sadly the optimism with which the century began for Waterford was ill-founded. Although the city had supported the winning side during the Nine Years War, the dilemma facing Waterford, that is, balancing loyalty to the crown in London with loyalty to the pope in Rome was not resolved and would dominate the next century. This dilemma was however beautifully and symbolically illustrated in folio 91of the *Great Parchment Book*. (p129)

Bearing sword of King Henry VIII

This sword was a gift of King Henry VIII of England in 1536, along with a cap of maintenance, to the mayor of Waterford, as a reward for loyalty at the time of the rebellion of Silken Thomas FitzGerald in 1534. The gifts were sent via William Wyse (of the famous Wyse family of the Manor of St John, who had been brought up with the young Henry), Waterford's emissary to the court at Greenwich. Wyse was given a letter of thanks, a promise of continued royal favour and the sword 'to be borne before the mayor from time to time within that our said city'.

The sword was used on ceremonial occasions, just as Edward IV's sword had been. In 1580 it was at the centre of an impressive welcoming ceremony when the city was visited by Queen Elizabeth's viceroy, Sir William Pelham, despite the fact that he had earlier denounced the citizens as 'the most arrogant papists that lived within the state'. A vivid account of his arrival records that the officers of the garrison 'issued out of the city with their companies, and near the shore presented his lordship with a mock fight, they retired to line the streets against his lordship's landing. The bulwarks [ramparts], gates and curtain [walls] of the city were beautified with ensigns [flags], and several cannon were discharged in a warlike manner, which were answered by all the ships in the harbour and a great number of pieces [cannon] on the quays. The soldiers also fired several volleys. The mayor and aldermen received his lordship in their scarlet robes and presented him with the city sword and the keys of the gates, which he immediately returned; and the mayor carried the sword before him to the cathedral. There were two orations made him in Latin on the way; and at his return from the church a third speech was made him at the door of his lodgings'.

This sword is an extremely fine example of the art of the sixteenth century European cutler. The handle is copper covered with silver openwork decoration of stylised plant ornamentation, the royal arms, an inscription 'V·O·P' and the Green Man motif. The guards or quillions are of tubular brass with dome-style finials, and may be later additions or replacements. Because this is a two-handed sword, there is a second guard of steel, with scalloped edge, 9.5 cm from the first. The blade is steel.

The scabbard is red velvet over wood with a central braid that was probably originally gold, running the length. There are three ornamental panels on the scabbard: a brass one, decorated, measuring 15 cm in length, marking the point at which the scabbard is split to accommodate the second guard. Further down is a silver-gilt decorated panel, about 6 cm, with crest-like motif within an oval. The third panel or chape, at the end of the scabbard, 10 cm in length, is beautifully decorated silver-gilt, showing the Tudor rose on the reverse and the royal arms on the obverse.

DATE:	c1536 A D
NUMBER:	WMT1999.1745
DIMENSIONS:	sword overall L 1470 x max W 470
	blade L 1130, handle L 280, pommel L 60,
	second guard W 115 scabbard L 1140 x max W 50,
	braid W 7, finial/chape L 10
MATERIAL:	sword silver, silver-gilt, steel, copper, brass
	scabbard wood, velvet, braid, silver-gilt, brass
PROVENANCE:	historic municipal collection
FURTHER READING:	Walton in McEneaney (ed) 1995

Cap of maintenance of Henry VIII

This was a gift, along with a bearing sword, of King Henry VIII of England to the mayor of Waterford in 1536. Henry's letter of 1536 states: 'And now at this tyme as a remembrance and evident token of our favours we have sent you by this brynger [William Wyse] a Capp of mainteynance to be borne at tymes thought by you necessarie before you the Maior being our officer of that our said Citie and your successors officers of the same. Given under our signet at our Manor of Greenewich the last day of Aprill in the xxviiith years of our reigne. To our right trustie and welbeloved the Maior and Cominality of our Citie of Waterford in our land of Ireland'.

A cap of maintenance was worn under the crown by the monarch from early Norman times and 'he to whom a cap of maintenance was granted need doff his cap to nobody'. It was, therefore, a significant mark of royal approval. A cap and a sword were traditional items in a mayor's regalia, although by the mid-sixteenth century they were more of symbolic importance.

This cap is made of red velvet, is embroidered with Tudor roses and marguerites and was probably made at the royal court. The velvet was very possibly produced in Lucca, Italy. The red rose is the symbol of the Tudor dynasty. The marguerites are motifs often repeated in Tudor decoration and on the clothing associated with Henry VIII. The symbolism is important as the marguerite represents Margaret Beaufort, Henry's grandmother. Margaret was the great great granddaughter of Edward III, helping to provide legitimacy for the Tudor dynasty's claim to the throne, as she was of royal blood.

A strip of baleen, supporting the crown of the cap, has been confirmed to be from a whale and carbon dating has shown that it is the same age as the cap. This is one of the oldest caps of maintenance in Europe and it is the only piece of Henry VIII's wardrobe to survive.

The bearing sword and the cap of maintenance were carried to Waterford by William Wyse who, soon afterwards, ceased to be Waterford's emissary to the royal court at Greenwich. Wyse however remained active in public life and was elected mayor of Waterford for a second time in 1540. In 1543 he paid yet another visit to Greenwich where he was knighted by the king. Three years later he was made a member of the Irish Council, a body that advised the lord lieutenant on how best to rule the country, a prestigious position he held until his death on 5 April 1557. The Dublin historian Richard Stanihurst, writing a generation later, paints an attractive portrait of William Wyse, twice mayor of Waterford, friend of Henry VIII and founder of a dynasty that would play a leading role in the affairs of the city for the next three centuries: 'Sir William Wyse, Knight, a worshipful gentleman, born in the city of Waterford, who deserving indeed the praise of that virtue whereof he bore the name, grew to be of great credit in the court and stood highly in King Henry's grace, which he wholly used to the furtherance of his friends and never abused to the annoyance of his foes. This gentleman was very well spoken, mild of nature, with discretion stout, as one that in an upright quarrel would bear no coals [grudge], seldom in an intricate matter gravelled [baffled], being found at all assays to be of a pleasant and present wit'.

DATE: 1536 A D
NUMBER: WMT1999.1746
DIMENSIONS: overall H 116 x overall Dia 397, crown H 114 x Dia 237
MATERIAL: velvet, felt, silk, metal, baleen
PROVENANCE: historic municipal collection
FURTHER READING: Walton in McEneaney (ed) 1995
Devitt forthcoming

Conservation generously funded by the Heritage Council

Statues

The medieval Franciscan friary was dissolved in 1540 but part of its church was re-opened as the Holy Ghost Hospital in 1545 by Henry Walsh who received a charter from King Henry VIII to establish an almshouse there. Catholic service continued to be held there until 1815. The hospital still survives today, although on a different site. A group of eight statues came to be housed in the original hospital chapel, thus ensuring their survival in the ensuing turbulent centuries. All these statues, except the stone head of John the Baptist, have been painted over several times, obscuring the carved detail. Originally they were beautifully painted in strong and vivid colours.

Unknown saint or angel (A)

This statue, fully carved in the round, is unique among wood sculpture in Ireland. The right arm is gone, the left arm incomplete; the figure looks therefore very narrow. The graceful poise, exquisitely chiselled head and richly undercut drapery reveal the hand of a master sculptor, probably Italian gothic. In the treatment of the features especially: the rounded cheek, delicately curved nostril and firmly modelled lips, the inspiration is classical.

DATE: 13th/14th century
NUMBER: WMT1994.0008
DIMENSIONS: H 1053 x W at base 211
MATERIAL: oak

Head of St John the Baptist (B)

This sculpture may have belonged to the Benedictine priory of St John, in the suburbs of Waterford. The Baptist is shown with long hair and curled beard, the features well-proportioned.

DATE: 15th century
NUMBER: WMT1994.0002
DIMENSIONS: H 250 x W 180
MATERIAL: sandstone

Enthroned Madonna and Child (C)

The Madonna and the Unknown Saint are the earliest of the statues and are very fine. The Madonna is carved from a single block of oak, with the back hollowed out like most medieval figures. She sits on a low throne supporting the child upon her left knee; her parted knees, sharply defined in the romanesque way, rise high above the throne. The poise of the head and neck give the figure a monumental dignity. The probable original colours were gold crown and hair, face and hands flesh-colour, carmine lips, red gown and blue mantle.

The child is depicted head-on, not turning towards His Mother, a pose essentially romanesque. The missing left hand possibly held a book, the Gospels; the right hand, also missing, was probably raised in blessing. The head is very worn, the hair was cut straight across the forehead and below the ears, another sign of an early date.

The arrangement of forms in a symbolic rather than naturalistic way suggests an Irish sculptor with continental romanesque influences. The statue is reverent and simple, in keeping with the lifestyle and practices of the early Franciscans. Statues of this nature were not brought into a country haphazardly by individuals; they appeared where a devotion was promoted by an organised community. This statue is testimony to the monastic orders being a conduit of Anglo-Norman and Italian influences.

DATE: c1300 A D
NUMBER: WMT1994.0004
DIMENSIONS: H 800 x max W 220
MATERIAL: oak

St Catherine (D)

This alabaster statue, the back hollowed out, is of St Catherine, identified by her symbols: the crown of martyrdom, the palm sheaf in her right hand (damaged), the broken wheel on the left and the head of the crushed emperor underfoot. She has long flowing hair. The drapery folds and the treatment of the features suggest fifteenth century English alabaster sculpture. This figure was probably produced locally but was inspired by an English statue of the saint. This statue may have been in the original Franciscan friary, or it may have belonged to St Catherine's Augustinian priory built just outside the walls of the medieval city, to the east.

DATE: 15th century
NUMBER: WMT1994.0007
DIMENSIONS: H 600 x W at base 262
MATERIAL: alabaster

St John the Baptist (E)

This gothic statue is carved of two blocks of oak dowelled together. The back is solid, but flat, indicating that the statue was probably placed against a wall. The beard, the book, the camel skin cloak and the lamb (the Lamb of God) identify this figure as St John the Baptist. It is probably local work and may have come from the Benedictine priory.

DATE: 15th century
NUMBER: WMT1994.0005
DIMENSIONS: H 900 x max W 300
MATERIAL: oak

St Stephen (F)

This late gothic statue probably came from the church of St Stephen's Leper Hospital and may be local work. The saint holds a book and stones, symbols of both his wisdom and death. He wears the vestments of a deacon, a pleated undergarment called an alb and a fringed open-sided dalmatic (T-shaped vestment) and carries a maniple over his left arm. He has carved wavy hair.

DATE: c1470 A D
NUMBER: WMT1994.0003
DIMENSIONS: H 557 x max W 190
MATERIAL: oak

PROVENANCE: chapel of Holy Ghost Hospital, gifted in 1994
FURTHER READING: MacLeod 1946, Hourihane 1984, Cochran thesis
                  forthcoming, Conlan 1988, Mooney in *JRSAI* 1956,
                  Lee 1996, Bradley 1987

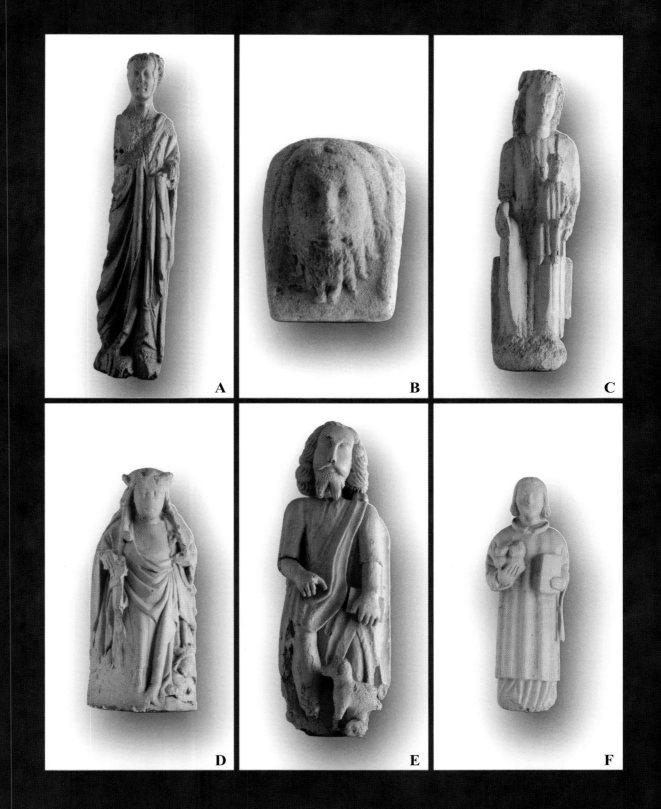

A

B

C

D

E

F

Charter of Queen Elizabeth I

This sumptuously-decorated charter of Queen Elizabeth I is one of seventeen royal charters preserved in Waterford, eight of which are on display in the museum. This charter is dated 1574 and is magnificently decorated. The first word on the charter is the queen's name, Elizabeth. The decorated capital of her name is used to enclose a portrait of the queen seated on her throne, dressed in rich red robes trimmed in ermine and wearing an ermine cape and a crown. Above the remainder of the word Elizabeth is a crowned lion holding an ensign or flag emblazoned with a fleur-de-lis. The D in *Dei* (God) is very elaborate and above the remainder of that word and the word *gracia* (grace) are the royal arms crowned and supported by a swag and foliage motif. The A of the word *Anglie* (England) is treated similarly to the D of *Dei* and above the remainder of the word is a white dragon holding an ensign emblazoned with a Tudor rose. The capital F in *Francie* (France) is a match of the previous two capitals and above the remainder of the word is a crowned fleur-de-lis, symbolizing Elizabeth's claim to be queen of France, as written in the title line of the charter.

On the top right hand corner is the coat of arms of the city of Waterford and for the first time we find the three barges, or galleys in this case, surmounted by three lions passant, the symbols of the English monarchy since the time of Henry II. The lions remained part of the arms of the city until 1953, when a new patent, issued by the Chief Herald's office included only the three galleys. Both sides of the charter are beautifully decorated in a renaissance fashion with flowers, foliage, insects and butterflies.

The charter is important in the development of the city as it proclaimed the city and its liberties (lands outside the walls but under its jurisdiction) as a separate county. Thereafter, as a county it was to be governed by a mayor and two sheriffs and not a mayor and two bailiffs as it had been since the thirteenth century. The only part of the city exempt from the jurisdiction of the mayor and sheriffs was 'the church and chapel of the Blackfriars and the place there, lately called Our Lady Chapel'. The Dominican priory (Blackfriars) had been dissolved in 1540 and James White of the famous merchant family acquired it on lease. It was granted to him in perpetuity in 1543 but was surrendered by Nicholas White in 1574, the year of Elizabeth's charter. It is probable that it was converted into a county court house at this time, thus explaining its exclusion from the franchises and liberties of the city. In the early seventeenth century it was used as a county court house and remained under county control until 1695, when it was surrendered to the city.

The charter also clearly stated the admiralty rights claimed by the mayor of Waterford - the very rights that had been so contentious in the previous three hundred and fifty years. A later charter, granted by Elizabeth in the twenty-fifth year of her reign, gave the Corporation the villages, towns and lands of Grange, Ballytruckle and the new lands adjoined to Waterford north of the river Suir, together with the abbey of Kilculliheen, previously in county Kilkenny.

The 1574 charter is evidence of the continued importance of catholic Waterford under Elizabeth, despite the fact that she had been excommunicated by the pope in 1570. During her reign, Waterford's close links with catholic Spain and France saw it come increasingly under the influence of the counter-reformation movement. Though it remained politically loyal during the various rebellions against the queen, its staunch loyalty to the old religion made it suspect. Elizabeth died in 1603 just as the last of the great Gaelic lords were defeated. Her successor, James I (1603-1625), would have little time for cities wishing to promote the concept of dual loyalty. Following a series of refusals by city officials to take oaths recognizing the king as head of the church, the chief justice of Ireland was directed in 1618 'to seize all the franchises and liberties of the city of Waterford and to order the acting mayor and sheriffs to desist from exercising their official functions'. The Chief Justice also demanded 'the surrender of the ensigns of mayoralty, the charters, the evidence, the plate, the jewels and other treasures'. This charter was among those confiscated by James's officials when the proud city was reduced to the status of an un-enfranchised village.

DATE: 1574 A D
NUMBER: WMT1999.1604
DIMENSIONS: L 710 x W 580
MATERIAL: parchment
PROVENANCE: historic municipal collection
FURTHER READING: Byrne PhD thesis 2001

The Great Parchment Book

The *Liber Antiquissimus Civitatis Waterfordiae*, also known as the *Great Parchment Book*, is one of the most remarkable compilations of any Irish municipality. It is an invaluable source for the history of Waterford, covering three centuries from the middle of the fourteenth century to the final entry of Mayor John Livet who governed the city during the unsuccessful siege by Oliver Cromwell in 1649. The book comprises some 233 folios of parchment, 229 of which contain scripted records, each 45 x 28 cm, bound in leather-covered oak boards of later origin. The script covers both recto and verso surfaces of most folios, although occasional leaves are blank. In the early sections of the manuscript some of the capital letters are rubricated. Later sections have lavish ornate capital letters, particularly on the folios recording the names of the mayors and bailiffs (sheriffs after 1574) annually elected to office.

The contents of the book do not proceed in regular order but may be categorised under the following five headings:
- Charters, petitions, returns, procedure for the election of the mayor and oaths to be taken by city officials
- Tables of customs levied at Waterford, fees and amercements (fines) in city courts and the assize of bread
- Acts made in the civic assemblies from the fourteenth century to the reign of Henry VIII
- Proceedings of the corporation, from the reign of Henry VIII to 1649, including the names of the mayors and bailiffs, admissions of freemen and acts for regulating the public affairs of the city and its citizens
- inquisitions and instruments relating to the rights and properties of the city

The fees and amercements in the city courts, the murage (tax for building the town walls) and customs anciently levied at Waterford appear in appendices two and three in the manuscript. A note above the appendices states that the particulars of the customs levied were taken from ancient rolls of Waterford, copied in 1474-1476 when James Rice was mayor. The manuscript contains entries in Norman-French, Latin, Hiberno-English and, from the mid-sixteenth century, standard official English.

The listing of mayors, bailiffs and later sheriffs makes it easy for historians to chart the rise and fall of various families in the city's ruling oligarchy. The names to dominate city politics between 1526 and 1649 are Walsh and Sherlock, with forty-seven instances of either a mayor or bailiff each. Wyse and Lombard are the next dominant names, followed by White, Strange, Madan, Comerford, Dobbyn and Lincoln.

The statutes are of particular value, providing vivid and fascinating details of the life of medieval Waterford and its citizens. A law in 1382 states that 'al hoggs, soues, bores, and al other swyne and piggs that sholde be founde by day or nyght walkyng within the saide citie ... shal be slayne and killed by thos or by others that bene specially deputid unto the said office'. Obviously pig control was a major worry for the authorities and illegal dumping also exercised their minds as much then as it does today. A law of 1475 states that 'no manere man, woman or childe putte no manere dunge, ramell or fylth into the ryvere over no key nor slippe of the citie,

ne into Saynte Mary strete, nether into the Kyngs ditches nor beside them from the marckette crosse unto Arondelis gate', the fine for these offences being 4d.

Public morals were also a concern of the city fathers: In 1430 it was ordained that 'no preste [priest] sholde have no wif or concubyne within the citie, and if they may be founde, the fynders shal have al ther clothes and thar bodies to the jayle of the said citie unto tyme thei shal mak a fyne'. A statute of 1566 criticises publicans: 'little weighing the fear of God, do sometimes for better utterance of their wines retain naughty corrupt women, by whose procurement and means other honest damsels are often driven to folly, to the great offence of God and dishonesty of the whole city'.

The recording of the mayoralty of Peter Aylward in 1566 is the outstanding example of decoration in the book. It is a startling mixture of symbols. The text begins with an elaborately decorated initial capital and says: *Tempore Petri Aylward Maioris Civitatis Waterford, Georgii Wyse et Nicolai Lumbard Ballivorum, Anno regni Regine nostre Elizabeth octavo 1566* (In the time of Peter Aylward, Mayor of the City of Waterford, and of George Wyse and Nicholas Lumbard Bailiffs, and in the eighth year of the reign of our Queen Elizabeth, 1566). The capital T encloses the royal arms. Above is the crown, over which is the motto *Nosce te ipsum* (Know thyself). Below is a stylised drawing of the city of Waterford seen from across the river as a jumble of walls, gates, houses and churches. The word *Portlarge* (Waterford) appears in the river where there are barges, galleys and moored ships.

At the top of the page and down the right-hand margin is a series of religious pictures - the infant Jesus with his hand raised in blessing and bearing an orb, reclines over all other imagery, both spiritual and temporal, an indication of his total jurisdiction over all things. Beside him is a dove representing the Holy Spirit. The Last Judgement is next, with the Risen Christ accompanied by saints, trumpet-blowing angels, and with the mottoes *Memento Mori* (Remember Death) and *Juste judicate* (Judge justly) at his back. The souls in purgatory are depicted, an image maybe intended to reiterate the Council of Trent's teaching on Purgatory (1563).

Next is an image of a woman behind whom rises a city. It is impossible to be certain who this represents as it has neither the halo of a saint nor the crown of a queen. Below is undoubtedly the Virgin, with the suckling infant in her arms, surrounded by foliage. Finally we see at the bottom left-hand corner the grinning head of the Green Man, a fertility figure beloved of medieval stonemasons and from whose mouth issue tendrils of intertwining branches, leaves and flowers. The Tudor rose and shamrocks also feature. This page, with its mixture of symbols, reflects the dilemma facing the city authorities - how to balance loyalty to Rome with loyalty to a protestant monarch.

DATE:	Late 15th - mid-17th century
NUMBER:	WMT1999.1596
DIMENSIONS:	L 420 x W 315
MATERIAL:	parchment, leather, oak boards
PROVENANCE:	historic municipal collection
FURTHER READING:	Byrne forthcoming, Gilbert 1885, MacNiocaill 1966, McEneaney (ed) 1995, Walton 1992

C̷ Petri Aylward maioris Ciuitatis
Waterford Georgii wyse et Nicolai
lumbard Balliuorum Anno regni ~
Regine nostre Elizabeth octauo ~ 1566

Eodem Anno subscript... recept... sunt ad
libertat... dict... Ciuitatis

Walterus wadding recept... est pro o...
Patricius walshe fil... Ricardi recept... est pro duobz. ẑ hardg. lapid
Iohes oten garrold recept... est pro duobz. ẑ hardg. lapid
Thomas appylbard recept... est pro duobz. ẑ hardg. lapid
Thomas Clatter recept... est pro duobz. ẑ hardg. lapid
Iohes Talbott recept... est pro duobz. ẑ hardg. lapid
Iohes Quemerford fil... Ricardi recept... est pro duobz. ẑ hardg. lapid
willus lumbard fil... Nicolai recept... est pro duobz. ẑ hardg. lapid
Thomas louch recept... est pro duobz. ẑ hardg. lapid
Iohes waydott recept... est pro duobz. ẑ hardg. lapid

Where This Cittie amongest other thynges by charter
hath authoryte to make such estatutes and ordynaces as shulde thought most
beneficiall for the comon welth of the same together with Cognyssance
of Plea. By force wherof certeyn lawes haue byne heretofore prouided
to restrayne the Neighbowres from vexing one another in sute before
forreyn Iudges   which prouysion notwithstanding sobers theinhabytantz
vppon Recoueries had agaynst them in the courtes of this Cyttie haue
soughte to aduoide thesame by wrytte of Erro̅ to the greate disquyet of
theire Neighbowres and slaunder of the Cowrtes And that most co̅
mouly practized by such as feele themselues Iustlie condempned ~
in thy demo̅ and thynke by that meane to delay the partie of dew
execution ffor redresse wherof and to thintente that bothe ~
                                                          the

Drawing of defences of Elizabethan Waterford

This is the earliest known map of any part of Waterford and is therefore of immense importance. This pictorial map depicts the defences along the southeast side of the city. It is attributed to Edmund Yorke, a military engineer who was sent over from England by the Privy Council in London, in the wake of the defeat of the Spanish Armada in 1588, to supervise the construction of outer fortifications or entrenchments around the city. The English authorities feared that the Spanish might launch an invasion of Ireland where they would expect to gain the support of much of the local catholic population. It was expected that the Spanish would initially try to seize one of the southern port cities or towns such as Waterford to use as a base for their invasion. To counter this fear the English embarked on a campaign to strengthen the defences of these ports.

Edmund Yorke arrived in Waterford in early 1590 to take charge of the works. The city provided 150 labourers and a further sixty were recruited from the surrounding countryside. They were engaged in the construction of defensible earthworks outside the city wall. Yorke sent reports and maps plotting the works back to the Privy Council and this map appears to belong to this set.

The caption on the map reads: 'Waterford towards the land by St John's gate with the march to Mrs Sherlock's abbey'. The latter is the large building that is depicted on the island outside of the city wall. It was the former Augustinian priory of St Catherine that was dissolved by King Henry VIII in 1539 and granted to the Sherlock family who were prominent merchants in the city. The map shows a new entrenchment around most of the 'abbey'. The island is delineated on the outer side by John's river, a tributary of the river Suir that is shown on the left hand side of the map. A tidal lake delineates the inner side of the island towards the city wall. At the mouth towards the river Suir there is a tidal mill. The lake was filled in for the laying out of the present Mall during the early eighteenth century.

The map is also of interest because it depicts a long section of the city wall, much of which still survives above the ground. At the northeast end is Reginald's Tower, located at the end of the quay along the river Suir. At the base of the tower the former blockhouse is shown with its cannons jutting out into the river, built in the middle of the sixteenth century and demolished in 1711. From Reginald's Tower the city wall runs southwest to Colbeck Gate. This tall building stood until the eighteenth century. Outside there is a bridge shown, giving access across the tidal lake to St Catherine's island. This bridge was located close to the junction of the present Catherine Street and the Mall.

From Colbeck Gate the city wall continued southwest to the former St Martin's Gate, also known as the Green Tower. The remains of this building, which was excavated in the early 1980s, can still be seen today at the end of Spring Garden Alley. From here the city wall turned south across what is now Parnell Street to a corner tower. The wall then turned southwest running parallel to the present Waterside and on to John's Gate. The latter was a large building that stood until the 1760s at the end of John's Street. Outside the gate, John's bridge is shown spanning John's

river. This medieval bridge is still in use today. A new entrenchment enclosed the area beyond the bridge and included a millrace, which still survives and served the former John's Mill. In the eighteenth century the mill here was re-developed and modernised by Thomas 'Bullocks' Wyse. It was described by Smith in 1746 as an 'ingenious mill which grinds, scists and bolts the several kinds of meal and flower at the same time; and near to it are considerable granaries erected, which will be both an advantage to the town, and to the profit of the proprietor'.

From John's Gate the city wall continued southwest for a short distance to the corner bastion or water gate in Grady's Yard, which still survives. From here the city wall still turns northwest to the Watch Tower, which is the last tower depicted on the map. The wall continues northwest across what is now Manor Street to disappear off the map. The earthworks or entrenchments that are depicted on the map appear to have been completed by the summer of 1590. The Spanish did not come to Waterford and the Yorke entrenchment eventually disappeared.

Ben Murtagh

DATE:	1590 A D
NUMBER:	WMT1999.1747
DIMENSIONS:	L 318 x W 213
MATERIAL:	paper
PROVENANCE:	acquired from Waterford City Library in 1999
FURTHER READING:	Murtagh in *Decies* 2001
	Hamilton (ed) 1885
	Kerrigan in *Decies* 1985
	McEneaney (ed) 1995

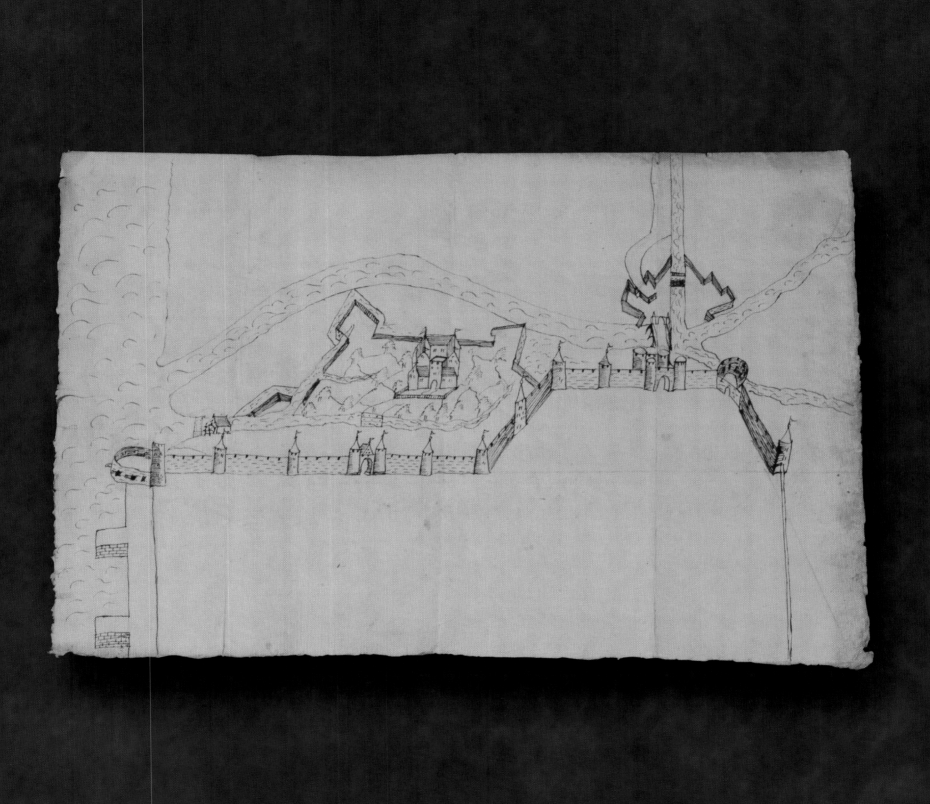

SEVENTEENTH CENTURY

WATERFORD

News of Queen Elizabeth's death in 1603 was received in Waterford with great joy. It was assumed that her successor, James I (1603-1625), son of the martyred Mary Queen of Scots, would restore the churches to the catholics. In a somewhat premature move, the catholic clergy began to take possession of the cathedral and other churches which had been transferred to the protestant church during Elizabeth's reign. However, by order of the Dublin government they were soon forced to return them and resort to having mass said in private houses. Surviving the catholic gunpowder plot to blow up both himself and parliament in London meant that King James was ill disposed to negotiation with the citizens of Waterford who refused to take the Oath of Supremacy recognising him as head of the church. In 1606-7 Waterford had no fewer than five mayors in quick succession; the first four refused to take the oath and were sent to Cork gaol. This resistance continued until 1618 when municipal government in Waterford was suspended and the charters seized and removed to Dublin.[1] For the rest of the king's reign the city was ruled directly by government appointees.

King James blamed Peter Lombard (1554-1625), the Waterford-born student of Peter White's school and archbishop of Armagh, for the state of affairs in Ireland, telling parliament that the Irish were only 'half subjects'. He alleged that 'Doctor Peter Lombard in Rome makes the catholics send their sons to seminaries in Spain, France, Italy and the Netherlands, who then return and act as traitors'.[2] Lombard and King James both died in 1625. Lombard's place as Ireland's representative at the Vatican was filled by another and equally famous Waterfordian, Father Luke Wadding, while James was succeeded by his son, Charles I (1625-1649).[3]

The citizens of Waterford petitioned the new king for a charter (on display in the museum) and as the monarch was short of money he graciously issued one for the sum of three thousand pounds. The city also has two maces which appear to have been re-fashioned during his reign by the application of his armorial arms. (p139) Charles was a supporter of Elizabeth's established church in both England and Ireland. The king's adherence to this church was not appreciated by the puritans in England who were tiring of his autocratic rule and his disregard for the institutions of parliament; neither did he win many supporters in Ireland, where the old religion still prevailed.

In 1637, as a result of a royal edict demanding the 'proper and decorous performance of Divine Service', Mayor Richard Butler became involved in a protracted argument with Thomas Wentworth, the king's lord deputy in Ireland.[4] The row arose over the ownership of the vestments and church plate of which the corporation had been given custody in 1577, during the reign of Elizabeth. The corporation had pledged four hundred pounds to the dean and chapter of the cathedral for the vestments and plate. Wentworth demanded the return of the vestments and plate without any compensation to the corporation. (p90, 107) Mayor Butler had no option but to comply and, as a catholic, it must have galled him to have to provide such venerable riches to the state church, without compensation. The letter from Wentworth to Mayor Butler survives and is displayed in the museum beside some of the disputed vestments.

The tension felt in Waterford was symptomatic of what the island as a whole was experiencing. Matters came to a head in 1641 with the outbreak of the rebellion which saw the massacre of the protestant planters who had settled in Ulster during James I's plantation. Protestant communities outside Ulster were also plundered. It was during these disturbances that Waterford admitted the Irish army of Lord Mountgarret, and for the next seven years, until it fell to Cromwell's parliamentary army in 1650, the city remained in catholic hands. During these years the city joined forces with the confederate catholics of Ireland. Their motto was *Pro Deo, Rege et Patria* (For God, King and Fatherland). The confederation's aim was to administer the catholic-controlled parts of the country pending a final settlement with the king. Representatives of this alliance of Old Irish, Old English and some New English met mainly at Kilkenny, though they also met occasionally at Waterford. The confederation's printing press was based in Waterford, Thomas Bourke being the printer. (p143) Father Luke Wadding, the Waterford Franciscan who founded the Irish College in Rome and was Ireland's agent at the Vatican, was kept informed of events in Ireland and was sent copies of the propaganda issuing from Thomas Bourke's press. It was at this time that a contemporary, when writing to Wadding, referred to Waterford as *Parva Roma* (Little Rome), a reference to its loyalty to the pope and the number of catholic scholars which emanated from it.[5] Despite the attempts to keep Rome informed and active in support of the principles espoused by the confederates, the reality was that there were various factions within the confederate camp and a consensus was difficult to secure. The whole matter was further complicated by the outbreak of civil war in England, a conflict which would later spread to both Scotland and Ireland. The confederates sought to obtain some measure of religious tolerance; in return the king expected support against the English parliament. All the optimism of finally reaching a settlement with a protestant monarch ended when Charles was executed for treason by parliament in 1649.

Oliver Cromwell set sail for Ireland in August 1649. He claimed that the southern ports were his primary objective, fearing they were most likely to give succour to the late king's supporters. He landed at Ringsend in Dublin and marched north to Drogheda where there was a massacre of the townspeople, carried out both as an object lesson to others who might resist, as well as in revenge for the massacre of protestants in the 1641 rebellion. The townspeople of Wexford fared no better when he finally decided to march south, and when New Ross surrendered, Cromwell informed the citizens that 'where the parliament of England has power, mass will not be allowed.'[6] By 24 November he was outside the gates of Waterford. The siege lasted nine days; however, the absence of artillery, bad weather, an outbreak of dysentery among his troops

and the need to find winter quarters combined to force Cromwell to lift the siege. On 2 December he marched away, describing it thus: 'so terrible a day as ever I marched in all my life'.[7] Cromwell left Ireland in 1650 leaving his son-in-law Ireton in command of the besieging army and in August of that year, Waterford finally surrendered to him. A cannon ball said to be from this siege is to this day embedded in the wall of Reginald's Tower. In London parliament ordered a day of thanksgiving to celebrate the fall of Waterford and notices were posted throughout the city of London to inform its citizens. (p143)

The capture of Waterford by the Cromwellians was followed by what can only be described as a campaign of ethnic cleansing. Hordes of homeless people, wandering the countryside and the towns of the south-east, were apprehended and transported to Barbados as indentured servants to English planters - to this day there is a small village in Barbados called Waterford. Many of the old merchant class were also driven out and, in theory at least, no catholic was allowed within the town walls. In the census of 1659 we find that over half the tax-paying householders within the walled city were newly arrived English planters.[8] However, if the suburbs were also taken into account, then the planters were outnumbered in a ratio of about two to three.

The respite between Cromwell's siege and that of his son-in-law gave the catholic church authorities (the church buildings were back in catholic hands since 1643) an opportunity to hide their treasures in the cathedral vaults. This subterfuge was only partly successful. A Kilkenny woman informed the city's Cromwellian governor, Colonel Sadlers, that treasure had been hidden in the vaults of the cathedral. Sadlers discovered one of the concealed vaults and found twelve hundred-weight of brass ornaments which he sold at nine pence per pound.[9] Neither the cathedral's silver plate nor vestments were found - an enquiry held in 1661 tells us that 'not finding silver plate they arrested several priests in their mass houses and in Irishmen's houses where there were a great store of plate, chalices, rings, and rich copes, as rich as ever seen in Spain'.[10] The vestments had been so well hidden by the catholics who had re-possessed the cathedral prior to the arrival of Cromwell that the Cromwellian looters failed to find them. When the monarchy was restored in 1660, the protestant church regained the cathedral and those catholics who hid the vestments either remained silent or were dead.

There must have been other, but unrecorded, attempts to conceal prized objects of religious veneration. The relic of the true cross escaped the Cromwellian plunder (p31), as did the 1629 ciborium and the Dempsy chalice. (p141) There is on record a story that a huge hoard of church plate and rings were discovered in a city centre cellar in 1824 and subsequently sold in London. The 1661 enquiry reveals that there was a great panic in the city, with people trying to conceal objects of religious and monetary value before Cromwell's parliamentary troops gained entry. Perhaps the beautiful Italian renaissance-style late sixteenth or early seventeenth century gold ring with an intaglio of a man in armour, was lost in the panic to conceal, prior to the fall of the city. (p145)

On being restored to the throne, Charles II (1660-1685) found himself in a no-win situation as far as the dispossessed Irish catholics were concerned. Petitions to the king from both the catholic merchant class still residing in Waterford and from those living abroad came to nothing. If the king re-instated their lands and property, he would face certain revolt from the parliamentary faction. As a result, the Irish catholics found the gates to their own lands and houses still barred against them. Waterford's new protestant corporation greatly resented both catholics and non-conformists and hoped to keep their numbers to a minimum. While the catholics felt aggrieved, the ruling class itself felt very insecure: not only was it in a minority, but its members had also conspired against the monarchy. William Bolton, one of the leading Cromwellian figures in Waterford and mayor

in 1662, had to perform a complete about-face when the monarchy was restored and was obliged to apply to the king for a pardon and confirmation of his lands at Faithlegg in county Waterford. The original royal pardon and confirmation of his lands are on display in the museum. The former owners of Faithlegg had been evicted by the Cromwellians and transported to Connaught, as many other landed catholic families had been and thus was born the slogan: 'To hell or to Connaught'.

In the dying years of Charles's reign a more tolerant attitude prevailed and several catholics were admitted as freemen of Waterford, a privilege allowing them to trade as merchants. To encourage trade the mayor and council commissioned Edmund Russell, silversmith and freeman of the city, to cut dies and strike copper tokens to be used within the city as coin.[11] Russell also made church plate including a beautiful silver chalice for the church of Ireland abbey church, Kilculliheen, in Waterford city. (p145)

On Charles's death the catholic James II (1685- 1688) became king of England. The city received a new charter in which the council members, who would elect their representatives to parliament, were named. In Waterford there was a comfortable majority of catholic councillors, but the number of protestant names is significant. What records survive suggest that the two groups worked harmoniously on the business of managing the city's affairs. The brief period of catholic restoration in Waterford ended with the surrender of the city to King William (1689-1702) in July 1690. The prompt surrender of the garrison meant favourable terms for the catholic inhabitants 'who were not to be molested in their properties'.[12] Thomas Wyse, a descendant of the William Wyse who had received the cap of maintenance and sword from Henry VIII, was a leading member of the city's ruling elite and the last catholic to serve a full term as mayor. He sent a petition to the king requesting that he honour his earlier promise 'not to molest the catholics in their properties'. The king remained true to his promise and so the Wyses held on to the lands and the manor of St John which they had acquired in 1536 when the monasteries were dissolved. The sealed petition to the king is on display in the museum, beside a Wyse family oak chest carved with the letters WW and the date 1693, probably the oldest piece of Waterford furniture to survive. (p147) A catholic would not again be elected to the city council until 1829 when yet another member of that famous Wyse family would take his seat.

Maces

The history of civic maces carried by the town serjeant begins about the middle of the thirteenth century but no examples from this period remain in either Britain or Ireland. A Commons petition of 1344 shows that the carrying of an ornamented mace was one of the privileges of the king's serjeants and it was felt that the use of civic maces was an infringement of that privilege. However the serjeants of London had the privilege by the mid-fourteenth century, followed by those of York (1396), of Norwich (1403/4) and of Chester (1506). By the mid-sixteenth century most towns of any standing had a silver mace.

Civic maces, like bearing swords, began as weapons, items used to protect the monarch or other powerful dignitary. With the passage of time and the development of a more stable society, its function became more ceremonial as the mace was now used to enhance the status of the individual being protected. Consequently maces, as well as swords, when carried before a high-ranking member of society, were ornamented to symbolise or convey the power and dignity of the individual rather than his or her need for protection.

When ceremonial maces came into use, the head of the war mace (the end with blade-like flanges) was borne uppermost and the small button with the royal arms on the base, downwards. By the 1460s, the head of the mace with the blade-like flanges, originally made for defence, degenerated into mere ornaments. The end of one of the early Waterford maces (not illustrated) still retains these flanges. Greater importance was now given to the end with the royal arms: this became bigger, resulting in the reversal of the holding position of the mace - the former offensive top now became the bottom of the mace.

With the exception of Waterford's civic maces, there are no surviving medieval maces in Ireland. The four Waterford maces have something of a chequered history. We know that among the gifts given to the city by Edward IV in 1461 was a mace. Three of the four surviving Waterford maces (two shown opposite) stylistically appear to date from the fifteenth century when silver mace heads were mostly plain (A) or plain with a cresting of leaves or flowers (B). The top of mace head (B) is a seventeenth century replacement.

Mace (A) is probably one of the earliest. There is little or no decoration on the head and the flanged end is simply decorated with a pattern that echoes the blade-like flanges of earlier offensive weapons. The circular silver plate that formed the top of the head is missing. It is likely that this missing piece was engraved with the royal arms or perhaps the arms of the city.

The third mace (C) is silver-gilt and could very well be the mace taken from New Ross in 1518. An official account of the battle between Waterford and New Ross states 'thirty-four of the leading citizens of Waterford, accompanied by many Spaniards, Frenchmen, Bretons and Irish ... came riotously with a fleet of boats in piratical or warlike fashion, variously armed, to wit, with surcoats, coat of mail, helmets, shields, spears, swords, lances, crossbows, darts, arrows, broadaxes, and bombards

or cannon and assaulted New Ross'. They did one hundred pounds worth of damage before being bought off by the gift of a silver gilt mace, to the value of twenty pounds. Mace (C) is silver gilt; its relatively small size, its similarity to the other maces in the collection and its decoration all indicate that it could date from about 1500 when maces were being more lavishly decorated.

The top of the silver-gilt mace head is almost identical to that on mace (B). Both are decorated with the armorial bearings of the Stuart kings of England. It must be presumed that these naively-drawn arms of the Stuart kings were seventeenth century additions. In 1626, following a request by the mayor and council and the payment of a fee of £3,000, King Charles I granted the city a new charter, known as the Great Governing Charter of Waterford. For the citizens of Waterford this was an historic occasion, for in 1618 under James I, the government of the city had been suspended and its charters and civic regalia withdrawn because the officials would not recognise the king as head of the church. The granting of the new charter put all this behind them - the city could once again function. We must assume that by placing the arms of the new monarch on two of the old city maces the citizens were highlighting both their gratitude and loyalty.

(A)

DATE:	mid-late 15th century
NUMBER:	WMT1999.1733
DIMENSIONS:	L 340, Dia of head 59
MATERIAL:	silver
PROVENANCE:	historic municipal collection
FURTHER READING:	McEneaney in Nolan and Power (eds) 1992

(B)

DATE:	mid-late 15th century
NUMBER:	WMT1999.1611
DIMENSIONS:	L 380, Dia of head 50
MATERIAL:	silver
PROVENANCE:	historic municipal collection

(C)

DATE:	c1500 A D
NUMBER:	WMT1999.4385
DIMENSIONS:	L 305, Dia of head 63
MATERIAL:	silver, silver-gilt
PROVENANCE:	historic municipal collection
FURTHER READING:	Walton in McEneaney (ed) 1995

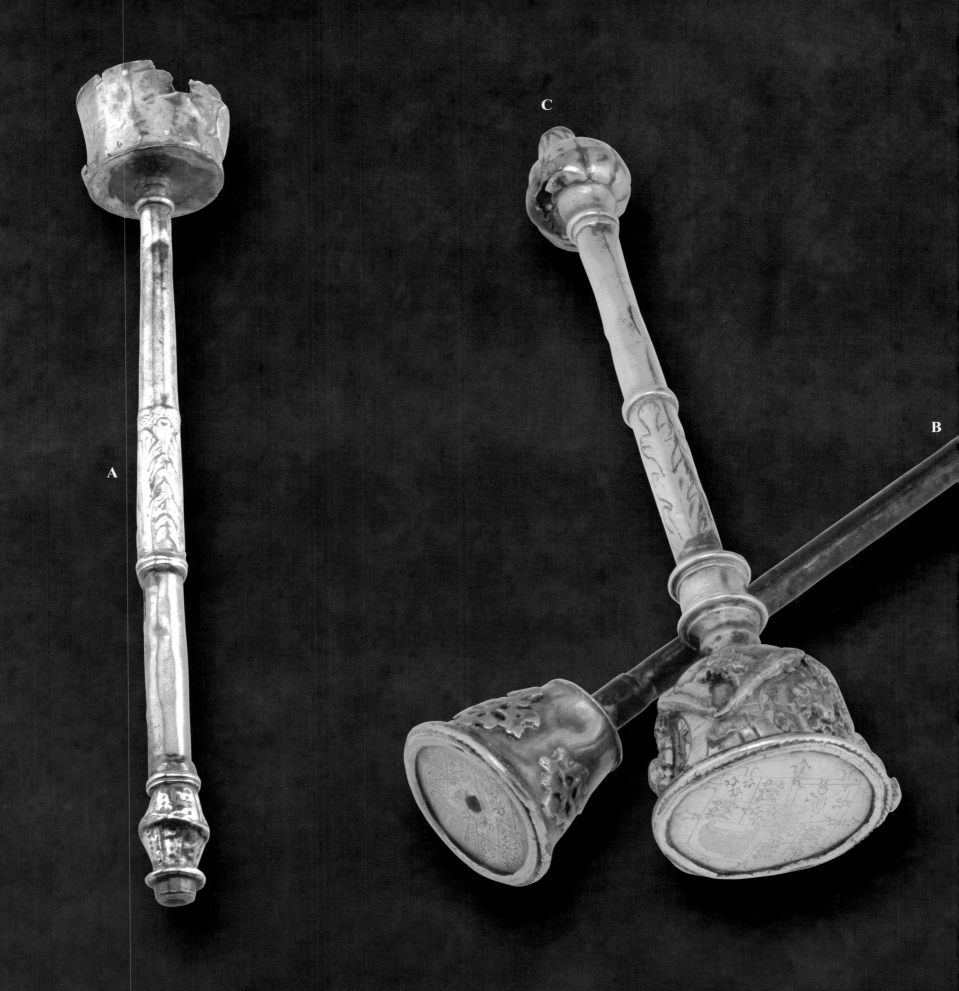

Ciborium

This elaborate ciborium is inscribed under the base: 'St Patrick's Waterford 1629'. St Patrick's church was a medieval foundation, its dedication suggesting that it may have pre-dated the arrival of the Anglo-Normans in 1170. It is not mentioned in records until 1468. It is again mentioned in 1603 when we are told that the soldiers at St Patrick's fort had 'pulled down the Tymbers and tooke away the seate and burned them for fire'. In 1615 the mayor of Waterford stated that repairs were underway at St Patrick's; both this and the date on the ciborium suggest that the church was in use for catholic service in the early years of the reign of Charles I.

The ciborium is of gilded copper. The base, stem, bowl and lid each have four applied winged cherubs' heads with stylised bodies. The cherubs are interspaced with bosses, infilled with niello. The lid is surmounted by a cross, now loose. Interestingly the entire cirborium is made in five pieces and held together by a long brass bolt into which is screwed a square nut. The nut is decorated with incised lines and dated 1629.

DATE:	1629 A D
NUMBER:	WMT1999.1750
DIMENSIONS:	H 390, Dia of bowl 136, Dia of base 168, weight 900 g
MATERIAL:	gilded copper
PROVENANCE:	St Patrick's church

On loan from the Bishop of Waterford & Lismore

Chalice

This fascinating silver chalice has a great story to tell. It is a typical early seventeenth century chalice and has no maker's mark. It has a deep bowl, internally gilded, and everted rim. The hexagonal stem has a slightly flattened globular knop with six chased designs around the centre. Above and below the centre are twelve decorated chased floral panels. The incurved hexagonal foot has one facet engraved with a crucifixion scene with a dove above and the instruments of the passion around. A second facet depicts a crowned St Catherine, holding a sword and a book, with a wheel (symbol of her martyrdom) and a steepled church to her right. On her left is what appears to be a crop of corn in a field. The scene is inscribed 'S Catharina'. A third facet is engraved with a picture of 'S Brigida' holding a crozier. Around her is a similar church and again a crop in the field.

At the base of the bowl are six panels, one of which contains the inscription 'IHS' surmounted by a cross and over a pierced heart. The second next panel is engraved with a stylised plant showing leaves, stem and root. The second next panel again is engraved 'MAR'.

At the base of the chalice is an inscription: *'R·D· Teiertius Dempsy me fieri fecit Anno Dom 1646'* (Teiertius Dempsy caused me to be made, the Year of Our Lord 1646). A second inscription, on the rim of the underside of the base, states: 'This Challice & Remonstrance is left by Fr Cullumb Morgan to the Parish Chappel of Waterford ... Obt Bilb [died in Bilbao] 8 Feb 1722 S N'. This fascinating inscription would suggest that the chalice (plus a remonstrance) was taken to the city of Bilbao, where a community of Waterford leather workers had been established. Among the merchant families who settled there at the turn of the eighteenth century, were Morgans. The chalice was left by Father Cullumb Morgan, to the old 'Big Chapel' of Waterford (the precursor of the Catholic cathedral begun in 1793 by John Roberts).

The third inscription, on the inside of the hexagonal base, suggests that the chalice never found its way back to Waterford as it was offered for sale at an auction in England in 1845. The inscription reads: 'This CHALICE lost for many years, or perhaps never having reached its first destination, was accidentally discovered at an AUCTION MART in MANCHESTER, and purchased by the Revd Daniel Hearne of the Diocese of Waterford and for 20 years Missionary Apostolic in Manchester. Pray for him and the Souls of John & Catherine Lee, the Parents of Daniel Lee Esquire, J P of Manchester who at his own cost restored this CHALICE to the Right Revd Nicholas Foran Lord Bishop of Waterford & Lismore. Pray also for the good Estate of Daniel Lee & of his Sisters Catherine, Kitty, Susannah Lee and Mary Anne Lee. Manchester November 8th 1845'.

DATE:	1646 A D
NUMBER:	WMT1999.1749
DIMENSIONS:	H 241, Dia of bowl 97, Dia of foot 132, weight 470 g
MATERIAL:	silver, silver-gilt
PROVENANCE:	Terence Dempsy
FURTHER READING:	Bilbao Acedos 2003

On loan from the Bishop of Waterford & Lismore

Pamphlet and Broadsheet

These two fascinating paper documents are representative of what was one of the most troubled decades in Irish history, 1640 to 1650.

Pamphlet

The earlier document is a pamphlet entitled: *ADMONITIONS BY THE SVPREME COVUNCELL OF THE CONFEDERAT CATHOLICKS OF IREAND*. This pamphlet was printed by Thomas Bourke in 1643 at Waterford, by command of the Supreme Council of the Confederate Catholics. Bourke's printing press in Waterford is best known for the printing of Patrick Darcy's detailed treatise known as the 'Argument', defending the legislative independence of the Irish parliament. Darcy, a constitutional lawyer, tried to keep the Irish parliament in being after it was prorogued in 1641 by the Dublin government. It was he who suggested the Confederate Catholic model and subsequently helped to draft its constitution. The confederation met mainly in Kilkenny but also in Waterford, and had Darcy's 'Argument', first stated in 1641, published in Waterford by Bourke in 1643. Darcy served on the supreme council of the Confederate Catholics and although he survived Cromwellian rule to resume his legal career, he lost his lands during the confiscations. Darcy's published works influenced the great scientist and political writer, William Molyneaux (1656-1698), and later the American colonists used his writings to advocate the rights of the colonial legislatures vis-à-vis Westminister.

The Admonitions (warnings) of the Supreme Council is essentially a small pamphlet of eleven leaves. It begins by explaining that since the last general assembly of the Confederate Catholics held in Waterford, a 'Solemn League and Covenant for the Reformation and Defence of Religion' had been issued by the Westminster parliament in London. This London document was an attack on the catholics of Ireland following the 1641 rising that saw the massacre of many protestant settlers in Ulster. The Admonitions is a propaganda document on behalf of the Confederate Catholics refuting the Solemn League and various other printed propaganda documents issued by the London parliament. Interestingly a number of the London parliament's propaganda documents including the 'Solemn League and Covenant' are reprinted within the pamphlet.

Thomas Bourke's printing works in Waterford has the distinction of being the oldest printing press in Ireland outside Dublin. It is known that copies of what issued from Bourke's press were sent to the agent of the Confederate Catholics in Rome, the Waterford Franciscan, Father Luke Wadding, in order to keep him informed of events in Ireland.

DATE:	1643 A D
NUMBER:	WMT1998.0002
DIMENSIONS:	L 183 x W 132
MATERIAL:	paper, binding modern
PROVENANCE:	purchased with assistance of Intacta Print & The Book Centre in 1998

Broadsheet

This broadsheet is entitled *An order of Parliament For THANKS-GIVING: Together with a DECLARATION of The Grounds and Reasons of it.*

The hopes expressed by the Confederate Catholics, that a compromise might be reached with the king whereby he would allow them practice their religion in return for their loyalty, came to nothing when the London parliament convicted King Charles I of treason and had him executed in 1649. Within months Cromwell and his parliamentary forces were in Ireland quashing all catholic resistance to the rule of the English parliament. The southern ports were Cromwell's main objective. They were the most likely places to be used by supporters of the executed king as a base from which the monarchy could be restored. It should be remembered that the motto of the confederate catholics was 'For God, For King and For Fatherland' and that cities like Waterford were comfortable with the idea of a protestant monarch, provided he was tolerant in matters of religion.

Cromwell failed to take Waterford in late 1649, however, the city fell to Ireton in August 1650. This broadsheet shows just how important the fall of Waterford was to the parliamentary cause.

The broadsheet is a bill or notice dated 30 August 1650 ordering the 'ministers of various churches and chapels in London and Westminster, and in the churches of England, Wales and Berwick on Tweed, to give thanks to the Lord God on September the first'. The order states specifically how the thanksgiving ceremony was to be conducted - 'The thanks-giving is to be held after the Psalms and before the sermon when the minister is to read out the Lord Deputy's account of the taking of the various strongholds by the Parliamentary forces, and then to offer their thanks'.

The Lord Deputy's letter is quoted in full on the order and gives an interesting insight into the mindset of the parliamentarians. The lord deputy achieved 'a wonderful and unexplained victory ... including the taking of many strong cities, towns, castles and garrisons. All this raised the spirits of the people who truly fear the Lord God and love his cause and people ... The work the Lord Deputy was carrying out pleased God, and Gods goodness was shown when Parliament Forces took Carlow and Waterford, a great and populous town and the most considerable harbour in all of Ireland. This victory occurred on Saturday 10th August, in which day a strong castle of Duncannon was also taken ... The forces put the surrender [of Waterford] to the workings of God'.

The reason the parliamentary forces believed Waterford's surrender was the result of divine intervention is clearly stated - 'an inspection of the town showed it to be better fortified, supplied and defended than the parliamentary forces had imagined'.

The order is printed on two leaves using a number of different typefaces. On the top of the document is the parliamentary seal showing two shields emblazoned with the harp of Ireland and the cross of St George representing England.

DATE:	1650 A D
NUMBER:	WMT1998.0001
DIMENSIONS:	L 500 x W 272
MATERIAL:	paper
PROVENANCE:	gifted by the late Nigel de la Poer, K M, in 1998

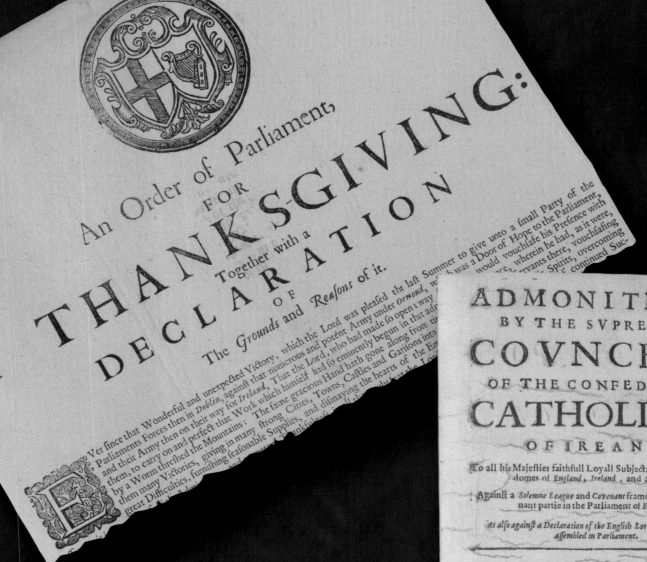

An Order of Parliament,

FOR

A THANKSGIVING:

Together with a

DECLARATION

OF

The Grounds and Reasons of it.

EVer since that Wonderful and unexpected Victory, which the Lord was pleased the last Summer to give unto a small Party of the Parliaments Forces then in *Dublin*, against that numerous and potent Army under *Ormond*, which was a Door of Hope to the Parliament and their Army then on their way for *Ireland*, That the Lord, who had made so open a way would vouchsafe his Presence with them, to carry on and perfect that Work which himself had so eminently begun in that admirable Victory, wherein he had, as it were, by a Worm threshed the Mountains: The same gracious Hand hath gone along from its servants there, vouchsafing them many Victories, giving in many strong Cities, Towns, Castles and Garisons into their hands, Spirits, overcoming great Difficulties, furnishing seasonable Supplies, and dismaying the hearts of the Enemy, and c. continued Suc-

---

ADMONITIONS

BY THE SVPREAME

COVNCELL

OF THE CONFEDERAT

CATHOLICKS

OF IREAND,

To all his Majesties faithfull Loyall Subjects of the three Kingdomes of *England*, *Ireland*, and *Scotland*.

Against a *Solemne League* and *Covenant* framed by the malignant partie in the Parliament of *England*.

As also against a *Declaration* of the English Lords and Commons assembled in Parliament.

Printed by Command of the said Supreame Councell, at VVaterford by *Thomas Bourke*, 26. Ian. 1643.

Chalice - Seventeenth Century

This chalice was made in Waterford by Edward Russell about 1670. On its base is the inscription *Deo et Ecclesia* (God & Church); underneath the foot *Dedit Hook* (Hook gave it). Pieces by Russell bear his initials together with the mark of Waterford.

The long tradition of goldsmiths working in Waterford goes back to Viking times. In the late thirteenth century we find the first named goldsmith, Roger the Goldsmith, a city official who may also have been involved with the mint operating in the city in the 1290s. Though there is no information on the operation of goldsmiths in the fourteenth and fifteenth centuries, it is very likely that there were goldsmiths, for in 1577 the city council decided the dissolve the Guild of Hammermen (a guild that included goldsmiths) and replace it with two new guilds, of Hammermen and of Timbermen.

It is not until 1582 that we find another reference to a Waterford goldsmith. Inscribed in stone on a beautifully executed memorial that stands in the nave of the old Franciscan friary at Greyfriars, is a Latin inscription that tells us that interred there is Cornelius Hurley, goldsmith, who died on 10 March 1582. Hurley is not a name normally found in Waterford, but is a Gaelic name possibly from west Cork. It may suggest that following the dissolution of the monasteries, the traditional Gaelic Irish goldsmiths lost their former major patrons and were forced to move to cities like Waterford where they might find patrons among the rich and sophisticated merchant class. We know that in the sixteenth century rich merchants like the Dobbyns were importing gold and silver objects from Spain, so it is natural to assume that they were also commissioning plate and jewellery locally.

Goldsmiths are not mentioned again in Waterford until 1657 when the Cromwellian planters, then running the city, granted a charter of incorporation to the Guild of Hammermen. Thirty-two crafts were embraced by this guild; the goldsmiths who were normally top of the list had slipped to fourth place after hammermen, blacksmiths and jewellers. The first Waterford goldsmith to be mentioned, following the restoration of the monarchy in 1660, is Edward Russell. Described as *Edmandus Russell faber argentarius*, his admission to the freedom of Waterford was recorded on 1 September 1674.

A few years earlier in 1667, in a response to a severe shortage of coinage in the city, the mayor and council had appointed Russell to cut dies for copper tokens. A surviving specimen, dated 1668, shows that for the obverse Russell adopted a version of the city arms with the words 'CORPORATION OF' in the surround, while the reverse bore the legend 'WATERFORD 1668' surrounding a castle with three flags flying and a tree on either side. Russell appears to have adopted a version of a triple towered castle (perhaps Reginald's Tower?) as a town-mark for his Waterford wares.

There are several surviving items of plate that can be confidently identified as his work. They are stamped with a shield bearing his initials ER and another stamp depicting the triple-towered castle, flying flags. The identified Russell items are a chalice and paten formerly from the church of Ireland parish church in Carrick-on-Suir, county Tipperary, both inscribed 'The gift of the Duke of Ormonds Troop to ye parish of Carrick, Anno Domini 1673'. A tankard by Russell, c1680, is on display in the National Museum of Ireland.

The exquisite chalice here is from the church of Ireland abbey church of Kilculliheen. This church and lands on the north side of the river Suir were made part of Waterford city by Queen Elizabeth in 1578. This beautiful chalice is on loan to the museum and forms the centre-piece of the seventeenth and eighteenth century silver collection. Edmund Russell pieces have for a long time been incorrectly attributed to Edmund Roth of Kilkenny. However thanks to the work of Dr Conor O'Brien, a more correct Waterford and Edmund Russell attribution has now been firmly established.

DATE: c1670 A D
NUMBER: WMT2000.0016
DIMENSIONS: H 150
MATERIAL: silver
PROVENANCE: Church of Ireland abbey church of Kilculliheen
FURTHER READING: O'Brien 2001 & forthcoming, Warren 1967

On loan from the Dean, Chapter and Select Vestry of Christ Church Cathedral

Ring with intaglio

This ring is another example of the very fine jewellery found in the Waterford excavations. The gemstone depicts a classical motif, a man in armour putting his hand into a fire and making an offering. The stone is sard or chalcedony and the engraving is carefully cut and polished and shows use of several tools. This is mounted on an oval bezel that is decorated with square bosses in relief on a sunken ground.

The classical subject and style of the intaglio indicate that it can only be of antique Roman or renaissance origin. However, it has been conclusively identified as of sixteenth or early seventeenth century date. This is borne out by the form of the ring, which is of late sixteenth century type. The probability is that both intaglio and ring are Elizabethan or early seventeenth century. It is very likely that the ring was imported rather than made locally and almost certainly the intaglio was imported as gem-cutting was a very specialised craft in the sixteenth century. It has been pointed out that the subject of the intaglio may be Mucius Scaevola, the Roman who, after his capture while attempting to assassinate Lars Porsenna, king of Clusium in Etruria, then besieging Rome, proved his dedication to his country by plunging his hand into the flames of a brazier. The story of Scaevola is related by the Roman historian Livy. An alternative is that the figure represents Mars.

The ring was found in organic layers dating from the thirteenth to the early seventeenth century.

DATE: c1600 A D
NUMBER: E527:1123:1 / WMT1999.0492
DIMENSIONS: Int Dia 22, stone L 14.5 x W 10.7 x Th 3.5
MATERIAL: gold, sard
PROVENANCE: Waterford excavations
FURTHER READING: Lightbown in Hurley & Scully 1997

Chest

This chest is probably the oldest surviving piece of Waterford furniture. It is made of oak, using a carcass frame with plain infill panels. It appears to have been acquired by the Religious Society of Friends when the Wyse family home, Newtown House, was bought by the Society who opened the famous Newtown School there in 1798. The chest is carved with the monogram 'WW' and the date 1693. A motif decorates the frame to the right and left of the monogram and date. We can presume that the chest belonged to a member of the Wyse family. Such chests were occasionally marriage gifts.

A chest was one of the most important items of furniture in a household, right through the medieval period and into modern times. We know from Waterford court cases as early as the thirteenth century that most households had chests in which to keep valuables. Thirteenth century records, relating to Waterford, show that wealthier people kept money, jewels, gold, silver and cloth in them. While these early wooden chests have not survived in Waterford, many of the barrel padlocks which were used to secure them, were found in the archaeological excavations. Muniments (documents) and plate were stored in chests like this for safekeeping and we know that the Waterford vestments survived by virtue of the fact that they had been stored in chests for over 120 years.

This is a fine example of seventeenth century oak furniture. The lock is missing. It is a remarkable survival of the original furnishings of the family house.

DATE: 1693 A D
NUMBER: WMT2002.0103
DIMENSIONS: L 1393 x H 620 x D 556
MATERIAL: oak
PROVENANCE: Newtown House

On loan from the Management Committee of Newtown School

EIGHTEENTH CENTURY
WATERFORD

Waterford was transformed during the eighteenth century from a walled enclave to a modern European city. Not only did it shake off the confining medieval defences but it also replaced some of the old twelfth and thirteenth century churches with what contemporaries considered gracious and modern buildings. The expansion of the thirteenth century city into the suburbs was mirrored in the eighteenth century with the diversion of the St John's river and the creation of new suburbs in Newtown. It is interesting that today in Waterford almost ninety per cent of the buildings of historic and architectural interest either date from the late twelfth-thirteenth centuries or the eighteenth century. As in the earlier period, the seventeenth and eighteenth centuries saw huge movements of people: Cromwellian settlers after 1650 and in the wake of the Williamite victory at the Boyne in 1690, new English, French and Dutch settlers. These settlers would put their indelible mark on the city, just as their Anglo-Norman predecessors had. However, the treatment of the displaced populations in each period was somewhat different: the Hiberno-Norse descendants of the Vikings were given the protection of English law and settled in the suburbs while their seventeenth and eighteenth century equivalents did not fare as well.

By the eighteenth century protestants controlled the Dublin parliament, and introduced a series of laws designed to exclude both catholics and non-conformists from public life. Catholic aristocracy and gentry had been decimated; by 1704 they owned only fourteen per cent of the profitable land of Ireland. Thomas Wyse, who successfully petitioned King William III (1689-1702) to retain his lands, was one of these fortunate catholic landholders. His son, Thomas 'Bullocks' Wyse (1701-1770), lived his entire life under the penal laws and yet he triumphed in adversity. A larger than life character, his nickname derived from his using bullocks instead of horses to pull his carriage as a protest against the penal law obliging any catholic who owned a horse to accept an offer of five pounds from a protestant wishing to purchase it. He developed a copper mine in county Waterford, using the copper for the manufacture of decorated snuff boxes.[1] Charles Smith, writing in 1746, described a mill capable of grinding different types of grain, which Bullocks devised as 'ingenious'.[2] Never one to be intimidated by authority, he removed part of the city's medieval defences to create easier access to his lands outside the bounds of the city. After 1756 he was a member of the Catholic Committee, the first body to give formal representation to catholic interests that were in the main commercial (p157).[3]

Not all were willing to remain in Waterford under the restrictions of the penal laws. Many fled the city to seek a livelihood in catholic Spain or France. In the Basque country of northern Spain a huge Irish community developed, the majority originating in Waterford. In the dying years of the seventeenth century the Waterford merchant families of Morgan, Grant and Furlong were settled there, with the Brownes and Powers joining them in the early eighteenth century. (p141) A tally of foreign merchants established in Bilbao in the eighteenth century shows the Irish as the second largest ethnic group after the French. Most of the emigrants were young single males, average age twenty-five, unwilling to live in Waterford as second-class citizens. Many of them left Ireland after the defeat and exile of the catholic King James II, even before the penal laws were enforced - religion appears to have been the motivation. In 1690 Miguel Morgan affirms that he left so as 'not to fall into heresy' and as late as 1800 Irish émigrés in Spain claimed to have left Ireland because of 'Cromwell the tyrant'. The vast majority of those who left were to become professional tanners.[4] Most of the émigrés kept the Jacobite dream alive, hoping for the day when James II or his heir would return from exile in France and reclaim the throne of England and restore the catholic hegemony. Indeed, it was one Antoine Walsh a rich Franco-Irish merchant, ship owner and slave-trader of Waterford descent, living in Nantes, who took Bonnie Prince Charles (grandson of James II) to Scotland in 1745.[5]

Other emigrants went to Cádiz in the south of Spain and, like those who went to Bilbao, some were of the merchant class; however the great majority came from families of comparative obscurity. Lorenzo Carew is a good example - he was born in Waterford in c1683 and probably had little either in the way of family capital or family connections when he left in c1713 and settled in Cádiz. Success came rapidly; he married a wealthy Portuguese lady who brought a large dowry and when she died he remarried, taking out Spanish citizenship in 1731. An extremely successful and wealthy merchant he never forgot his city of origin and in the 1750s presented to the Catholic Chapel in Waterford six silver candlesticks and a magnificent silver reliquary crucifix. (p159)

Following the death of his only child, he negotiated with John St Leger, S J, the parish priest of St Patrick's, and founded a home for poor widows in Waterford. He may also have assisted St Leger acquire premises for a new church, St Patrick's in Jenkins's Lane. Bequests to relatives and charitable institution in Waterford are frequently found in the wills of Cádiz merchants with Irish connections. The cathedral treasury contains many bequeathed pieces of church plate, including a chalice and paten from Thomas Walsh 1771 and a silver incense boat and thurible which are now on display in the museum. (p161) The links with Spain continued until the end of the eighteenth century when Irish communities in the Basque country and Cádiz were absorbed into the local population. Yet, through trade the connection between Spain and Waterford continued, as evidenced by the story behind one of the smallest of the city's treasures, the miniature on ivory of Xaveria Wiseman, née Strange. (p163) She was the daughter of Peter Strange, a member of an old Waterford catholic family. She married James Wiseman, the son of a Waterford merchant who had emigrated to Seville in the early eighteenth century. Their son, Nicholas, born in Seville in 1802, was destined to become the first catholic cardinal of England since the death of Cardinal Wolsey in 1529.

In time some of the catholics who remained in Waterford, though excluded from civic office, were, from 1710 onwards, allowed to become freemen. As early as 1704 the corporation dropped commercial restrictions against catholics and others, although the minutes record that the motive for the removal of these restrictions was 'the great decay of trade in the city'.[6] Interestingly the museum possesses a large bronze mortar made in England in 1707 for Michael Tonnery, a Waterford catholic apothecary. Its existence demonstrates that some catholics, particularly those with specialist skills, not only remained in business but apparently flourished. (p165) In 1727, of the twelve persons accepted as freemen of Waterford, four were catholic and, by 1740, seven of the fourteen admitted were catholic. By this time Waterford had presbyterian, baptist and quaker meeting houses and three catholic mass houses, one in the city and two in the suburbs.[7]

The protestant ruling class were the great builders of the eighteenth century. In 1724 the church of Ireland began rebuilding the old churches that formerly belonged to the catholic church. St Patrick's church in Patrick Street was rebuilt in 1727 and shortly afterwards, in 1734, the old Norse foundation of St Olaf was rebuilt. St Patrick's church had what Charles Smith, the contemporary historian describes as 'a handsome altar-piece on which is painted the Glory by van der Hagen'.[8] Presumably van der Hagen received this commission around 1736, for in that year the mayor and council paid him the princely sum of twenty pounds for the now famous 'View of Waterford' that hangs in the Council Chamber. It is the oldest view of an Irish city and its painter is regarded as the father of Irish landscape painting. (p167)

The commissioning of the view of Waterford is a sign that economic prosperity had returned after all the turmoil of the previous century. Streetlights were installed in 1732 and a system of rating householders was devised to cover maintenance costs. What we know today as the Mall was created in the 1730s when the Pill or St. John's river was diverted and the area it occupied, reclaimed. Rows of very fashionable elm trees were planted to make a pleasant walkway, and opposite Reginald's Tower a bowling green was laid out. In 1741 the Oxford-educated, church of Ireland bishop of Waterford and Lismore, Charles Este (1696-1745), commissioned the renowned German born architect, Richard Castle (1695-1751), to build what was to become the finest eighteenth century ecclesiastical palace in Ireland. He also commissioned a portrait of himself by one of the greatest portrait painters of his age, Jean Baptiste van Loo (1684-1745). (p169) The new bishop's palace is symbolic of the outward looking and expansionist city. Reversing the orientation of the original palace which he demolished, his new palace now overlooked the old town wall out on to the newly created Mall.

The old medieval cathedral, now in protestant hands, received the attention of a number of church of Ireland prelates, starting with Mills, the builder of St Patrick's and St Olaf's. This Oxford graduate entertained plans as early as 1730 for the rehabilitation of the medieval fabric of the cathedral. He had a great interest in what was happening to similar churches in England and he commissioned the Bristol architect, William Halfpenny, to produce plans and drawings of Waterford's medieval cathedral.[9] However, by 1740 he had decided the better option would be to build anew but his untimely death in May 1740 put an end to the project. Two fine eighteenth century paintings, exterior and interior views, give us some idea of the splendour of the medieval cathedral. (p171, 173) Bishop Mills, who obviously agonized over the fate of the cathedral, may have commissioned the paintings. The untimely deaths of both Bishop Mills in 1740 and his successor Bishop Este in 1745 seems to have put the cathedral project on hold. Este's successor, Richard Chenevix, was left with an unfinished bishop's palace, so his first priority was its completion and the commission was given to the Waterford architect, John Roberts. In 1773 Thomas Ivory was commissioned to report on the condition of the medieval cathedral and he recommended that it be taken down and replaced. In January 1774 a joint committee of

the corporation and church authorities resolved that 'the plain plan omitting the rustic work laid before the committee by Mr John Roberts for rebuilding the cathedral appears to be most eligible of any as yet produced to us'. The estimated cost of demolition and rebuilding was £3,704.5s.6p.[10] The massive undertaking of demolishing a fine medieval cathedral and its replacement by a new building in the classical style indicates the self-confidence of Waterford's religious and civic oligarchy. During the demolition of the cathedral the vaults into which the medieval vestments had been placed for safe keeping before the fall of Waterford in 1650 were discovered and the vestments recovered. (p90, 107) It was perhaps a sign of the harmonious relations between the protestant and catholic communities that on their discovery the kindly Bishop Chenevix presented them to the catholic dean Dr Hussey. The cathedral was completed in 1780 and the spire in 1788. Roberts was now well on his way to transforming Waterford - he very probably built Faithlegg House completed in 1773 for Cornelius Bolton, a descendant of the Cromwellian soldier, later Mayor of Waterford in 1672. Roberts was also responsible for Newtown House as the country seat of the catholic landowner John Wyse, a descendant of another famous family.[11] A pair of contemporary paintings, both on copper, show the interior of Newtown House. One features John Wyse with his wife and brother enjoying a musical interlude in the print-room and the other depicts John in his study. (p175) The beautiful plasterwork shown in the paintings is no longer a feature of the house. When the Pennsylvania Quaker, William Savery, visited the house early in 1798, he found his co-religionists busily removing the stuccowork. The house had been sold for use as a school to the Religious Society of Friends who found the over decorative plasterwork anathema to their preferred simple architectural tastes.[12]

In 1792 the quakers had built a new meeting house, now housing Garter Lane Arts Centre, and this building too is very plain. It is in stark contrast to William Morris's house, built by John Roberts, less than two hundred metres away, now the Chamber of Commerce building. Built at a cost of £10,000 for one of Waterford's wealthiest protestant merchants of Cromwellian planter stock, it contains what is beyond doubt one of the finest staircases in Ireland. The stuccowork in the oval stairwell is believed to be the work of Michael Stapleton.

The city fathers were also in a building mood though in the case of the leper hospital they did so out of compunction. The Rev William Downes took a case against the council claiming that they were obliged to provide a leper hospital for 'the sick and maimed poor of the city' because the medieval leper hospital had been closed by the city fathers who had neglected to put that hospital's endowment to further use. Prince John had founded the original hospital in 1185 and the new one, sited on John's Hill, was completed six hundred years later by John Roberts In 1788 Roberts was a member of a consortium that 'leased a plot of ground under Dundory Wall as a site for a playhouse and assembly hall'.[13] This imposing nine-bay, two-storied building situated on the Mall, forms a piece with the cathedral and bishop's palace prompting Edward McParland to write in *James Gandon, Vitruvius Hibernicus:* 'Waterford more than any other city in the country in the late eighteenth century succeeded in expressing its civic dignity with fitting architectural grandeur'.[14] The city council purchased the building in 1813 for use as a new town hall and in 1836 acquired from Dublin Castle the magnificent Waterford Glass chandelier which graces the Council Chamber. The chandelier had been commissioned in 1786 by the Duke of Rutland for Dublin Castle on the instigation of Thomas Penrose, architect and kinsman of the glass factory founders. (p177)

Civic dignity ranked high in the consciousness of eighteenth century Waterford. When the lord lieutenant the Duke of Westmorland visited in 1783 he was given the freedom of the city, the scroll being presented in a gold freedom box emblazoned with the arms of the city on its base and those of the duke on the domed cover. (p179)

Nor was the city averse to acknowledging the achievement or generosity of one of their own. In 1779 the city council voted that Henry Alcock, the outgoing mayor, 'be given 200 guineas to be laid out on a plate with the city arms engraved thereon'. The gesture was intended to acknowledge his benevolence 'in supplying the poor, at his own expense, with provisions during the time of great scarcity'. The piece is marked by two goldsmiths, one Dublin - that of Thomas Jones and the other Waterford - Anastasia Fleming of Broad Street, a catholic goldsmith who presumably sub-contracted the work to a Dublin maker.[15] Her son, Ignatius, born in 1766 was an accomplished goldsmith and a very fine christening cup dated to 1800 is a reminder of his skill. (p181) The same year as the mayor received the honorarium for the purchase of the silver salver, the city sheriffs also received twenty guineas 'to be given to each of the late sheriffs by this Board to purchase such piece of plate as they shall think proper testimony of the sense of this city of their good conduct during their sheriffalty' - one of the sheriffs Thomas Ivie purchased a gold topped walking stick. (p181)

By the 1790s relations between catholics and protestants in Waterford were much improved. In 1793 under the terms of the Catholic Relief Act, catholics were admitted to the parliamentary franchise on the same terms as protestants; the few remaining restrictions on their holding land were removed and most civil and military posts were open to them. The only substantial discrimination which remained was their exclusion from membership of parliament. Many members of the establishment in Waterford supported these reforms, as shown by the stone tablet commemorating the building of the first bridge across the Suir at Waterford. The tablet (now on view in the museum) was erected by an exclusively protestant council and refers to 1793 as 'a year rendered sacred to national prosperity by the extinction of religious division'. When the Catholic Relief Act became law James Wyse, a leading catholic merchant and owner of four ships, on behalf of the catholic community thanked the protestant members of parliament for Waterford for their 'very decided support'.[16] A year earlier the same council had leased to the catholic community a plot of land on which to build a new church replacing the 'Big Chapel' . It says much for the status and wealth of the catholic community in Waterford that it should build the first post-reformation catholic cathedral in the British Isles. It is equally remarkable that the catholics should commission a protestant architect to build their cathedral. This was Roberts's last work; it is also his masterpiece - 'a perfect epitome of Georgian taste ... possibly the greatest forgotten building in the history of eighteenth century building in Ireland'.[17] He died on 24 May 1796, at the age of eighty-two, shortly before the completion of the cathedral. In his lifetime he had transformed Waterford, creating many of the city's greatest architectural treasures.[18]

Who and what paid for all this work? Certainly the money generated from overseas trade helped, for Waterford was the third busiest port in eighteenth century Ireland. The success of the port was in no small measure due to the realisation by the city council, as early as 1704, that if Waterford was to flourish then it needed the efforts, skills and contacts of more than the small protestant ruling elite. By the end of the eighteenth century Waterford was a booming port, part of a far-flung and diverse trading world involving 400 ports in Britain, Holland, Germany, Scandinavia, France, Iberia, the West Indies, mainland America and Newfoundland. Salt pork, salt beef and butter were the stalwarts of Waterford trade and just as in the halcyon days of the thirteenth century the city's hinterland grew rich as once again the merchant princes of Waterford found markets for their produce. There were about fifty vessels belonging to the port in 1770 and the great majority of the merchant ship-owners were catholic. In 1775 over 120 merchant families lived in the port of Waterford, slightly more than half of whom were catholic, a third protestant and nearly one fifth quaker.[19]

The quakers were a minority group constituting no more than two per cent of the city's population. They were dissenters who arrived in 1654 and who, like catholics, suffered under the discriminatory penal laws. By the 1780s they were among the leading figures in Waterford overseas trade, becoming so wealthy they began to diversify. The glass factory was founded in 1783 by George Penrose and his nephew William, members of the most successful quaker merchant family in the city. It operated until 1851 and the glassware it produced was so prized for the quality of its craftsmanship that the National Museum of Ireland began to acquire pieces from as early as 1880.[20] The chandelier in city hall is an early example of the factory's craft but prized among the museum collection is an early decanter, one of the few surviving with the name Penrose on its mould-impressed base (p183).

Glassmakers and goldsmiths were not the only highly skilled craft workers in the city; there were also a number of watch and clock makers. Francis, Henry and William Maddock were prominent catholic watchmakers residing on or near the Quay. A grandfather clock made by William in 1783, the same year as the glass factory opened, today marks time in the Council Chamber, City Hall, while a pocket watch he crafted, also in 1783, and still keeping perfect time, represents him in the musuem. (p181). William was kinsman of another William Maddock who captained the Mary Ann, a ninety-ton Waterford-built ship that made over thirty voyages between 1766-1771. Another relative, Luke, was also a watchmaker in St John's, Newfoundland and subsequently became a very wealthy ship owner and merchant there, focusing on the Waterford-Newfoundland trade.[21]

Newfoundland, in North America, was one of Waterford's most important trade routes. By 1770 the route absorbed between ten and fifteen percent of the city's exports. Not only did the city's merchants provision the English ships sailing from Bristol and the West Country ports to Newfoundland for the fishing season, but Waterford fishermen and mariners themselves found much needed employment there. Thousands of 'green men' (inexperienced fishermen) travelled seasonally to work on the Grand Banks from the second half of the eighteenth century onwards. In time those who went out to work seasonally in the fishery became permanent settlers and it is estimated that about 33,000 people, drawn overwhelmingly from Waterford and its hinterland, settled in Newfoundland prior to 1820. By this time over half the population of the island of Newfoundland was Irish and spoke with what has been described as a Waterford or south-east of Ireland accent that persists in places right up to today. Contemporaries sometimes described Newfoundland as 'Transatlantic Ireland' but one writer went further saying that it was more correct to call it 'Transatlantic Waterford'. He claimed that 'Friars from Waterford hold the Irish bishopric of St. John's as a baronial fief entail ... all the leaders of Parliament are Waterfordians and all the place holders'.[22] The first bishop of Newfoundland, James Louis O'Donel arrived as Prefect Apostolic in 1784 following a request from the Irish of Newfoundland to the bishop of Waterford. On retiring to Waterford in 1807 he was given a large silver cup by the catholic community of St. John's in recognition of his work. Today the cup is both a tribute to Bishop O'Donel and a reminder of the tens of thousands of Irish men and women who braved the cold north Atlantic in search of a better life. (p187)

The migration to Newfoundland from the south-east of Ireland was the largest mass migration from a single region prior to the Great Famine of 1845-1849. This exodus gave social mobility to those willing to work hard and brave the seas. It also acted as a safety valve for the ever-increasing population. Though the migration had ceased by 1830 its impact on Waterford's hinterland was one of the factors ensuring that the south-east region would escape some of the worst effects of the Great Famine.

Thomas 'Bullocks' Wyse

In the eighteenth century the Wyses of Waterford were an almost unique survival from a past era - a catholic landowning family that had held onto both their lands and their faith through wars and persecutions. Their power base was on the edge of the city at the Manor of St John's (on the site of the Good Shepherd Convent, now part of Waterford Institute of Technology). Like the Waddings, Sherlocks, Comerfords and Lombards, they had belonged to the Catholic junta that had ruled the city since the middle ages. They had survived the confiscations of Cromwell and William III and the penal laws through a combination of political astuteness, luck, and the genetic good fortune that had provided them with one (and no more than one) capable head of the family in times of crisis.

Such a man was Thomas Wyse (1701?-1770), lord of the manor in the mid-eighteenth century. As the head of an ancient and illustrious family, he chafed at the penal laws that treated him as a second-class citizen. He devoted his energy and his talents to changing all that. Catholics were barred from acquiring land, so he built up a whole series of industries instead. In 1750 he took a lease of the lands of Tankardstown near Bunmahon and reopened the old copper mines there. At least two paintings, done on copper from these mines survive. (p175) We know that Thomas Wyse set up a 'manufactory at Waterford [that produced] painted snuff-boxes, trays and waiters in imitation of Birmingham and Japan ware'. He established mills at Pouldrew near Kilmeaden and on the Pill at St John's. In 1757 he and two others set up the Catholic Committee to campaign for civil rights. Deprived of his horses by the famous penal law that allowed protestants to buy them for a mandatory five pounds each, he harnessed bullocks to his carriage and defiantly drove through the city in style - hence his nickname of 'Bullocks' Wyse. Finding the medieval Bowling Green Gate near the approach to his manor too narrow for this carriage, he commanded his tenants to assemble one Sunday morning, and got them to demolish it while the protestants were all in church.

'Bullocks' had, however, an Achilles heel. The three sons for whom he built up his family's prestige - Francis, John and Richard - proved to be spoiled wastrels. Moreover, under the penal laws upon the death of a catholic landlord his estate had to be 'gavelled', that is to say, it had to be divided equally between the sons. The motive was obvious - to produce smaller and therefore weaker catholic landowners. So the best that Thomas could hope for was that his estate would only be divided into three. But there was worse to follow. For if one of the sons conformed to the established church he could inherit the whole lot. And that is precisely the course followed by 'that abandoned reprobate my youngest son' Richard, who 'took the soup' and ousted his elder brothers and father.

Fate, however, intervened, for Richard died childless in 1764. Nevertheless, the last years of 'Bullocks' were clouded by disappointment with the fecklessness of his sons and trepidation at the explosion of anti-catholic feeling that erupted among the protestant establishment of Munster in the 1760s. He died, embittered, in 1770.

This is a fine half-length portrait of 'Bullocks' in young to middle age, depicted in blue velvet. The painter has not been identified. 'Bullocks' had at least two other portraits of himself painted, as a young and as an older man (also in the museum), both by John Lewis, a portrait and scene painter in Dublin theatres. This portrait is a more intimate one. The frame may be original. A paper label on the back of the portrait records that it was the property of Thomas Houghton (Margaret, daughter of 'Bullocks', married Thomas Houghton of Kilmannock House near Arthurstown in county Wexford) but it subsequently passed back to the Wyse family, who have loaned it to the museum.

The famous *Green Book of the Wyses*, a compilation of the muniments associated with the family from 1199 to 1867, was begun by 'Bullocks' Wyse. This extraordinary source for the history of Waterford is also on loan to the museum.

Julian Walton

DATE:	c1740 A D
NUMBER:	WMT2002.0015
DIMENSIONS:	L 710 x W 593 (canvas)
MATERIAL:	oil on canvas
PROVENANCE:	the Bonaparte Wyse family
FURTHER READING:	Bonaparte Wyse forthcoming

On loan from Henry Bonaparte Wyse

Candlesticks and reliquary crucifix

The pair of candlesticks here are part of a set of six presented to the 'Chapel of Waterford' in 1751 by Laurence Carew, of Cádiz in Spain. They stand on tripod legs and are sixty-seven centimetres high. As a group they are most impressive. Laurence Carew was one of the most generous benefactors of both the catholic church and the catholic community in eighteenth century Waterford. He is known to have founded the home for poor widows attached to St Patrick's catholic church (off Jenkins Lane). He made an elaborate provision for the funding of this almshouse from his house rents and from his wife's dowry and stipulated that after his death, it was to be administered by his son-in-law, Nicholas Langton.

In 1752 he gifted the same 'Chapel of Waterford' with a very splendid reliquary crucifix. The reliquary possibly at one stage contained a relic of the true cross. The scroll-like details on the stand of the cross, reflect eighteenth century Spanish architectural motifs. The cross is particularly interesting in that it has been signed and dated by the maker - Francis Dearens 1751 - and bears the inscription, added a year later, 'Pray for Mr Laurence Carew 1752'.

One of the most beautiful eighteenth century buildings in Cádiz today is the Hospital de Mujeres, now used as the diocesan headquarters. In 1746 Laurence Carew and his wife contributed 10,000 pesos towards its building. The chapel contains some fine works of art, notably El Greco's 'Ecstasy of St Francis' and a painting of St Patrick, shown expelling the snakes from Ireland. The painting of St Patrick was a gift of Laurence Carew who also endowed one of the side chapels dedicated to the Child Jesus. Carew was, no doubt, a man who embraced his new homeland and was indeed embraced by it. He did not, however, forget the city of his birth and his generosity is still remembered in these beautiful pieces of eighteenth century Spanish silver ware.

Candlesticks

DATE:	1751 A D
NUMBER:	WMT1999.1768 & 1769
DIMENSIONS:	H 670, weight 5,000 g
MATERIAL:	silver

Crucifix

DATE:	maker's mark 1751, inscription 1752 A D
NUMBER:	WMT1999.1767
DIMENSIONS:	H 620
MATERIAL:	silver

PROVENANCE:	The Big Chapel, subsequently the Cathedral of the Most Holy Trinity Waterford
FURTHER READING:	Walton & O'Flanagan forthcoming

On loan from the Bishop of Waterford & Lismore

Monstrance throne

This magnificent silver monstrance throne was intended to hold a monstrance in which the Blessed Sacrament was placed for exposition, traditionally for forty hours, after the Benediction ceremony. Like monstrances of this period, the throne is decorated so as to represent rays issuing from the host as a central sun. The size of the throne suggests that an impressive monstrance must once have stood under its very elaborate crown. Liturgically, this is very typical of the continental and Spanish emphasis on the majesty and glory of the triumphant catholic ritual. When used in Waterford, it would have been in complete contrast to the spareness of the reformed protestant ceremony. This contrast is very obvious by comparing these pieces of émigré silver with the elegant simplicity of the Russell chalice. (p145)

Forming part of the decoration on the rim of the crown are three plain panels with inscriptions. The two side panels have identical inscriptions that read 'belonging to Paul White' while the centre panel has the date 1729. The flamboyant style of this monstrance throne suggests that it is a gift from Irish émigrés living in Spain. The Whites were a famous Waterford and Clonmel family who were prominent in the ecclesiastical and civic life of Waterford from the fourteenth century. It is very probable that Paul White or his father had emigrated to Spain in the late seventeenth or early eighteenth century when the public practice of the catholic faith was prohibited.

DATE: 1729 A D
NUMBER: WMT1999.1771
DIMENSIONS: H 1200, weight 14,000 g
MATERIAL: silver, oak
PROVENANCE: The Big Chapel, subsequently the Cathedral of the
                          Most Holy Trinity Waterford
FURTHER READING: Walton & O'Flanagan forthcoming

On loan from the Bishop of Waterford & Lismore

Incense boat and thurible

The very finely wrought incense boat and thurible were used at High Mass, Benediction and at funeral services. These are again very probably Spanish as there seem to have been a tradition of Irish émigrés in Spain bequeathing both church plate and money to the churches and charitable institutions in Waterford. Both items are inscribed 'Gift of Thomas Valois alias Walsh' and are dated 1771. We have no evidence to connect these pieces to the famous Walsh family, of Waterford origin, living in Nantes, France. It is likely, however, that they are a gift of Thomas Walsh living in Spain, possibly Cádiz. The French form of the name Walsh - Valois - was used also in Spain though in that country it was pronounced 'Baloys'. The cathedral treasury also has a chalice and paten inscribed *'Ora pro* [Pray for] *Do[mino] Tho[m]a Valois alias Walsh 1771'*.

Incense boat (left)
DATE: 1771 A D
NUMBER: WMT1999.1772
DIMENSIONS: H 140, weight 350 g
MATERIAL: silver
PROVENANCE: The Big Chapel, subsequently the Cathedral of the
                          Most Holy Trinity Waterford
FURTHER READING: Walton & O'Flanagan forthcoming

On loan from the Bishop of Waterford & Lismore

Thurible
DATE: 1771 A D
NUMBER: WMT1999.1770
DIMENSIONS: H 230, weight 970 g
MATERIAL: silver
PROVENANCE: The Big Chapel, subsequently the Cathedral of the
                          Most Holy Trinity Waterford
FURTHER READING: Walton & O'Flanagan forthcoming

On loan from the Bishop of Waterford & Lismore

Xaveria Wiseman, née Strange

This is an exquisite miniature portrait, painted in watercolours on ivory. It is of Xaveria Wiseman, the mother of Cardinal and Archbishop Wiseman (1802-1865), the first English cardinal since the death of Cardinal Wolsey in 1529, and head of the catholic church in England.

Xaveria Wiseman, née Strange, was the daughter of Peter Strange, of Aylwardstown near Glenmore, Waterford. The Stranges were an old catholic landowning family, based at Dunkitt and Drumdowney. Dispossessed under Cromwell, they acquired Aylwardstown through marriage into that family and built a Georgian residence onto the side of the Aylward tower-house. Xaveria was the second wife of James Wiseman, the son of a Waterford merchant, also James, who had emigrated to Seville in southern Spain in the eighteenth century, another Waterford refugee from the penal laws. Xaveria and James Wiseman had three children: James, Nicholas (born 1802) and a daughter Frasquita, all born in Seville. In 1805 after the death of her husband, Xaveria returned to her family home with her children. Nicholas and his brother were sent to a boarding school in Waterford between 1808 and 1810. Nicholas then went to Ushaw College in Durham, England, during which time he made the decision to become a priest. On the re-opening of the English College in Rome in 1818, Nicholas was sent there with five companions to train for the priesthood. In 1824 he graduated as a doctor of divinity and was ordained a year later. He had a brilliant academic career. Appointed vice-rector of the English College in 1828, he remained in that position until 1840. During these years he made trips to Ireland and England where he lectured and founded, with Daniel O'Connell, the *Dublin Review* in 1836. Such was his reputation in Europe at this time that he received visits from the likes of Macaulay and Gladstone.

He was consecrated a bishop in 1840. After the achievement of catholic emancipation in 1829, the catholics of England succeeded in winning back the right to have proper bishoprics and consequently in 1850, Wiseman, who had been instrumental in the campaign, became the head of the catholic church in England with the title of archbishop of Westminster. He was also made a cardinal. During a triumphant visit to Ireland in 1858, Wiseman visited Waterford and his boyhood home. He was feted by the people and given a civic reception and banquet in City Hall. In his speech he spoke fondly of the influence that his mother had on his formative years: 'all I know is, that from her to whom I owe my education, as I had the misfortune to lose my father in infancy, from her whose warmest recollections and most affectionate feelings were connected with this city, and with the neighbouring place where she was born, I remember to have heard histories which remain engraved on my memory, that tell me what my ancestors had to endure to preserve the faith, how they shared in the confiscations and spoliations of property which were the heirlooms of every Catholic in those days. Friends of mine since then have thought it kindness to find in the Record Office in Dublin, the original decrees of confiscation and spoliation of the property my ancestors possessed here, but all this has been nothing compared to the tales she told me of the secret, unseen sacrifices, by which some of her ancestors preserved the faith to themselves and their children'.

Wiseman died in 1865 at the age of sixty-three. An obituary in the *Times*, generally no friend to catholicism, stated: 'Yesterday the body of Cardinal Wiseman was solemnly buried at the Roman Catholic Cemetery of St Mary's at Kensal Green, amid such circumstances of ritual pomp as, since the Reformation at least, have never been seen in this country and, we may add, amid such tokens of public interest and almost of sorrow as do not often mark the funerals even of our most illustrious dead. Altogether the feeling among the public seemed deeper than one of mere curiosity, a wish perhaps to forget old differences with the Cardinal, and render respect to his memory as an eminent Englishman, and one of the most learned men of his time'.

The nicely-detailed portrait shows the cardinal's mother as a grey-haired but not necessarily old woman. The artist has not been identified. She is dressed in an old-fashioned way with a lace fichu over her shoulders; her hair, in an old-fashioned style, is uncovered. The miniature is also shown here at its actual size.

DATE:	late 18th century
NUMBER:	WMT2002.0099
DIMENSIONS:	L 51 x W 40 (painting)
MATERIAL:	ivory
PROVENANCE:	purchased at auction with the assistance of the Friends of the National Collections of Ireland and of Waterford Civic Trust
FURTHER READING:	Dowling in *OKR 1974* Caffrey 2000

Mortar

Both Viking age and medieval mortars were found in the Waterford archaeological excavations and are now part of the museum's collection. This bronze mortar, although of a later date, is of particular interest because it is inscribed 'Michael Tonnery, Apothecary in Waterford 1707'. Michael Tonnery is known to have been a catholic and it is particularly interesting that a catholic was flourishing in business at a time when the penal laws were in operation.

The mortar is decorated with bands of leaves and berries and with fleurs-de-lis. It was used by an apothecary or chemist at a time when medicines were made locally at the apothecary's premises. Much store would have been placed in the skill of the apothecary, who was considered to be learned and accomplished in the days before off-the-shelf remedies were available. It is known that this mortar was last used by White's chemists in O'Connell Street, close to the museum. In the last hundred years of its working life, the mortar was used for breaking up dried varnish into powder. The powder was applied by sailors to their hands to improve their grip when handling the rigging on a ship.

Henry Tonnery, also an apothecary and very probably Michael's son, died in Waterford in 1791 aged 112. Perhaps the Tonnerys had secret recipes that aided longevity! The mortar is typical of mortars made in England in the late seventeenth/early eighteenth century and was almost certainly made there.

DATE: 1707 A D
NUMBER: WMT1999.1786
DIMENSIONS: H 284, Dia of top 368
MATERIAL: bronze
PROVENANCE: purchased with the assistance of Bausch & Lomb

View of Waterford by van der Hagen - 1736

Commissioned by Waterford Corporation in 1736, this is the first view in oils of the city of Waterford by an artist who has been described as the first important name in landscape painting in Ireland. The Minute books of Waterford Corporation record the order 'that Mr William Vanderhagen be paid twenty pounds out of the Revenue for the picture or draft of the Quay, houses thereon, and River and opposite lands to it now hanging up in the Council Chamber unless cause be shown to the contrary this day four weeks'. Another order reads 'that Alderman Samuel Barker buy a frame for the said picture at the charge of the Revenue not exceeding Five Guineas'. Four months later, on Michaelmas Day, the payment had presumably not been made as the order is repeated to pay the painter .

William van der Hagen (died 1745) was probably English born of a Dutch family and lived in Ireland for over twenty years from the early 1720s. Among his first commissions was an altarpiece in St Patrick's church in Waterford (that had been re-built in 1727), described by Smith in 1746 as 'a Glory of Vander-Egan's well performed'. The painter must have spent a considerable time in Waterford, as several other of his Waterford works are recorded by Smith as follows: 'at the Christmas [family] home of Whitfieldstown, some well executed landscapes of the late Vander-Egan, and other good pieces, including a picture of St John Baptist. The hall is painted in *Clara Oscura* with several of the heathen deities and in it stands two statues of Neptune and Amphitrite. Smith goes on to say that in Curraghmore there were 'beautiful paintings ... with several landscapes. The ceiling is painted in perspective, and represents a Dome, the columns seeming to rise, though on a flat surface. There was 'A spacious room entirely painted by Vander-Egan in Landscape, in which kind he much excelled ... several lesser pieces by the painter in the house but that which seems to excel the rest is a fine representation of the landing of King William at Carrickfergus'.

In his entry on the Exchange, Smith states: 'in the council-chamber is a very large perspective view of the city, finely painted by Vander-Egan.' In this council chamber the decision was made to commission a painting that in time was to prove a very valuable record of the city in the 1730s.

In the foreground is Ferrybank on the north side of the river. We see a pastoral scene and a cluster of buildings including Sion Hill house, built by the Popes, a wealthy merchant family. In front of these houses, though not visible, was a ferry landing as there was no bridge across the Suir at Waterford until 1794. In the foreground to the extreme left the abbey church of Kilculliheen can be identified. The breadth of the river is accentuated by the artist and the eye is immediately drawn to this great thoroughfare, where many sailing ships lie at anchor in mid-river while smaller boats are docked at the quayside. The quay with its terracotta, ochre and cream to mid-brown buildings, standing tall and majestic overlooking the river, is a visual delight. The rolling countryside with neat cultivated fields almost comes to the base of Reginald's tower. Beyond that, arranged almost like steps of stairs and so drawing the eye upwards, is the bell tower of the old Franciscan friary, followed by the great tower of Christ Church cathedral. The cathedral tower dominates the city that spreads out before it to the west. Both the choir and nave of the cathedral are visible.

Along the quay and close to Reginald's tower are arranged the great public buildings; the Custom House, built of brick, with stores occupying the ground floor has two matching flights of stone steps providing access to the first floor offices. Next is the Exchange, a truly splendid building with its arcaded front supported by stone pillars of the Tuscan order. This building, erected in 1714, has an Italian hipped roof with a beautiful octagonal cupola. It was here in the Exchange that the city council met and this van der Hagen painting adorned the council chamber there until it was moved in 1813 to the new City Hall on the Mall. Further along the quay are the homes of the merchant princes - tall buildings of three, four and even five storeys. Most of these are narrow with their gables facing the river. They are finished in the Dutch style and were known as 'Dutch Billies'. It is known that there were many Dutch and French settlers in the city following the victory of William of Orange at the Battle of the Boyne in 1690 and these no doubt influenced local architecture. These Dutch-style gables are also to be seen in the beautiful line drawing of the city published in Smith's history of 1746.

Right of centre, beyond the quay front, can be seen the tower of Blackfriars, the old Dominican priory which in 1736 functioned as a county courthouse. Beyond this again can be seen the tower of the city courthouse or Guildhall, where the city council had met since the thirteenth century before it moved to the Exchange on the Quay after 1714. All that is visible of the Guildhall in the painting is the octagonal cupola topped with a stone spire. Beyond this again the city merges into the countryside.

Enclosing the city to the west - the extreme right of the painting - are the massive towers and walls of the medieval fortifications. These serve a twofold function, framing the city to the west and creating a counter balance with the towers of the Cathedral and Greyfriars at the opposite side of the city. Less than forty years earlier these fortifications ran along the quay, as shown in a 1690 drawing of the city. In the distance beyond the city the undulating countryside is marked by cultivated fields while high on one hill can be seen a windmill. Beyond that the blue sky is mirrored in a small lake.

This painting is more than simply a view of a city experiencing rapid change; it is also a statement by the new oligarchy that this is their city. Certainly most of their grandfathers had been born elsewhere but this new generation was of Waterford and the pride they felt in their city was what caused this painting to be commissioned. For over two and a half centuries it has presided over council meetings, a reminder to all that this is no mean city.

DATE:	1736 A D
NUMBER:	WMT1999.6249
DIMENSIONS:	L 2140 x W 1280
MATERIAL:	oil on canvas
PROVENANCE:	municipal collection
FURTHER READING:	Smith 1746, Crookshank & Glin 2002
LOCATION:	City Hall

VIEW OF
WATERFORD
1736
Painted by Vanier Hagen

Charles Este (1696-1745)

Charles Este was the church of Ireland bishop of Waterford and Lismore, 1740-1745. Born at Whitehall, London, in 1696, he received his early education at Westminster School. In 1715 he entered Oxford University and proved himself an accomplished classical scholar, receiving two arts degrees in 1719 and 1722 respectively. Having taken holy orders, he was appointed a chaplain to Hugh Boulter, archbishop of Armagh (1724-1742), and accompanied him to Ireland in 1724.

Boulter was to become one of the most powerful men in church and state in eighteenth century Ireland. Este benefited from his significant powers of patronage and was nominated to various lucrative church positions in Armagh, including the archdeaconry in 1730. When the diocese of Ossory fell vacant Este was appointed bishop in 1732, through the influence of Boulter. While at Kilkenny he undertook many additions to his palace and was largely responsible for transforming a late medieval tower house into an elegant eighteenth century residence. Este was awarded the degree of doctor of divinity by Trinity College, Dublin in 1736.

Four years later he was advanced to the see of Waterford and Lismore. Although he was one of the shortest serving bishops in the history of the diocese, Este left his mark on the city's landscape. He commissioned a new residence on the Mall, the old palace being in a state of serious disrepair. He sought the permission of the archbishop of Cashel for this undertaking and in his letter Este gave details of his plans. The front of the proposed building was to be built of stone and brick and the whole edifice was to be crowned with a proportional cornice and plinth of hewn stone. The parlour was to be wainscoted, while the hall and staircase were to be finished partly with wainscot and partly with stucco. All floors were to be made of Swedish timber or oak. To bring these proposals to fruition, Este employed the services of the most renowned architect of the period, the German born Richard Castle (1695-1751). Castle has to his credit some of Ireland's finest houses, including Powerscourt House and Russborough House both in county Wicklow, the Rotunda Hospital and Leinster House in Dublin, Carton House in county Kildare and Westport House, county Galway. Este's palace in Waterford (now the offices of the city engineer) is regarded as a national architectural treasure, being described as the finest eighteenth century ecclesiastical palace in Ireland.

The bishop commissioned a portrait of himself, in his House of Lords robes, by one of the greatest portrait painters of the age, Jean Baptiste van Loo (1684-1745). The artist had worked in Turin and Rome, establishing a considerable reputation before settling in Paris in 1720. Moving to London in 1737, van Loo became the favourite painter of the then prime minister, Sir Robert Walpole. Este's will states 'To the Mayor and Corporation of Waterford, after my wife's decease, I bequeath my picture painted by Vanloe'. However, the painting has not been recorded as ever entering the collection of Waterford Corporation. Fortuitously it was acquired by the Waterford Treasures Museum in 2000. The painting is not signed but the words 'Charles Este, Bishop of Waterford' appear on the canvas.

Charles Este, one of the most sophisticated and cultured men to rule over the diocese of Waterford, and who brought a distinct breath of internationalism to the city, died on 27 November 1745, aged forty-nine years.

Eugene Broderick

DATE:	c1744 A D
NUMBER:	WMT2000.0012
DIMENSIONS:	H 870 x W 666 (canvas)
MATERIAL:	oil on canvas
PROVENANCE:	purchased and conserved in 2000 with the assistance of the Friends of Waterford Museum of Treasures

Line drawing by the late Noel Cusack of the Bishop's Palace built by Charles Este.

Christ Church Cathedral Exterior

This early eighteenth century bird's eye view shows both Christ Church Cathedral and the Widows' Apartments. In the foreground of the painting are a number of figures dressed in red robes, while others are dressed entirely in black. There is also a horse-drawn carriage and we may assume that the assembled group represents the dean and chapter together with the mayor and corporation. The rolling countryside is seen in the distance. This painting is a companion piece to the interior view and the two pictures have matching frames.

In this view, the tall square bell tower dominates the cathedral. Though not obvious from the painting, the tower marks the point where the early-thirteenth century portion of the building begins. That part of the building to the right of the tower dates from the mid-twelfth century. It is not possible to tell if the tower was actually built in the thirteenth century or if it was added later, but it certainly was there before 1374, for in that year we know it collapsed during a storm. The steep crenellated battlements of the tower suggest a re-building in the late fourteenth or fifteenth century. The northern and southern aspects of the slated roof show a crenellated parapet and both the eastern and western gables rise just above the line of the slated roof in a series of low steps. A row of clerestory windows run the length of the building, all furnished with twin lancets, suggesting that the windows of the twelfth century nave were altered to correspond to those of the thirteenth century choir. The aspect of the painting does not allow us view the east end and the features of the west end are not visible as they are shown in shadow.

Also shown in the painting is a series of chapels, erected along the northern flank of the building, all probably dating from the fifteenth century. The three-bay chapel in the foreground is unnamed in the Halfpenny drawing of 1739. Next is an open space under the tower and to the left the chapter house with chimney visible, where the dean and twelve members of the cathedral chapter met. Alongside is a chapel dedicated to St Catherine and St James, built by James Rice, a man who served as mayor of the city on eleven occasions between 1467 and 1486. Rice planned to build the chapel in 1481 but work was not begun until 26 March 1482 and the bishop of Ossory consecrated the structure in December of the same year. It took only nine months to build and was no doubt rushed, so that it would be finished prior to Rice's departure on pilgrimage to Santiago de Compostella in Spain. Within the chapel a large gothic mensa tomb, regarded as one of the finest of its kind in Ireland, was sculpted for Rice and his wife, Catherine Brown. Along the sides of the tomb are arranged figures of the apostles. On the top, in place of the usual life-like effigy, is a well-carved, open-eyed, cadaverous figure - a reminder of the decay of the present life. Arranged around the figure is the following inscription:

> 'Here lies James Rice,
> One time citizen of this city,
> Founder of this chapel,
> And Catherine Brown his wife,
> Whoever you may be, pass by,
> Stop, weep as you read.

> I am what you are going to be,
> And I was what you are.
> I beg of you pray for me!'

Remarkably, this tomb was saved when the cathedral was demolished in 1774 and is today preserved within the eighteenth century cathedral.

On the right of the painting, opposite the west end of the cathedral, stand the Widows' Apartments, built in 1702. Smith, writing in 1746, describes it as a 'large plain brick building, with a hip roof and two returns, fronted with a court yard and two iron palisades'. Over the middle door, on a plate of black marble, in gold letters, is an inscription: 'This Apartment funded by the right reverend Dr Hugh Gore, late Lord Bishop of Waterford and Lismore, for the use of clergymen's Widows and was erected in the year of our Lord 1702 by Sir John Mahon, knight, surviving Executor of his Lordship's last Will and Testament'.

Three hundred years after its foundation, Hugh Gore's apartments still fulfil their original function, however today both widows and widowers are accommodated, as are all religious denominations.

This painting is unsigned, though it has been suggested that it could be the work of one of the many Dutch artists who were seeking commissions in early eighteenth century Ireland. A comparison between this exterior view and the 1739 William Halfpenny drawings of the exterior of the cathedral suggests that the painting pre-dates the drawings. On the Halfpenny drawings, a tall wall links the chapter house to the north-facing entrance doorway that is situated next to the fifteenth century three-bay chapel. In the painting, this wall does not exist and a number of plants are seen growing against the west wall of the chapter house. Though this evidence is not conclusive, it is very probable that this painting and probably its companion interior view, were commissioned in the early decades of the eighteenth century, possibly by Bishop Mills (1708-1740), the man who commissioned the Halfpenny drawings and agonised over the fate of this historic building.

DATE:	early 18th century
NUMBER:	WMT2002.0102
DIMENSIONS:	L 1095 x W 747 (canvas)
MATERIAL:	oil on canvas
PROVENANCE:	Christ Church Cathedral
FURTHER READING:	Stalley 1981

On loan from the Dean, Chapter & Select Vestry of Christ Church Cathedral
Conservation generously funded by the Heritage Council

Also illustrated is a pen and ink drawing of the exterior of John Roberts's Christ Church Cathedral by Charles Newport Bolton c1874.

Christ Church Cathedral Interior

This painting is one of a pair of early to mid-eighteenth century paintings of the medieval Christ Church cathedral in Waterford. It affords us a remarkable record of this historic building prior to its demolition in 1774, when it was replaced by a classical cathedral, designed and built by John Roberts.

This interior view is of particular importance: not only is it the sole surviving interior view of Waterford's medieval cathedral but it is probably the only eighteenth century painting of the interior of any Irish medieval cathedral.

The painting shows the interior of the building, looking west, from the high altar. Some of the architectural features are obscured by what at the time, were relatively recent furnishings. Clearly visible on the right are box pews and an impressive pulpit; on the left is an elaborate episcopal throne surmounted by angels and beside this are the stalls of the mayor and corporation. The galleries, placed at the west end of the chancel and incorporating a large organ, are also late-seventeenth century additions. These alterations to the medieval cathedral were probably carried out between 1666 and 1691 under the direction of the very wealthy Hugh Gore, bishop of Waterford and Lismore.

Looking beyond these seventeenth century additions, we can read the history of the building through its architecture. The nave at the west end was constructed some time in the twelfth century in the romanesque style, though many of the features were altered in the early thirteenth century when the cathedral was enlarged. The painting shows rounded arches with round-headed windows in the clerestory. In this early portion of the building, the clerestory does not appear to have a passageway or triforium; this is confirmed by a plan of the cathedral dated 1739.

It is presumed that work on the substantial gothic extension to the twelfth century structure, seen clearly in the foreground of the painting, was carried out sometime after 1210 when King John visited Waterford and endowed the cathedral with substantial amounts of land. At the top right hand side of the painting the thirteenth century triforium clerestory is very visible as are the gothic mouldings surrounding the opes. The thirteenth century piers, again very obvious on the right hand side of the painting, are complex in form with the main shaft rising unbroken to support the vault ribs. The date of the original vault is confusing. Close examination of the painting leaves little doubt that a vault was at least intended, if not in fact erected, in the thirteenth century. The timber vaulting, so beautifully captured in the painting, is very probably a later replacement of a stone-vaulted ceiling. We know that the cathedral tower was blown down in 1374 and so perhaps the original stone vault roof was damaged at this time and had to be removed. Charles Smith notes in his 1746 history that 'in 1522 Bishop Nicholas Cumin and Robert Lombard the dean adorned the choir and chapel with an arched or vaulted ceiling and in the last [seventeenth] century, bishop Gore went to considerable expense beautifying it'. It is logical to accept Smith's 1522 dating for the ceiling as Waterford was a thriving and prosperous city at that time.

This eighteenth century painting captures not just a moment in time but a segment of history. We see part of the old romanesque cathedral that would have been standing when Strongbow and Aoife were married in the city in 1170. Henry II must surely have attended mass here in 1171, as would his son King John in 1210. The gothic extension, begun in John's reign, would witness the installation here in 1394 of Robert Reed, the first bishop of the united dioceses of Waterford and Lismore. Bishop Reed is said to have intoned the *Te Deum* as the royal party of King Richard II entered the cathedral for Reed's first public mass in Waterford.

The cathedral experienced its heyday at the end of the middle ages when its clergy, dressed in cloth-of-gold vestments sparkling in the candlelight, performed elaborate ceremonies here. Sadly it was the focus of bitterness and dispute in the reigns of Elizabeth and her successor James I and suffered much destruction of its works of art under the Cromwellian regime. Surviving all this, Bishop Gore modernised it in the seventeenth century though it is clear from the painting that the two styles did not mix. It is easy to see why it exercised the minds of so many church of Ireland prelates in the eighteenth century who, in the end, decided to replace it. Recently, a portion of one of the thirteenth century gothic piers, a survival from the 1774 demolition, has been exposed in the floor. It is beautifully worked in oolithic limestone carried to Waterford from Dundry near Bristol. The irregular shape of the pier shows that it marked the point where the twelfth century cathedral met the thirteenth century gothic extension. The pier and this painting are wonderful reminders of a cathedral that has been classed with Christ Church cathedral and St Patrick's in Dublin as the three finest medieval cathedrals in Ireland.

DATE: early 18th century
NUMBER: WMT2002.0101
DIMENSIONS: L 1095 x W 753 (canvas)
MATERIAL: oil on canvas
PROVENANCE: Christ Church Cathedral
FURTHER READING: Stalley 1981

On loan from the Dean, Chapter & Select Vestry of Christ Church Cathedral
Conservation generously funded by the Heritage Council

Also illustrated is an interior view of John Roberts's cathedral that replaced the medieval cathedral in 1774. It is by Thomas Malton senior and was executed about 1790.

John, Mary Anne and Francis Wyse

These are important works in the history of Irish art as depictions of Irish eighteenth-century interiors are rare. They are painted in oils by George Mullins, who 'worked at Mr Wise's manufactory at Waterford and painted snuff-boxes and waiters in imitation of Birmingham ware'. Moreover, they are painted on copper that - according to family tradition - came from the family's mines near Bunmahon.

When Thomas 'Bullocks' Wyse passed on in 1770, his estate was divided under the terms of the Gavel Act between his two surviving sons. Francis the elder inherited the Manor of St John's; his younger brother John received the lands at Newtown. Francis remained a bachelor, but John married well. His wife, Mary Anne Blakeney from Ballyellin, county Carlow, was not only the daughter of another Catholic landowner but a beauty as well. She was nicknamed 'Murdering Moll' from the devastating effect of her flashing eyes on the young men of Waterford. She and John had a healthy crop of children, including a son and heir Thomas, nicknamed 'Gentle Tom' to distinguish him from his grandfather 'Bullocks'.

As a younger son who had unexpectedly inherited a sizeable estate, John needed a stately home to go with it. Hence the building of Newtown House in 1786, the work of local architect and builder John Roberts, who had already created Waterford's protestant cathedral, was currently at work on the Assembly Rooms (now City Hall), and would finally produce the roman catholic cathedral as well. Roberts had recently completed the town house of William Morris (now the headquarters of the Chamber of Commerce), an astonishing achievement with its impressive façade, ornate doorcase, delicate oval cantilever staircase, and magnificent stucco ceilings. If Newtown House, as originally built for John Wyse, was on a par with Morris's house, then it was a masterpiece. We get some idea of the elegance of its interior from the larger of these two paintings, showing John, Mary Anne and Francis Wyse in the print room. They are in relaxed mood and Mary Anne holds a lute.

The smaller oval painting shows John Wyse, wearing a turban, seated in his library atrium, presumably also at Newtown. On a paper beside him is written 'Arts & Science' and items relating to those pursuits, including a globe, are shown, some on the table and others depicted on the decorative plasterwork in the niche behind him.

One would hope that John Wyse, 'Murdering Moll' and their children were happy in their lovely new home. Fate, alas, soon overtook them. John had borrowed money all round him, and the cost of building Newtown must have been crippling. By the mid-1790s he had run up debts of over £30,000. Newtown had to be sacrificed, and in the mid-1790s it was sold to the Society of Friends for their provincial boarding school. When the Pennsylvania Quaker William Savery visited Waterford in January 1798, he found his co-religionists busily removing from house and garden all 'offensive' ornamentation such as the prints and stucco-work seen in the background of George Mullins's beautiful paintings.

Julian Walton

John, Mary Anne and Francis Wyse

DATE:	c1786 A D
NUMBER:	WMT2002.0016
DIMENSIONS:	L 714 x W 615
MATERIAL:	oil on copper
PROVENANCE:	the Bonaparte Wyse family
FURTHER READING:	Crookshank & Glin 2002

On loan from Henry Bonaparte Wyse

John Wyse

DATE:	c1786 A D
NUMBER:	WMT2002.0019
DIMENSIONS:	L 653 x max W 555
MATERIAL:	oil on copper
PROVENANCE:	the Bonaparte Wyse family
FURTHER READING:	Crookshank & Glin 2002

On loan from Henry Bonaparte Wyse

Chandelier

This magnificent chandelier is the largest and finest piece of old Waterford glass in existence and hangs in the council chamber in City Hall Waterford. This is a traditional thirty-two light chandelier. The frame is brass and the centre column is mounted with a series of crystal centrepieces, the largest of which is an Adams urn - an acorn shaped vessel which was traditionally used on chandeliers of this type.

There are thirty-two solid flat faceted arms in two tiers of sixteen each. Each arm is capped with a scalloped topped candleholder, mounted on a flat bobeche on the lower tier and a cup-shaped bobeche on the upper tier. This was designed to prevent hot candle wax dripping down.

The solid metal staging that the arms are mounted on is enclosed by a richly cut large bowl which used deeply incised swag cuts enclosing panels of closed diamond cuts. The tip of the bowl is finished with very deeply cut upright blazes that refract the candlelight brilliantly.

Underneath the large bowl the centre column continues with covering crystal pieces, one being a variation on the Adams urn higher up. From the end of the column is suspended a solid finial which is flat faceted for maximum refractive effect.

The chandelier has a fascinating history. It was commissioned in 1786 by the Duke of Rutland who was the lord lieutenant of Ireland from 1784 until his death at the age of thirty-three in 1787. It is very possible that family connections ensured that the chandelier commission went to Waterford because the owners of the factory, George and William Penrose, were kinsmen of the architect Thomas Penrose who worked as inspector of civic buildings. In the late 1780s Thomas Penrose was responsible for the conversion of the Battle Axe Hall at Dublin Castle to a Presence Chamber.

We must presume that as inspector of civic buildings and architect for the castle project, Thomas Penrose used his influence and encouraged the Duke of Rutland to pay a visit to Waterford. While in the city the duke purchased the chandelier at a cost of £277 for the Presence Chamber in the castle. The patronage of the duke must have been a great boost to the fledgling company and no doubt the huge amount expended on the chandelier helped the new concern's cash flow. The fact that the company was capable of undertaking such a large piece, within so short a time of opening, shows the extent to which the factory depended on imported English labour and expertise. Workers who were coming green to the craft, within the short few years that the factory had been open, could not have acquired the skills necessary to make such a complex piece.

The doubling of the glass excise duties in England in 1777 had been a catalyst for the migration of English glassworkers to Ireland, especially after 1780 when the Irish parliament won the right of free trade from the British parliament. With Ireland free to export glass and the heavy duty placed on English glass, workers began to leave England, some going to France but many to Waterford. The advantage the Penrose family made of these legislative changes can be seen from the evidence given before a Commons Committee appointed in 1785 to enquire into the commercial relations between Great Britain and Ireland. This committee met only two years after the Waterford factory opened and reported that 'a Mr. Hill [the compounder and technical expert at Waterford], a great manufacturer at Stourbridge, had lately gone to Waterford and taken the best of the workers that he could get (between fifty and seventy) in the county of Worcester'.

On completion the chandelier became the centrepiece of the Presence Chamber in Dublin Castle and James Malton described it as 'an elegant glass lustre, of the Waterford Manufactory; purchased by the late Duke of Rutland, when Lord Lieutenant, on visiting the city; which cost two hundred and seventy seven pounds'. Rutland died in 1787 before the room was complete but the chandelier hung there until the 1830s before returning to Waterford where it adorns the council chamber along with two twentieth century Waterford chandeliers.

Thomas Penrose, the architect responsible for the Presence Chamber, is thought also to have had a private practice in Dublin and Waterford. It is believed that he was the architect of the long demolished, but once very beautiful terrace of three houses at Adelphi Quay, built in the 1780s for his first cousins William (founder of the glass factory) and Samuel Penrose. He is also known to have designed a stone bridge to span the river Suir at Waterford but his plans were not acted on, the commission being given instead to the American architect Lemuel Cox who built a timber bridge across the Suir in 1793.

DATE:	1787 A D
NUMBER:	WMT1999.6250
MATERIAL:	glass
PROVENANCE:	municipal collection
FURTHER READING:	O'Dwyer in *Bulletin of IGS* 1996-7
	Elviller 1953
LOCATION:	City Hall

Freedom Box

The certificate conferring the freedom of the city of Waterford was presented in this box to John Fane (1759-1841), tenth earl of Westmorland, who was appointed lord lieutenant of Ireland in January 1790. The hallmarks and maker's mark reveal that it was made of 22 carat gold by Alexander Tickell (sometimes Ticknell) in Dublin in 1790. The lid is engraved with the coat of arms and motto ('Bring nothing vile to the altar') of the Fane family and the base is engraved with the arms of Waterford city with its motto *'Urbs intacta manet Waterfordia'*, the city of Waterford remains untaken. It appears from council minutes that Westmorland was not the first lord lieutenant to receive the honour in a gold box. Just over a century earlier the lord lieutenant, the earl of Clarendon, on visiting the city in September 1686, was given the freedom in a gold box. That box cost the corporation £15-10s and was made by William Smith who was sheriff of Waterford in 1680, master of the guild of hammermen in 1684 and mayor in 1689.

In Waterford the granting of freedom dates from Norman times. It was a coveted honour sought by citizens, denizens (foreign residents) and suitably qualified merchant strangers. In addition to conferring enviable status on the recipient, it provided very advantageous and preferential trading concessions for those admitted to the liberties and franchise of Waterford. Freemen were exempt from tolls, taxes and customs dues within the city suburbs and port. These privileges also extended to other towns in Ireland, allowing freemen to trade free of taxes and tolls throughout the entire country.

The son of a freeman qualified automatically for admission; however, other applicants had to satisfy several stringent conditions. Only royal subjects who had been born in England, Ireland or Wales were eligible. Candidates were required to be of full age, of good character and must be vouched for by a senior municipal official and be a householder in the city where he must have had at least three years residence. An apprentice, having served a seven year apprenticeship, could be admitted to the liberty on the recommendation of his master, while a freeman's widow also qualified but was required to take an individual oath with the sacrament. Those of Irish blood were required, prior to application, to have 'the King's liberty under seal' (approval of the English authorities). They must also dress in English apparel, speak English and live in the English manner.

From 1536 onwards the fee for being admitted to the freedom included supplying the city with two half barges of stone, no doubt used to build and repair the city's defences. The punishment for breaking the city ordinances was very often the loss of the freedom of the city. The freedom remained an important honour right to the end of the eighteenth century and while catholics were admitted to the freedom, they were prohibited from voting in elections until the passing of the Catholic Relief Act of 1793. Under the 1832 Reform Act, freedom was no longer the basis of franchise and gradually the concept became redundant. In 1876 the Municipal Privileges Act established the practice of conferring honorary freedom on individuals who distinguish themselves in some field of endeavour. To date in Waterford this honour has been conferred only on twenty-nine individuals.

The museum has also on display a second gold freedom box presented to Benjamin Wilson Esq in 1743 by the Corporation of Dublin. It was made by Robert Calderwood of Dublin.

DATE:	1790 A D
NUMBER:	WMT2000.0001
DIMENSIONS:	Dia 66
MATERIAL:	gold
PROVENANCE:	on loan from Mary Macnamara junior
FURTHER READING:	FitzGerald & O'Brien 2001
	O'Brien forthcoming
	Byrne forthcoming

Verge watch

Clock and watchmakers were also members of the hammermen's guild that was given a charter of incorporation by Waterford Corporation in 1657. The Maddock family is the best known and most prominent of the catholic watchmakers in eighteenth century Waterford. The movement of this fine verge watch in silver pair cases, silver pendant and bow, is signed Wm Maddock of Waterford, No 956; the case is by Thomas Appleby, mark T.A., hallmarked Chester 1783. The watch has a full plate fire gilt movement with round pillars, pierced and engraved masked cock, with silver regulator disc. It has plain three arm gilt balance and blue steel spiral hairspring. The dial is white enamel with Arabic numerals, the hands are gold beetle and poker hands. This watch, made c1783, together with a grandfather clock in the council chamber in City Hall, are excellent examples of William Maddock's work. Watchmaking was and remains an extremely skilled craft. Not only is this watch expertly made but it is also very beautiful. The tiny key used to wind it still survives. The printed watch paper reads 3rd Oct 1837 by E Pearce-Lanson.

William was one of three watchmakers by the name of Maddock residing on or near the Quay in eighteenth century Waterford. A kinsman, Luke Maddock, had been a watchmaker in St John's in Newfoundland and subsequently became a merchant and shipowner there, focusing on the Waterford-Newfoundland trade. He was one of the Irish merchants to go bankrupt in the collapse of the trade with the ending of the Napoleonic wars and was bought out by Thomas Meagher who afterwards returned to Ireland, taking up residence at Waterford.

Another kinsman, William Maddock, was possibly the watchmaker's father or uncle. He captained a ship called the Mary Ann, built in Waterford in 1756, trading mainly with English ports. The Mary Ann made thirty voyages under his command between 1766 and 1771.

DATE:	c1783 A D
NUMBER:	WMT2002.0077
DIMENSIONS:	Dia 360
MATERIAL:	silver
PROVENANCE:	on loan from a private collector
FURTHER READING:	O'Brien 2001 & forthcoming
	Mannion in *Decies* 2003

Walking stick

This gold-headed walking stick is inscribed 'Dan'l Ivie Esq'r Sheriff Waterford, 29 September 1778'. The walking stick was a gift of the corporation to the outgoing sheriff.

On 15 January 1779 Waterford Corporation voted that the outgoing mayor and two sheriffs, Daniel Ivie and Thomas Alcock, be given gifts in recognition of their service to the city. In the case of the sheriffs it was resolved 'that twenty guineas be given to each of the late sheriffs by this Board to purchase such piece of plate as they shall think proper as a testimony of the Sense of the City of their good conduct during their sheriffalty'.

The head of the walking stick is stamped three times with the maker's mark F·S·. The only Irish goldsmith or jeweller of this period having the initials F S known to us is Francis Smith of Carrick-on-Suir. It would therefore seem that Daniel Ivie spent his honorarium locally, as would be expected.

DATE:	1779 A D
NUMBER:	WMT1996.0001
DIMENSIONS:	L 870
MATERIAL:	gold, wood
PROVENANCE:	purchased in 1996
FURTHER READING:	O'Brien forthcoming

Child's mug

This child's mug was made in Waterford by Ignatius Fleming junior about 1800. It is of baluster form, sits on a reeded rim base and has a five-form handle. The base is stamped ·FLEMING and the inside stamped I·F. There were a number of gold and silversmiths working in eighteenth century Waterford but the Flemings are probably the most interesting. They were catholic and worked for three generations in the business in Waterford and unusually the wife of one of the Flemings was herself a silversmith.

The Corporation minutes of 29 June 1749 record that 'Ignatius Fleming, silversmith, was admitted to the freedom of the city as other Roman Catholics are on his petition now read'. In Waterford at this time there existed an atmosphere of tolerance and for some years during the mid-eighteenth century, close to half of those admitted annually to the freedom were catholic. Ignatius died in 1755 and was survived by a wife and three children; his eldest son Robert followed in his father's footsteps. Described as a 'Papist', Robert was admitted to the freedom of the city in 1769. He probably made the beautiful silver-gilt monstrance now in the treasury of the Cathedral of the Most Holy Trinity in Waterford. It is dated 1776 and although it is not hallmarked, it bears the maker's mark R F in Roman capitals.

Robert died in the late 1770s and in 1784 his widow Anastasia, named as Ann Fleming, registered under the Act of 1783, obliging gold and silversmiths to register in the Assay Office in Dublin. Her premises were on the corner of Broad Street and the Square in Waterford. In 1779 she was commissioned by the corporation to make 'a large silver salver with the arms of the city engraved thereon' to be presented to the outgoing mayor for his generosity to the poor during a time of great need in the city. Her son Ignatius, baptised in January 1766, was admitted to the freedom of Waterford in November 1796 and registered under the 1783 Act in 1802. It was Ignatius who made the exquisite child's mug shown here.

DATE:	c1800 A D
NUMBER:	WMT2002.0078
DIMENSIONS:	H 760, Dia of top 720
MATERIAL:	silver
PROVENANCE:	on loan from a private collector
FURTHER READING:	O'Brien 2001 and forthcoming

Penrose decanter

This twenty-six centimetre high decanter has a noticeably wide pouring lip as is common to most Penrose decanters. It has a generous swelling body and high comb flutes. High quality lead has been used in the glass-mix, giving the decanter a heavy weight and clear colour. It is cut with pendant semi-circle arch motif filled with fine diamonds and has trefoil splits between the arches. There is prismatic cutting on the shoulder and the neck has three rings. The words 'Penrose Waterford' are moulded on the base.

The history of glass making in Waterford can be traced to the Ballynegerath (Ballynerath) glass house established in county Waterford in 1622. Little is known of this establishment other than that it produced a variety of glassware and supplied it to the upper echelons of society. However, the earliest mention (1729) of glassmaking associated with the city is that of the Gurteens glass house, situated about two miles from the city on the northern banks of the river Suir. The proprietor of this establishment was John Head, and his factory was more than likely in operation for a few years before this date. However in 1840, a year after John Head's death, the contents were sold and the premises and accompanying lands were let. These lands were again let in 1762 and Ryland, writing in 1824, mentions that the glass house itself was in ruins. It was almost another sixty years before glassmaking resumed again in Waterford.

The Free Trade Act of 1780 repealed the prohibitive excise duties imposed on Irish glass in 1740 and in 1783 the quaker merchants, George and William Penrose, established their extensive glass works in the city. £10,000 was initially expended and, during its first years in production, the factory employed between fifty and seventy workers. The most prominent of these workers was John Hill, also a quaker, a renowned glassmaker from Stourbridge, one of the most reputable glassmaking areas in England. He brought with him about a dozen skilled glassmakers to the Penrose factory, but he was the only person who knew the secret of mixing the glassmaking materials. Within a few years the quality of Penrose glass had attracted a discerning clientele, including the royal family; and the company was exporting most of its produce to America, Canada, Newfoundland, the West Indies and many European countries.

Following a disagreement with William Penrose's wife Rachel, John Hill left Waterford. But before he departed he gave his friend, Jonathan Gatchell, a clerk with the firm, the secret glassmaking formula. William Penrose died in 1796; three years later George also died and the factory passed out of the Penrose family. Rachel Penrose, in a poem written in 1785, captures wonderfully the trials and anxieties of her husband William (Billy) who appears to be running a number of businesses at the time.

'My Billy's mind oft full of care
he to the fire turns his chair
And thus by him I'm oft addresst
My Jewel what does thee think best
Of money matters and provision
Of business in each division,

Of Glass House and of this man's order,
Of such a glass, with such a border
Decanters goblets and of crofts
And of the new ware house and the loftes
Of buying beef and also pork
Of getting butter round from Cork
To these I little can reply
But my good will and feeling sigh
And wishes it was in my power
To soothe the cares of every hour.'

John M Hearne

DATE: 1789 A D
NUMBER: WMT1999.1774
DIMENSIONS: H 260, Dia of base 90
MATERIAL: glass
PROVENANCE: on loan from the National Museum of Ireland
FURTHER READING: Dunlevy 1989
Gatchell Letters, 2 Vols, NMI
Hearne in *Decies* 54, 1998
Waterford Crystal 1968
Westropp 1980

Decanter & Water jug

This flint glass decanter with three neck rings is cut with basal flutes and flat slices. Unlike the Penrose ware, the maker's name was not impressed on the base of glass made in Waterford in the nineteenth century. We are fortunate that the bill of sale for the decanter here survives, telling us that Joseph Grubb purchased it on 23 October 1804. (The museum subsequently purchased this piece from the Grubb family). The decanter was purchased as one of a pair that cost eight shillings and eight pence, a considerable amount of money at the time. The handwritten bill states that it was purchased from 'Ramsey Gatchell and Co'.

The water jug is beautifully crafted of flint glass with hobnail diamond cut on the body and elaborate prismatic cutting on the neck. There is flat cutting on the handle. The jug is thought to date from c1830.

Following the death of George Penrose in December 1799 a partnership of James Ramsey, Ambrose Barcroft and Jonathan Gatchell assumed control of the former Penrose glassworks. However, this partnership was dissolved in 1811 following the death of Ramsey; Gatchell assumed sole control of the glassworks until 1823. In January of that year he formed a new partnership with his brothers James and Samuel and his son-in-law, Joseph Walpole. Within a few months Jonathan Gatchell died and in his will the glassworks was to be inherited by his youngest son, George, when he reached twenty-one in 1835. Until then the business was to be run by the existing partnership. However, by 1830 all the remaining partners had died and control of the Waterford Glassworks passed to Jonathan Wright, son of Jonathan Gatchell's sister, Susannah.

Significant technological changes had occurred within the firm between 1825 and 1830. A steam engine had been acquired and a new designer, Samuel Millar, had initiated designs to accommodate cutting wheels powered by steam. Many of these designs have remained up to the present. In 1835 at age twenty-one George Gatchell took control of the glassworks and almost immediately formed a partnership with George Saunders. By this time, however, the Irish glass industry was in terminal decline resulting from mounting debt and crippling excise duties, with the Waterford Glassworks paying £11,936 in such duties between 1831 and 1835. The partnership between Gatchell and Saunders lasted for twelve years. During that time the company's products were exhibited at the Royal Dublin Society's Exhibitions of 1835 and 1836, winning silver medals at both. In 1848 the partnership was terminated and George Gatchell assumed sole control of the glassworks. Two years later he exhibited again at the Royal Dublin Exhibition and, in 1851, Waterford Crystal was exhibited for the last time at the Great Exhibition in London's Crystal Palace. Here, Gatchell displayed a diverse range of crystal ware including a magnificent ornamental centrepiece for a banqueting table, consisting of forty pieces of cut glass. By this time however, Gatchell had decided to close the business. Unable to attract the capital investment necessary to consolidate the enterprise the glassworks finally closed in October 1851 and six months later, the steam engine, office furniture and other materials and tools were sold.

Although George Gatchell failed to keep the Waterford Glassworks afloat, his persistence and attention to quality was to make the name of Waterford a byword for craftsmanship and excellence in glassmaking throughout the world.

John M Hearne

Decanter

DATE:	1804 A D
NUMBER:	WMT1999.2159
DIMENSIONS:	H 233, Dia of base 90
MATERIAL:	glass
PROVENANCE:	purchased in 2003 from the family of the late Isabel Grubb

Jug

DATE:	c1830 A D
NUMBER:	WMT1999.2159
DIMENSIONS:	H 195, Dia of base 100
MATERIAL:	glass
PROVENANCE:	On loan from the National Museum of Ireland
FURTHER READING:	Dunlevy 1989
	Hearne in *Decies* 54 1998
	Gatchell Letters, 2 Vols, NMI
	Waterford Crystal 1968
	Westropp 1980

Newfoundland urn

This magnificent urn was presented to the first catholic bishop of Newfoundland. The urn, or two-handled cup, was made in Bristol in 1807. The bowl has a foliage pattern at the base and a band of vines at the top. The lid has a similar pattern as the base and is surmounted by the sea-god Neptune. The long elegant swan neck handles are decorated with a foliage motif.

The status of Irish catholics was not altered by crossing the Atlantic to Newfoundland; here also the anti-catholic penal laws limited their religious and political rights. Eighteenth century English officialdom viewed the catholic community in both Ireland and Newfoundland with suspicion and their possible support for foreign invaders, namely the French, added to this sense of distrust. In Newfoundland tensions increased when catholics began to outnumber the protestants, leading many to claim that the Irish were taking all the best fishing rooms, while others complained about the marriage of Irish women to protestant settlers, as the children of such unions were raised as catholics. By about 1790 the inhabitants of English origin could no longer regard the Irish as simply fishermen and themselves as planters with superior rights because by then large numbers of Irish had made Newfoundland their home.

The relaxation of the penal laws in the late eighteenth century paved the way for the establishment of a catholic hierarchy in Newfoundland, who did much to reduce tension and improve the status of the catholic Irish community. Catholic emancipation paved the way for the Irish to participate in the government of the island. In 1783 the catholics of St John's received permission to build a chapel and a group of Irish merchants, led by the Waterford-born Luke Maddock (kinsman of the Waterford watchmaker, see p181), approached the bishop of Waterford for an authorised priest to have jurisdiction over Newfoundland.

In 1784 James Louis O'Donel (1737-1811) was chosen as prefect apostolic of Newfoundland. Son of a prosperous farmer, the Knocklofty-born O'Donel was a Franciscan priest whose ability to speak Irish made him an ideal candidate. He encouraged order among members of the Irish community who often engaged in violent faction fighting. He used his influence to maintain the peace when in 1800 a mutiny of United Irishmen among soldiers of the garrison was uncovered. The calming influence of O'Donel and his successors Lambert and Scallan (all Franciscans from the south-east of Ireland) worked towards official acceptance of the church while reversing the state of near chaos that had existed in the church due to the penal laws. O'Donel had to tackle the problem of unauthorised 'strolling clergymen', one such confrontation resulting in serious riots in Ferryland between the supporters of O'Donel and those who supported the unauthorised priest. However, by 1790 he had three authorised priests in place, which did much to encourage stability. He gradually established his authority, while his collaboration with the English governors of Newfoundland ensured his survival and that of the catholic church.

He was made bishop in 1796, the first English-speaking catholic bishop in North America. In poor health from 1804, he finally left Newfoundland in 1807. He was presented with this silver urn on which the inscription reads: 'Presented to the R Revd Dr O'Donel, by the Inhabitants of St Johns Newfoundland, as a Testimony of their Esteem for his Pious, Patriotic and Meritorious Conduct, during a Residence among them of Twenty Three Years.' He died in 1811 in Waterford, aged seventy-four.

DATE:	1807 A D
NUMBER:	WMT2003.0006
DIMENSIONS:	H 525 x max W 353
MATERIAL:	silver
PROVENANCE:	on loan from a private collection
FURTHER READING:	Byrne in Nolan & Power (eds) 1992
	Byrne (ed) 1984

NINETEENTH
CENTURY

WATERFORD

Of the vast numbers of Irish moving to North America in the eighteenth and nineteenth centuries, only a tiny minority ever returned. Newfoundland's transatlantic migratory cod fishery was an exception to this; up until the late eighteenth century most Irish migrants to Newfoundland were seasonal workers or temporary residents who eventually returned home. All of this was to change dramatically with the advent of the Napoleonic wars and the recession that ensued. Increasingly Irish servants now settled in Newfoundland, married and raised families. It was a different story however for successful merchants like the Meaghers, whose wealth afforded them the opportunity to return to Ireland.[1]

Thomas Meagher senior, was born in county Tipperary about 1759 and moved to St John's, Newfoundland in the early 1780s where he worked as a tailor. At this time most of the population of St John's were men from England and Ireland who had gone there for a season or two to work at the fishery. Nineteen out of twenty tailors in St John's were Irish but Meagher was one of the few to advance to mercantile status when in 1808 he acquired a sixty-ton brig for deep-sea trade. In 1809 he was carrying out a trade that was typical of a Newfoundland merchant, shipping dried cod from St John's to Waterford and arriving back the following spring with salt pork, beef, butter and oatmeal as well as servants to work in the fishery.

Meagher's entrance to the maritime trade coincided with a boom in the cod economy. The final years of the Napoleonic wars witnessed a rising demand in Europe for Newfoundland fish. This was especially the case in Spain where a lowering of tariffs on cod imports from the island in 1808 resulted in a virtual monopoly by Newfoundland merchants. Prices soared as did the wages of fishermen. The traffic in passengers and provisions from the port and harbour of Waterford to St John's increased dramatically between 1809 and 1815. The demand for cod in Waterford and its hinterland also expanded, an indicator of rapid population growth there, particularly among the poor.

However the Newfoundland cod fishery entered a recession in the wake of the Napoleonic wars. Trade with Spain dropped drastically in the face of high tariffs and competition from Norwegian fish. Late in 1815 Meagher admitted his two sons as full partners in the business. As the family was not involved with the south European markets, it was not as exposed as other firms who fell into debt when this market collapsed. Meagher and sons took advantage of bankrupt houses to expand their clientele, and Thomas Meagher senior was appointed joint trustee for a number of notable Newfoundland estates, including that of Luke Maddock from Waterford.[2]

Meagher returned to Ireland with his wife and son Henry in 1817 while Thomas junior remained in St John's to continue company operations. A crucial factor in Meagher's successful relocation was the considerable capital, in excess of £20,000, which he had accumulated in St John's and now deposited in Newport's bank, Waterford. He leased an imposing Georgian villa at Ballycanvan just outside the city, formerly the residence of the Boltons, a landed family of Cromwellian origins. In 1819 Thomas senior leased extensive premises in Hanover Street (the site of the present museum building) and his son, Thomas junior, left Newfoundland, marking the end of the family presence in St John's. None of them ever returned.

In 1820 with the transatlantic provisions trade in rapid decline, the Meaghers decided to abandon it. The same year Thomas junior married Alicia Quan who lived in a Georgian house on the Quay (the site of the present Granville Hotel). Her father had leased the house from the Newports who were declared bankrupt in 1820; as the Meaghers were the leading creditors they now acquired an interest in the house. When the Quans themselves were declared bankrupt in 1823 the Meaghers stepped in and bought out the entire interest. Thomas Meagher junior and his wife Alicia Quan now took up residence in what had been his wife's family home and it was here that their four children including Thomas Francis would be born.

Alicia Quan died in 1827 and four years later the Meagher family withdrew completely from maritime trade.[3]

With the house on the Quay no longer central to their business interests it was leased to Charles Bianconi, the Italian carriage entrepreneur who converted it to a stagecoach station. Edward Cummins had a business relationship with Bianconi and converted part of the Quay premises to a hotel (which it remains to the present day). Thomas junior and family moved to a house in William Street and finally to a house on the Mall called Derrynane, after Daniel O'Connell's home in Kerry. This house became known nationally with the arrest there of his son Thomas Francis in 1848.

After only two years residency in Waterford, Thomas junior became active in public life and in 1823 he was admitted to the Chamber of Commerce and appointed treasurer. Originally almost exclusively a protestant preserve, the composition of the chamber was in transition as the catholic merchant community expanded and became more politically engaged. Meagher's re-location in Waterford coincided with the emergence of the city as a major centre in Daniel O'Connell's campaign for Catholic Emancipation - the right of catholics to sit in parliament. (p197) In 1823 O'Connell established the Catholic Association, a largely middle class organisation. A year later he made the momentous decision to expand the membership - this had the effect of introducing, for the first time, the great mass of ordinary Irish catholics into the political process. Thomas junior was appointed secretary of the Waterford branch of the association in 1824. This was a pivotal appointment in the evolution of Meagher's political career. Waterford became the focus of O'Connell's campaign in 1826 when the liberal protestant, Villiers Stuart, challenged the Beresfords, a powerful ascendancy family, for a seat in parliament. Under the leadership of O'Connell and the Waterford branch of the Catholic Association, the large catholic electorate produced a victory for the liberal Villiers Stuart. His election was a seminal event in modern Irish politics and

a critical moment in the history of the first mass movement of organised democracy in Europe.[4]

The election of O'Connell as MP for Clare in 1828 forced the British parliament to pass the final Catholic Relief Act in 1829. Catholic Emancipation had been achieved and O'Connell entered the Westminster parliament in London in 1830, the first Irish catholic to do so. A year later he was elected MP for county Waterford.[5]

Following the success of emancipation, Meagher junior and his son Thomas Francis became involved in O'Connell's movement for the repeal of the Act of Union and the re-establishment of an Irish parliament. O'Connell and Meagher junior became close personal friends and in 1841 O'Connell, still fighting for repeal, was elected as the first catholic mayor of Dublin in over a hundred years, his election having been facilitated by the passing of the Municipal Reform Act 1840. The Newfoundland-born Thomas Meagher junior received a similar honour in Waterford when he was elected mayor in 1843. (p199)

Emancipation and later Repeal attracted more interest and financial support from the Irish abroad than any other previous political movement in Ireland. There were substantial subscriptions from the Newfoundland Irish who appear proportionately to have been more generous than the rest of the Irish Diaspora in North America. The Irish in America also followed with great interest political matters in Ireland. When in 1853 Thomas Meagher junior went to America with his daughter-in-law to visit his son Thomas Francis, he was feted by a number of Irish American groups. The Sons of Erin in Cincinnati presented him with a walking stick, cut from a tree growing on George Washington's grave, in recognition of his work for the cause of Ireland. (p199) Thomas junior was also a prominent supporter of charitable institutions both in St John's and Waterford. He had been treasurer of the Benevolent Irish Society in St John's and later held the same position in the Trinitarian Orphan Society in Waterford. He was also a benefactor of the Sisters of

Charity to whom he presented a silver chalice and paten. (p199)

The second Irish catholic to be elected to the Westminster parliament after emancipation was a Waterford man, Thomas Wyse, who secured the seat for Tipperary in 1830. A year earlier, he had the distinction of being the first catholic to sit on Waterford City Council since the seventeenth century. (p201) Although both Wyse and Thomas Meagher junior were intimately involved in O'Connell's Catholic Association they were from completely different backgrounds - Meagher, the Newfoundland-born son of an emigrant tailor and Wyse, the heir to the Manor of St. John and a member of a family that could trace its ancestry back to the middle of the fourteenth century. Thomas Wyse had been the election agent for Villiers Stuart who had so dramatically defeated the conservative Lord George Beresford. Indeed it could be said that Wyse's organisational ability was critical to the electoral success. He wrote a history of the Catholic Association but, unlike Meagher, he refused to become involved in the movement for the repeal of the Act of Union and consequently broke with O'Connell. He represented Waterford city in parliament from 1835 to 1847 and, as a supporter of the British Whig (Liberal) government, he threw his energies into educational reform and was instrumental in the setting up of the National School system.[6]

Wyse is perhaps better remembered today because of his marriage to Letitia Bonaparte, niece of Emperor Napoleon Bonaparte. The marriage was a disaster. Letitia was one of the recipients of a mourning cross commissioned by Madame Mère, Napoleon's mother, to mark the death of the Emperor. (p201) When Wyse lost his parliamentary seat in 1847 the Foreign Secretary Lord Palmerston offered him the post of ambassador to the new kingdom of Greece, thus saving him from falling into obscurity. Thomas's efforts in securing Greek neutrality during the Crimean war 1854-56 saw him honoured with a knighthood in 1856 exactly 313 years after his ancestor

William Wyse was knighted by King Henry VIII. On his death in 1862 Sir Thomas was given a state funeral by the king and queen of Greece.[7]

In his refusal to support repeal of the Act of Union, Wyse represented the last of the old Jacobite tradition - catholics who were loyal to the crown. Yet interestingly he favoured interdenominational education and in this he was much more of a radical than many of his contemporaries.

Thomas Francis Meagher (p203-209) was, like Thomas Wyse, educated by the Jesuits at Stonyhurst in England. There Thomas Francis Meagher learned to play the clarinet in the school band and ran foul of the school authorities on one occasion when he refused to play because the recital was organised to celebrate an anniversary of the British victory at Waterloo. Both Thomas Francis Meagher and Thomas Wyse split with Daniel O'Connell but here the similarities end. Wyse split because he would not support O'Connell's repeal movement, believing instead that Ireland's future lay within the United Kingdom. Meagher and the Young Irelanders broke away because they believed that O'Connell's meek acquiescence following the proclaiming of the famous Clontarf monster meeting in 1843 and his subsequent alliance with the Whigs, who had no interest in federalism, had made the repeal movement a redundant political force.

Thomas Francis Meagher's break with O'Connell took place in Constitution Hall, Dublin, on 28 July 1846 when Meagher made his famous 'sword speech' against O'Connell's resolution that members of the Association pledge to repudiate physical force in any and all circumstances. The speech propelled Thomas Francis Meagher to the forefront of national politics and was to have a significant influence on latter day revolutionaries such as Pearse and Griffith.

An attempted armed insurrection did occur in 1848 when the Young Irelanders rose in rebellion. For his part in the rebellion Meagher was transported to Van Diemen's Land from where in 1851 he dramatically escaped, arriving in America in 1852. Meagher himself went on to fight in the American Civil War, was promoted to Brigadier-General and praised for his bravery at the battles of Antietam and Fredericksburg. After the war he was appointed Secretary and later Acting Governor of Montana Territory. He died in 1867 having fallen overboard from a steamboat into the Missouri river.

Waterford figured prominently in early nineteenth century Irish politics, with all shades of the political spectrum being represented, unionist, constitutional nationalist and republican. As the century came to a close the city once again came into focus as the leader of the reunited Home Rule Party was John Redmond the MP for Waterford. Nineteenth century Waterford had seen huge change as the political pendulum swung between constitutional and revolutionary politics.

The upheaveal experienced by Waterford in the nineteenth century was not confined to the political sphere but was mirrored with equal drama when the city underwent its own industrial revolution and emerged on the international stage as a leading player in shipbuilding and food-processing.

The development of shipbuilding in Waterford saw the quakers once again to the fore as they owned all three of the city's main shipbuilding yards. White's shipyard opened in 1819 and began building its first ship, the Erin, in 1820. Plying the Waterford-London route it was still in service in 1842, a testimony to the quality of the materials and workmanship. In 1832 Whites built the schooner Hellas for Bewleys of Dublin which was the first ship to bring tea directly from China to Ireland. In 1837 they built for the Pope Brothers of Waterford the Zenobia, one of the earliest steam ships to make the passage around the Cape of Good Hope to India. The jewel in the crown was the Merrie England built in 1856, the largest and finest sailing ship ever built in the port of Waterford and probably the

longest ever built in Ireland. The famous Penrose family who had established the glass factory in 1783 also operated a shipbuilding yard in Waterford from 1856 to 1870.[8]

The giants of Waterford's industrial revolution were the Malcomsons, also quakers, who opened the Neptune Ironworks in 1843. It was from here that in 1846, a ship called the Neptune was launched and had the honour of inaugurating the London-St. Petersburg service. As the SS Neptune steamed up the Neva river she was greeted by His Imperial Majesty Czar Nicholas I, who decreed that the ship be freed for all time from port dues. In return the Czar was presented with a suite of Waterford glass.[9]

This was the great age of iron ship-building in Waterford. Some forty steamers were built at the Neptune Yard, all of them for Malcomson Brothers, who held the largest fleet of iron steamers in the world from the mid-1850s to the late 1860s. There were five transatlantic passenger liners built at Waterford for the Malcomson-owned London-Le Harve-New York line. The Malcomsons also owned the famous cotton mill in Portlaw, county Waterford where they established Ireland's most successful model village. The international dimension of their great business empire includes the ownership of a half share in several coal mines at Herne in the Ruhr Valley in Germany where the collieries were appropriately named Hibernia, Shamrock and Erin, the latter remaining in operation until 1986.[10] Despite the success of many of their business ventures Malcolmson Brothers declared themselves bankrupt in 1877. Little remains today in Waterford city to remind us of their great industrial empire except for a large stock anchor. It differs from a regular anchor in that it has only one fluke. The anchor is five metres high and was used in the launching of ships from the Neptune Ironworks on Canada Street/Park Road. Today it stands in the museum foyer as a symbol of our maritime history. (p9)

Another nineteenth century Waterford industry that, like the Malcomsons, had a strong international dimension was Henry Denny and Sons. Henry Denny's grandfather was a cooper in 1788, one of probably well over a hundred such craftsmen who made barrels for the Newfoundland provisions trade while his father was a boot-maker, no doubt providing boots to the local and Newfoundland market where there was a huge demand for Waterford boots and shoes. A member of the church of Ireland, Henry was born in Waterford in 1789. He entered a partnership with a long established general merchant in 1820 and by the early 1830s had his own business. Henry entered the bacon business at a time when the Newfoundland salt pork provisions trade had gone into terminal decline. Waterford provisions merchants now directed their attention to the more lucrative and discerning London market where the demand was for unsalted meat. This was a good move as the general decline in prices after the Battle of Waterloo in 1815 did not affect these specialist products. Pig meat became a huge component of Waterford's overseas trade, with over half of Irish bacon and ham exports going through the port. Between 1826 and 1846 bacon exports from Waterford increased by sixty-three percent. A report of the Solicitor General in 1860 stated that Waterford produced two-thirds of Irish bacon exported to London and sourced its pigs from as far away as Connaught. Waterford was also exporting half of all cured bacon into London. The city's pre-eminence in the bacon trade was attributed to the perfecting of the curing process by Henry Denny. It was such technological innovation that allowed Denny access to a new and affluent consumer society just emerging in Britain. By aligning his products with the new grocery chain stores, Home & Colonial, London & Newcastle and Liptons, Denny was positioning his branded product at the forefront of the convenience food and luxury meat market. By the time of his death in 1870 at the age of eighty his company Henry Denny and Sons was, despite its great success, still very much a local industry.

In 1872 a second factory opened in Limerick with a third opening in Cork in 1888. Experiencing competition from America, Denny & Sons, as the company was now called, became involved in improving the quality of Irish pigs with Charles Denny writing a book on pig breeding. As the quality of Irish pig-meat improved so did the renown of Denny. Workers from the Waterford plant were enticed to Russia and Canada during the 1890s to help start up bacon industries in those countries. It is interesting to note that in Waterford, young men still sometimes refer to a girlfriend as 'the lack' - a name derived from the Russian for 'girl' and introduced into colloquial speech by the returning bacon factory workers. In 1898 Denny & Son took over and moved to Richardson's Queens Bacon Stores in Morgan Street. This was one of the most modern meat factories in the country using both electric light and machinery.

Overseas expansion began in 1843 when Thomas Denny was sent to London to co-ordinate developments in Britain, a necessary move given the trend towards free trade in 1842 which lowered tariffs on imported goods to meet Britain's growing consumption needs. Low food prices were now favoured in Britain as they helped keep industrial wages low, thus keeping British industry competitive. In 1885 Denny & Son formed an association with a German firm J D Koopmann of Hamburg. Then following Bismark's introduction of protectionist policies Denny and Koopmann moved their operation to Denmark. Denny now brought to the Danish economy unrivalled production and marketing expertise. In 1888 they acquired a pig processing company in Chicago. The American business failed as it produced bacon with a higher fat content than its Irish or Danish equivalent and could only find markets in the poorer parts of Britain. In 1894 Denny & Son took over Koopmann of Hamburg and opened a sales office there, dealing mainly with liver, kidney and offal meat products.

In Britain in 1887 Edward Denny was a founder of the London Provision Exchange. His son Frederick became Chair of the Exchange from 1909-1921 and was then the most influential person in the meat industry in Britain.

During the Great War 1914-1918 Denny & Son supplied the British armed forces with 820,000,000 pounds of bacon by weight (worth fifty million pounds), making the company one of the leading meat producers in the world. During the inter-war years the company expanded into Northern Ireland. In 1933 one of the managers of the Waterford plant in Morgan Street won a gold medal in England for his sausage recipe. (p211) During the Second World War Denny & Son supplied both the British and American armed forces. If the old adage is true that 'an army marches on its stomach' then Denny & Son of Waterford can take a little credit for the allied victories in both the First and Second World Wars!

In 1941 the skinless sausage was invented and in 1947 the company began an association with the Swedish firm Lars Slagterier. In 1953 it won the contract to supply the American armed forces. The following year Denny founded Amagraze Ltd, in Brisbane, Australia to produce lamb and beef products. In 1964 E M Denny New Zealand was formed for the same purpose. Despite this expansion, the post-war economic climate proved very challenging for the industry at home and abroad and many factories were forced to close. The historic Waterford facility closed in 1972 after almost 140 years in operation. The Tralee plant was also in trouble. However market research was undertaken indicating that Denny was a strong brand and had a strong brand loyalty. In 1982 Denny was acquired by Kerry Foods who still produce the famous gold medal sausage. Kerry Foods, as part of their programme to modernise the Tralee plant, employed Danish bacon experts to train its workforce. It is not unreasonable to speculate that these Danish experts had been trained by people who themselves had been trained by Denny in the late nineteenth and early twentieth century.[11] This move, viewed in the broader context of that never-ending circle of migration and emigration and the cultural transfers that accompany this process, meant that we in Ireland were experiencing the return of the Vikings - this time however they were bringing home the bacon.

Daniel O'Connell (1775-1847)

Daniel O'Connell was the MP for the county of Waterford, 1830-1831. He was born near Cahirciveen, county Kerry, on 6 August 1775. At an early age he was adopted by his wealthy and childless uncle, Maurice 'Hunting Cap' O'Connell, and brought up by him at Derrynane. In 1791 he was sent to school at St Omer and Douai, in France. Here he witnessed, at first hand, some of the horrors of the French revolution and these fostered in him a deep conviction of the abhorrent nature of violence for political ends. O'Connell entered Lincoln's Inn in 1791 to train as a barrister, being called to the Irish bar in 1798. The rebellion of the United Irishmen in that year reinforced his hostility to politically motivated violence.

O'Connell became active in the campaign for catholic emancipation. In pursuit of this objective, he founded the Catholic Association in 1823. O'Connell believed that a more popular movement was required for success and to that end he established the catholic rent, whereby associate membership was open to all on the payment of a penny a month. This initiative transformed catholic opinion in Ireland into something like a gigantic political party. Waterford was one of his areas of strongest support, with an active local committee that included Thomas Wyse and Thomas Meagher. It was Wyse who devised the electoral strategy of harnessing the political force of the predominantly catholic forty-shilling freeholders in a direct challenge to the protestant ascendancy. Success was apparent in 1826 when Villiers Stuart, a protestant supporter of catholic emancipation, defeated one of its most bitter opponents, Lord George Beresford. This strategy was emulated, with success, in other constituencies. In 1828 it was employed in Clare, where Daniel O'Connell himself was a candidate. His victory was a major factor in the government's decision to grant emancipation, for which achievement O'Connell gained the title the 'Liberator'.

In the 1830 general election O'Connell presented himself as a candidate for the Waterford county constituency. In the 1840s O'Connell began a vigorous campaign for the repeal of the Act of Union. Since emancipation had been gained by a popular agitation, he adopted similar tactics in this struggle. Once again Waterford was one of the places to give him widespread support. O'Connell declared that 1843 would be the year of repeal. So-called 'monster meetings' were organised throughout the country and were intended as displays of the power of organised democracy. One such gathering took place in Waterford city on 9 July, attracting a crowd in the region of 300,000. Repeal was not achieved, however, O'Connell cancelling a meeting at Clontarf on 8 October 1843, for fear of bloodshed. He was arrested a few days later and charged with conspiracy and sedition. In May 1844 he was sentenced to one year's imprisonment. The House of Lords reversed the verdict in September of the same year and ordered his release.

The momentum for repeal, however, was gone and a group that became known as Young Ireland was challenging O'Connell's political dominance of the movement. A split finally occurred in July 1846, an event in which Thomas Francis Meagher, the son of one of O'Connell's most loyal and staunch Waterford supporters, Thomas Meagher, played a central role, when he delivered his famous 'sword speech', a moral justification for the use of physical force.

Worn down by political setbacks, deteriorating health and the advent of famine, Daniel O'Connell died in Genoa, Italy, on 15 May 1847, while on his way to Rome. Waterford Corporation's decision to hang a portrait of the Liberator by Stephen Catterson Smith, President of the Royal Hibernian Academy, in the council chamber was a recognition of his distinguished service to his country and his association with the city and county. We know that this painting was hanging in city hall by 1883 when a portrait of his friend, Thomas Meagher, was placed there. The Waterford portrait may be similar to the portrait of O'Connell painted by Catterson Smith in 1871 for city hall, Dublin, destroyed by a fire in 1908. The Waterford painting is signed 'Catterson Smith R H A Pinxit'.

Eugene Broderick

DATE:	mid-19th century
NUMBER:	WMT1999.6251
DIMENSIONS:	L 2375 x W 1459 (canvas)
MATERIAL:	oil on canvas
PROVENANCE:	municipal collection

Conservation generously sponsored by the Heritage Council

Thomas Meagher (c1789-1874)

Thomas Meagher was the father of the patriot, Thomas Francis Meagher. He served as the first catholic mayor of Waterford since the seventeenth century and represented the city as an MP for ten years. Meagher was born in Newfoundland c1789, where his Tipperary-born father was a wealthy merchant, who had made his fortune on the prosperous Waterford - Newfoundland trade route. Meagher junior settled in Waterford in 1819 and a year later he married Alicia Quan, a member of a prosperous local family. Meagher quickly established himself as one of the city's most influential merchants.

In 1823, Daniel O'Connell founded the Catholic Association to campaign for emancipation. Meagher became a member and was appointed secretary of the Waterford association. He played a very important role in the 1826 election when Villiers Stuart successfully challenged Lord George Beresford. Meagher was elected the first mayor of the reformed Waterford Corporation in 1843 and was re-elected for another term in 1844. As mayor, Meagher was a fiercely loyal supporter of O'Connell and was very active in the unsuccessful struggle for the repeal of the Act of Union in the 1840s. In 1847 Meagher was elected as MP for Waterford city. Re-elected in 1852, he retired from politics in 1857.

The latter part of his political career was overshadowed by the actions of his son, Thomas Francis, who associated himself with the Young Ireland movement. Thomas Francis Meagher was transported to Van Diemen's land for his part in the abortive rising of 1848. He escaped to America in 1852, and his wife Catherine visited him there in 1853, accompanied by her father-in-law. During this visit, Thomas Meagher was presented with a gold-topped walking stick by a group of Irish exiles resident in Cincinnati, Ohio. Cut from a tree growing on the grave of George Washington, this walking stick was given as a mark of recognition that Meagher was the father of 'a gallant and gifted son'. It was also given in admiration of his 'character as an Irish gentleman and representative in the British House of Commons where, in the midst of treachery and corruption', he was always found the 'earnest friend of the people'. He was also a generous benefactor of the charities and religious orders of Waterford city. The chalice and paten here were gifts by Meagher to the Sisters of Charity. This silver chalice, the bowl internally gilded, is inscribed: 'The Gift of Thomas Meagher Esqre to God and our Lady of Charity 1842. Pray for him'. The maker's initials are I.S. and the hallmarks show that the chalice was made in Dublin. The paten is silver, gilded on the upper side.

Thomas Meagher died on 27 August 1874, his obituaries recalling a life dedicated to public service. In 1883 a portrait of Meagher in his mayoral robes and chain was acquired by one of his mayoral and parliamentary successors, John A Blake, and hung in the council chamber of City Hall, Waterford, appropriately enough at the right hand side of the portrait of Daniel O'Connell. Meagher's portrait (by an unidentified painter), recently conserved, is now displayed in the museum, giving due recognition to this distinguished man.

Eugene Broderick

Walking stick

DATE:	1853 A D
NUMBER:	WMT1999.1798
DIMENSIONS:	L 900, top L 35
MATERIAL:	wood, gold
PROVENANCE:	gifted in 1954

Chalice & paten

DATE:	1842 A D
NUMBER:	WMT2003.0016 & 2003.0017
DIMENSIONS:	H 221, bowl Dia 73; paten Dia 109
MATERIAL:	silver
PROVENANCE:	gifted by the Sisters of Charity in 2003

Portrait

DATE:	c1883 A D
NUMBER:	WMT1999.6252
DIMENSIONS:	L 940 x W 740 (canvas)
MATERIAL:	oil on canvas
PROVENANCE:	municipal collection

FURTHER READING:	Broderick in McEneaney (ed) 1995
	Decies 54 2003

Conservation generously funded by Bausch & Lomb

Sir Thomas Wyse (1791-1862)

Thomas Wyse, grandson of John Wyse of Newtown House, was born in 1791, possibly in Newtown. Educated at Stonyhurst, England, and Trinity College Dublin, he took his degree in 1812 and entered Lincoln's Inn to study law. In 1815 Thomas went on the Grand Tour of Europe, in the course of which he visited Emperor Napoleon Bonaparte's younger brother, Lucien Bonaparte, prince of Canino, who lived near Rome. There he met Lucien's pretty daughter the Princess Letitia, the 'Venus of the Bonapartes', aged eleven. Returning several years later, he found her grown into a young beauty and fell in love with her. They were married in Viterbo in March 1821. This portrait of Thomas, painted about 1824, is by his sister Harriet, a talented artist who had received formal training.

Alas, the couple were ill-matched: Thomas was a cold, scholarly, talented man in his thirtieth year, Letitia a flighty socialite of sixteen. They had two sons: Napoleon Alfred, born in Italy, and William Charles, born in 1826 in Waterford. Within two years, Letitia had fled Waterford amid much melodrama and the marriage was over. Her subsequent career, involving three further children by different partners, was a cause of perpetual embarrassment to Thomas.

Meanwhile, Thomas had thrown himself into the heady world of Irish politics. He was the author of the political strategy that was central to the eventual success of the struggle for catholic emancipation. He proposed that the predominantly catholic, and heretofore politically subservient, forty-shilling freeholders be organised to challenge the political dominance of parliamentary representation by the protestant ascendancy. As agent for the pro-catholic candidate, Henry Villiers-Stuart, in the Waterford county by-election of 1826, Wyse played a leading role in securing victory for Villiers-Stuart. This strategy was emulated, with success, in other constituencies, most notably in 1828 when Daniel O'Connell was elected in county Clare. The government, alarmed by these developments, decided to grant emancipation a year later. In the same year Wyse was elected the first catholic member of Waterford Corporation since the seventeenth century and his valuable contemporary account of the campaign for catholic rights, entitled *Historical Sketch of the Late Catholic Association*, appeared. Wyse was elected MP for county Tipperary in 1830 and he represented Waterford city from 1835 to 1847. Relations between him and O'Connell deteriorated further when Wyse refused to support repeal of the Act of Union. As a Catholic unionist he remained committed to Ireland's connection with Britain.

As a supporter of the Whig (Liberal) government, Thomas threw his energies into educational reform, setting up the national school system which gave people throughout Ireland access to free elementary education; he chaired the secondary education committee which recommended the establishment of interdenominational state-financed secondary schools; and he supported the proposal to establish provincial university colleges, also to be interdenominational - the 'godless' Queen's Colleges of Cork, Galway and Belfast. In seeing religious strife as a major cause of Ireland's economic and cultural backwardness, and in striving to overcome this through educating the youth of the nation together, Sir Thomas (he was knighted in 1856) was a man before his time and one of the great Irish educationalists of the nineteenth century. Wyse was also one of the commissioners for the building of the new Houses of Parliament at Westminster. The architect was Augustus Welby Pugin, who became acquainted with Wyse and built him a residence at Lisduggan, in the suburbs of Waterford. In 1849 he was appointed british minister at Athens where he remained until his death on 16 April 1862. He was given a state funeral by the king and queen of Greece, a fitting tribute to the career of a man who had brought distinction to the various positions he held during his life.

DATE:	c1824 A D
NUMBER:	WMT2002.0013
DIMENSIONS:	L 800 x W 650
MATERIAL:	oil on canvas

Bonaparte plaque

Sir Thomas Wyse's marriage to the Princess Letitia Bonaparte ended in scandal and disgrace and his relations with his sons remained embittered to the end. In order to prevent any Bonaparte claim whatsoever on the Wyse estates, Sir Thomas disinherited both sons. However, when these estates were sold under the Encumbered Estates Act, his elder son Napoleon Alfred bought them back. In 1862, after the death of his father, he returned to live in Waterford at the new Manor of St John's which his father had erected. His mother came to live with him, and a stone plaque bearing the imperial eagle and shield of the Bonapartes (but not the arms of the Wyse family!) was erected over the entrance. It was defiantly inscribed 'Letizia Bonaparte Wyse'. According to the Waterford News, this plaque was 'elegantly cut in stone by Mr M Carew sculptor of this city'.

DATE:	c1862 A D
NUMBER:	WMT2001.0019
DIMENSIONS:	plaque Dia 175
MATERIAL:	marble

Mourning cross

Upon the death of Emperor Napoleon in exile at St Helena in 1821, his strong-willed mother - known as 'Madame Mère' - commissioned twelve jet crosses set in gold, one to be given to each female member of the Bonaparte family. The cross given to Letitia passed to Harriet Wyse, sister of Sir Thomas, and hence to the present representatives of the family, from whom it is on loan to Waterford Treasures.

Eugene Broderick and Julian Walton

DATE:	19th century
NUMBER:	WMT2001.0017
DIMENSIONS:	L 50 x W 35
MATERIAL:	jet, gold

PROVENANCE:	the Bonaparte Wyse family
FURTHER READING:	Bonaparte Wyse 2004
	Auchmuty 1939
	Smith in *Decies* 2002

On loan from Henry Bonaparte Wyse

Thomas Francis Meagher (1823-1867)

Meagher the Young Irelander

Thomas Francis Meagher was born in Waterford city on 3 August 1823 into a wealthy catholic middle-class family. His early education was at Mount Sion and, at eleven years of age, he attended the Jesuit-run boarding school, Clongowes Wood College in county Kildare. In October 1839, aged sixteen, he was sent to another Jesuit College, Stonyhurst near Preston in England. Within a few months of his arrival he, as first clarinettist in the college orchestra, refused to play during a concert celebrating the anniversary of the Battle of Waterloo. The concert was subsequently cancelled as Meagher stated that he would not sound a note in praise of England's victory. That clarinet is the one featured here. It was made by Dalmaine & Co, Late Golding & Dalmaine, Soho Square, London.

Meagher left Stonyhurst in August 1843 and returned to Waterford where he quickly immersed himself in nationalist politics and initially supported Daniel O'Connell's repeal movement. But Meagher, along with many younger members, quickly tired of the conservatism and compromising politics of O'Connell and this faction became known as the Young Irelanders. In 1845, Meagher helped establish a new '82 Club to commemorate the achievement of legislative independence by the Volunteers in 1782. The members wore special uniforms and Meagher urged that the '82 Club should be developed as a Young Ireland forum. This here is Meagher's original coatee, part of the uniform. It was donated to Waterford Corporation in 1886 by a Mr Donegan of Cork.

In 1846 a split occurred in the movement when the Young Irelanders refused to accept O'Connell's attempt to force members to adopt a pledge repudiating physical violence in any and all circumstances. When this matter was debated in Dublin on 27 July 1846, it was Meagher, in what has become known as the 'sword speech', who refused to accept this ultimatum. The split in the repeal movement came in January 1847 with the formation of the Irish Confederation and Ireland moved a step closer to revolution. In March 1848 Meagher was part of a delegation sent to Paris by the Confederation to congratulate the new French government. When he returned he brought with him the tricolour of green, white and orange. This flag subsequently became the Irish national flag and was first publicly flown in Waterford on 7 March 1848. The 'sword speech' enunciated a moral justification for the use of physical force in pursuit of political independence and propelled Meagher into the forefront of nationalist politics and along a career path even he could not have envisaged. A revolution did occur in 1848 and for his part Meagher was transported to Van Diemen's Land from where in 1851 he escaped, arriving in America in 1852. As a result of his actions in pursuit of independence Meagher earned the sobriquet, 'Meagher of the Sword'.

In May 1852 Meagher arrived in New York. He had left a wife, Catherine behind in Van Diemen's Land and in February 1852 she had given birth to a son, who died four months later. In 1854, Catherine gave birth to a second son, Thomas Bennett Meagher, but she died shortly after the birth. This child was brought up by his grandfather Thomas Meagher junior in Waterford. Thomas Francis married Elizabeth Townsend in 1855 and was called to the New York bar in the same year. In 1856 he founded his own newspaper, *The Irish Citizen* and in 1857 he became an American citizen. At the outbreak of the Civil War in April 1861, Meagher was unequivocal in his support for the Union and the Constitution. He volunteered for Union service in April and fought with the 69th New York Regiment at the Battle of Bull Run in July 1861. Meagher was appointed Brigadier-General and commander of the Irish Brigade in October 1861 (confirmed by Congress, February 1862) and led the Irish Brigade at the Battles of Fair Oaks, Gain's Mills, Malvern Hill, Antietam and Fredericksburg during 1862.

clarinet

DATE:	early 19th century
NUMBER:	WMT1999.1799
DIMENSIONS:	L 590 x max W 74
MATERIAL:	wood, ebony, ivory, brass

coatee

DATE:	mid-19th century
NUMBER:	WMT1999.1790
DIMENSIONS:	L 950 x circumference 860

Meagher of the Sword

After the devastation of the Brigade at Chancellorsville in May 1863, Meagher resigned when he was refused permission to recruit new men to the Brigade. In the summer of 1863 the Napper Tandy Light Artillery, Brooklyn, presented him with a specially commissioned sword. This is an ornate 1850 staff officer's sword with decorative engraving and has a panel containing a spread wing eagle and another panel with a large US etched onto the blade. It has an engraved silver grip and the pommel is topped with a large eagle. This sword was made by the Ames Manufacturing Company, Chicopee, Massachusetts. It bears the inscription 'Presented to Thomas Francis O Meagher by the members of the Napper Tandy Light Artillery, as a small token of their high admiration of his sterling devotion to the cause of Ireland and liberty'. The silver plated steel scabbard has mounts of heavy cast brass with stands of arms and acorns with oak leaves on the drag. A second, less ornate and lighter 1860 sword bearing the inscription 'Tiffany's & Co, New York', has the emblem of an eagle with, on either side, three flags. The brass scabbard is plain. Although adopted in 1860 it did not become standard until after the heavier 1850 model was discontinued in 1872. Meagher's widow, Elizabeth, gifted this sword to Waterford Corporation in August 1886. Both swords were modelled on French originals.

Meagher was re-appointed to active command in December 1863 and was appointed to the Etowah District, south of Chattanooga, Tennessee. He formed part of the general officers' honour guard that accompanied President Lincoln's lying in state in April 1865 and, like all civilian generals, resigned his commission on 15 May 1865. That same year President Andrew Johnston appointed Meagher secretary of Montana Territory. During his brief tenure, 1865-1867, while he acted as both secretary and acting governor, Meagher was fully aware of Montana's untapped resources and sought to prepare her for statehood. In attempting to frame a constitution for the Territory, he fell foul of both Democrats and Republicans and of other powerful interests, many of whom did all in their power to keep Montana in a state of anarchy and confusion. His death by drowning on 1 July 1867 at Fort Benton, Montana was shrouded in mystery. Many believe that he was murdered by his enemies. His body was never found.

staff officer's sword
DATE: c1850 A D
NUMBER: WMT1999.1794
DIMENSIONS: sword: handle L 150, blade L 770, scabbard L 820
MATERIAL: sword steel, brass, silver
                     scabbard metal

sword
DATE: c1860 A D
NUMBER: WMT1999.1793
DIMENSIONS: sword: handle L 138, blade 790, scabbard L 970
MATERIAL: sword metal, wood, leather
                     scabbard brass

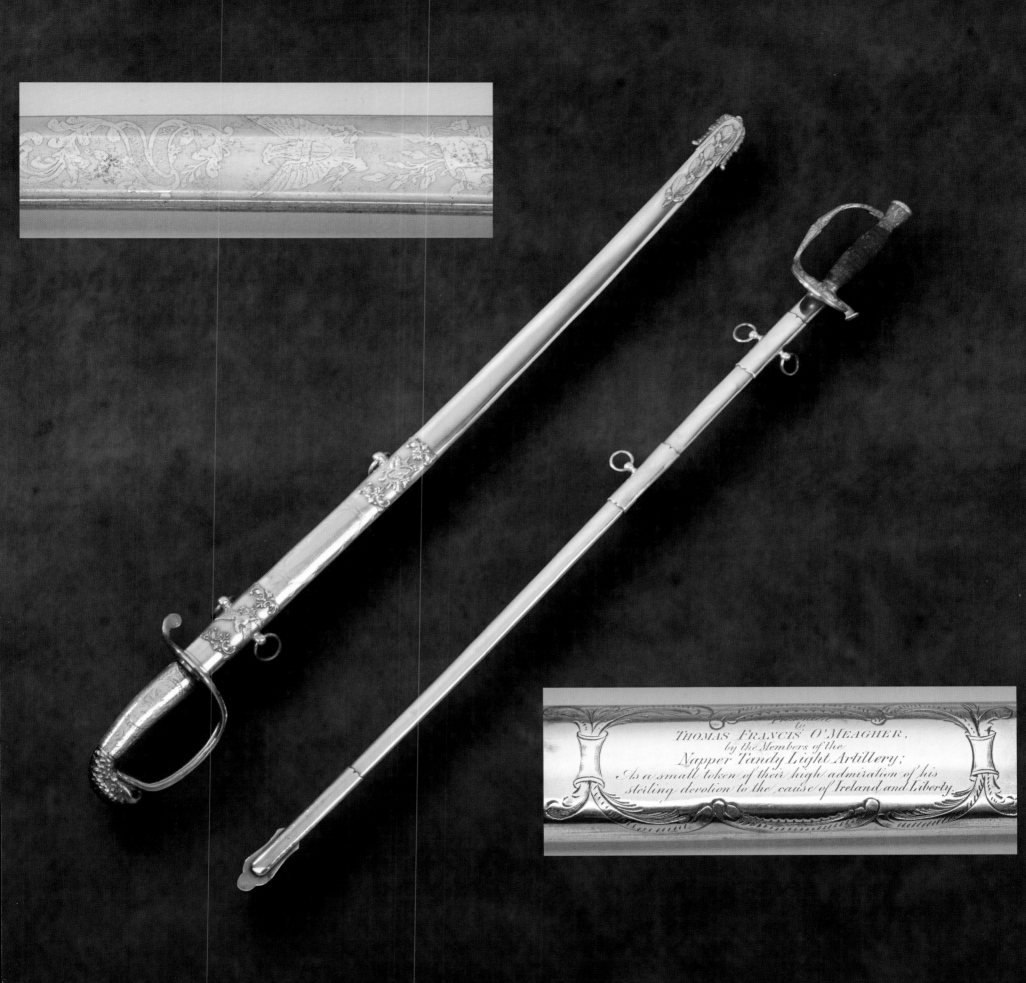

Presented to
THOMAS FRANCIS O'MEAGHER,
by the Members of the
Napper Tandy Light Artillery;
As a small token of their high admiration of his
sterling devotion to the cause of Ireland and Liberty.

Recognition in Ireland

In August 1886 Meagher's widow, Elizabeth presented some of the General's personal possessions to Waterford Corporation. She had intended to come to Waterford herself to make the presentation, but was unable to do so. Two of these treasures, the Kearney cross and Fort Sumter medal were presented to Meagher in 1863. The Kearney cross was named in honour of General Philip Kearney who was killed during the Battle of Chantilly, in 1862. Kearney, a veteran of the Mexican and Italian wars, won the French Legion of Honour for bravery at Solforino. Following his death, Brigadier General David B Birney succeeded him. On 13 March 1863 Birney authorised the decoration in Kearney's honour. It was designed as a 'cross of valour' and is inscribed with the words 'Kearney Cross' on one side and 'Birney's Division' on the other. In June 1863 Meagher was the first recipient of the Kearney cross. It was presented to him at New York's Astor House by Alderman Farley and was inscribed, 'To General Meagher, Kearney's friend and comrade'. In 1863 Meagher was presented with the Fort Sumter medal, also known as the Gillmore medal after its creator, Major General Quincey Gillmore who, in 1863, issued orders creating the medal. Unlike the Kearney cross that was a divisional decoration, the Sumter medal was a medal of honour for gallantry and meritorious conduct and was commissioned to reward valour in the Union Army in operations before Charleston. It was designed by James Pollock, director of the Mint and crafted by the artist Christian Schuller.

Mrs Meagher also presented the corporation with a 'sprig of green' similar to that worn in the caps of the soldiers of the Irish Brigade during the battle of Fredericksburg. It was this 'sprig of green' that was used to identify the Brigade's dead after the battle. A United States Army general officer's buff coloured silk net sash, belonging to Meagher, was also donated. Mrs Meagher also donated two regimental flags to the corporation. One, a double pointed pennon, the top half red and the bottom white, is inscribed '5th Regt. Irish Brigade'. This seems to correspond to the flag of the 28th Massachusetts (part of the Irish Brigade) that the Confederates claim to have taken (a large red and white flag with the number one in the centre) after the Battle of Fredericksburg. The second flag is a blue square of eighteen inches and is embroidered with thirty-four white stars. There were thirty-four states in the Union at the outbreak of the Civil War. This flag would almost certainly appear to be the Union canton from a national flag, perhaps the national colour of one of the regiments. These are currently in possession of Waterford Museum of Treasures, awaiting conservation.

sprig
NUMBER: WMT1999.1792
DIMENSIONS: L 130

sash
DATE: mid-19th century
NUMBER: WMT1999.1791
DIMENSIONS: L 1700, tassel L 230
MATERIAL: silk

medals
NUMBER: WMT1999.1795 (Kearney cross) & WMT1999.1796 (Fort Sumter)
MATERIAL: silver, copper

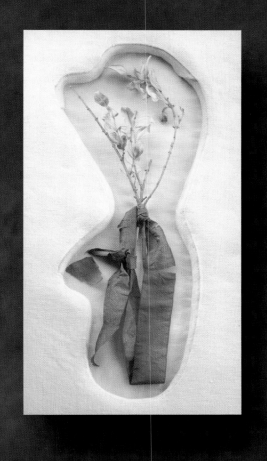

Meagher remembered

In August 1886 a crowd of over 60,000 lined the streets of Waterford to welcome the American party who had come to gift the city with the memorabilia of one of its most famous sons, Thomas Francis Meagher. One of the more interesting items gifted to Waterford Corporation at the ceremony was a large oil on canvas portrait of General Meagher in the uniform of a major general, painted by T F Gallagher of New York, a native of Waterford. Gallagher was himself in attendance and presented the painting to the mayor, Richard Power. Gallagher, along with a Mr Ford of the *Irish World*, organised the presentation ceremony from the American side. The portrait of Meagher was one of two painting of the general by Gallagher. The other painting was presented by Mrs Meagher to the Society of Montana Pioneers in 1878 and now hangs in the offices of the Bank of the Rockies, White Sulphur Springs, Montana. These paintings were probably painted in 1865, prior to Meagher leaving New York for the West.

But even in death Meagher proved to be controversial. On 8 November 1889 Montana was admitted to the Union as its forty-first state. This led to a bitter dispute as to which of the new State's cities would be its capital. In a run-off between Butte (supported by the copper-king, Marcus Daly) and Helena (supported by another copper-king, William A. Clarke), Helena narrowly won. When Helena was chosen, Daly set up the Meagher Memorial Association. Its purpose was to erect a monument to Thomas Francis Meagher in the grounds of the State Capitol Buildings, Helena. $20,000 was raised by public subscription, mainly from the Irish miners at Daly's Anaconda copper mine, for the bronze statue designed by Irish-born sculptor, Charles J Mulligan of Chigago. The American Bronze Foundry, Chigago, cast the statue and the granite pedestal was designed by Charles Lane and constructed by James Welch and Company, Butte, Montana. It was unveiled and dedicated on 4 July 1904. The inscription on the base of the monument reads: 'In Ireland, in America, he invited no man to danger he was not ready to share ... he gave all, lost all for the land of his birth. He risked all for the land of his adoption, was her true and loyal soldier, and in the end, died in her service'.

It was a fitting tribute to one credited with the speedy assimilation of the Irish into *post bellum* American society.

John M Hearne

portrait

DATE:	c1865 A D
NUMBER:	WMT1999.1797
DIMENSIONS:	L 1260 x W 850
MATERIAL:	oil on canvas
PROVENANCE:	municipal collection
FURTHER READING:	Hearne (ed) forthcoming
	Decies 59 2004
	Catton & McPherson 2001

Brigadier-General
THOMAS FRANCIS MEAGHER
U. S. Army
BORN AUGUST 3ᴿᴰ 1823
DIED JULY 1ˢᵗ 1867

The Denny gold medal

The Denny family has its origins in Kerry, but by the beginning of the eighteenth century some of the family had come to Waterford to participate in the lucrative transatlantic trade. John Hall Denny was a cooper in the 1780s and his son, Abraham Denny was a shoemaker and prominent local politician and father of Henry Denny who was born in Waterford in 1879. In 1820, Henry entered partnership with the long established general merchant, Simon Max. However, by the early 1830s Henry began trading on his own account as a provisions merchant in Bridge Street in the city. By 1835 he had moved to the Queen Street premises that the firm was to occupy until the end of the nineteenth century. In 1898 Denny bought a rival company, Richardson's Bacon Stores, in Morgan Street where the firm was to remain until closure in Waterford in 1972.

From the beginning, Henry directed almost all his products towards the growing British market, concentrating on the most lucrative market, London. Emphasis on quality and guaranteed under the Denny 'Star' brand, Denny bacon and ham monopolised the London market. In 1860, Denny made a significant technological innovation by perfecting the curing process. It was an innovation that was to allow Denny access to a new affluent consumer society just emerging in Britain. By aligning his products with the new grocery chain stores such as Home and Colonial and Liptons, Denny positioned his branded products at the forefront of the convenience food and luxury meat market.

Henry Denny died in 1870 and his eldest son, Abraham now took control of the firm. He initiated the expansion of the firm to Limerick, 1872 and Cork, 1888. Abraham and his son Charles played an important role in the Irish pig industry, improving the quality of pigs by engaging in selective breeding. Such was the renown of the Waterford workers that many Denny workers were sent to Canada and Russia during the 1890s to help organise the bacon industries in those countries.

In 1880 Henry Denny's youngest son, Edward established Edward Denny & Co in London and began the international expansion of the company. Between 1885 and 1900 it had operations in Germany, Denmark and America. Indeed it was the Denny technological and marketing expertise that helped develop the Danish bacon industry during this time. By the time he died in 1905, Edward Denny was one of the most powerful men in the international meat industry. During World War I, Denny was appointed official supplier of meat to the War Office and during the course of the war, supplied 820 million lbs of bacon valued at around £50 million. The company retained this contract during the Second World War and afterwards continued its expansion into Sweden, Australia and New Zealand.

In 1933, at an international food fair in Manchester, England Denny was awarded a gold medal for its sausage recipe and George Goodfellow, manager at the Waterford plant, accepted it on behalf of the company. The medal is inscribed 'Presented to Geo Goodfellow, Henry Denny & Sons Ltd for making the finest quality sausage. John Crampton & Co Ltd, Manchester December 1933'. George Goodfellow later became an Irish citizen and was one of the founder members of the Waterford International Festival of Light Opera. In 1935 Denny opened a factory in Portadown and in 1941 they invented the skinless sausage. But after the war the company's fortunes declined due to a lack of investment and increased competition. With the onset of Ireland's entry into the European Economic Community, Denny closed its historic Waterford factory in 1972 and in 1982 Kerry Foods bought out the Denny Irish operation. This medal is a link to one of Ireland's first multinational companies and Waterford's industrial revolution.

John M Hearne

DATE:	1933 A D
NUMBER:	WMT2003.0012
DIMENSIONS:	Dia 25
MATERIAL:	gold
PROVENANCE:	gifted by George Goodfellow junior in 2003
FURTHER READING:	*Dennys 1820-1970* 1970

The smaller illustration shows the medal at actual size.

Dr Cormac Macnamara
1944-2004

As this book was going to print, the death occurred of Dr Cormac Macnamara,
a great friend and supporter of Waterford Museum of Treasures.
The Director and staff would like to acknowledge his contribution
to the success of the museum in its formative years.

Ar dheis Dé go raibh a anam dílis

EDITORS

Eamonn McEneaney is a graduate of Trinity College Dublin. He has published widely on the history of medieval Waterford. He wrote *Discover Waterford* (2001), edited *A History of Waterford and its Mayors* (Waterford Corporation 1995) and contributed to *Late Viking Age and Medieval Waterford Excavations 1986-1992* (Waterford Corporation 1997) and *Waterford History and Society* (1992). He is currently Director of Waterford Museum of Treasures and Curator of Reginald's Tower. He is a member of the Heritage Council.

Rosemary Ryan was a teacher, then worked for eight years on *Irish Arts Review*. She is Education Officer / Documentation Officer at Waterford Museum of Treasures. In 2002-03 she led the Cultural Heritage digitisation of a museum collection project. She is married with two daughters.

CONTRIBUTORS

Dr Eugene Broderick teaches history and English in Our Lady of Mercy Secondary School in Waterford City and is a part-time lecturer in social history in the Waterford Institute of Technology. A graduate of NUI Cork, he has MA and PhD degrees in history. He has contributed many articles to books and journals pertaining to Waterford's history.

Clíodna Devitt has a BA degree in History of Art and Archaeology from UCD, a Diploma in Woven Textile Design [1983-1986 NCAD], MA Thesis in Textile History [1987-1989 Faculty of History of Art and Design, NCAD]; participated at Textile technical course [1989-1990 International Centre for the Study of Ancient Textiles [CIETA, Lyon]; a 3-year post-graduate diploma on Textile Conservation [1989- 990 Textile Conservation Centre, Hampton Court]; opened her studio in Dublin [1992 - Clíodna Devitt Textile Conservation Studio]; and is an Accredited Conservator of the United Kingdom Institute for Conservation.

Dr John M Hearne is a native of Waterford city and teaches history and economics at St Paul's Community College and history at Waterford Institute of Technology. For the last four years he was editor of *Decies*, the journal of the Waterford Archaeological and Historical Society. He was a contributor to *A History of Waterford and its Mayors*. He has been published widely in national and international publications and is co-editor of the forthcoming publication by Irish Academic Press, *Thomas Francis Meagher: The making of an Irish American*.

Ben Murtagh was awarded an honours degree in history and archaeology by the National University of Ireland, Dublin, and subsequently a masters degree in archaeology from the same institution. He has worked as a professional archaeologist on the city walls of Waterford for many years. He is Vice-Chairman of the Waterford Archaeological and Historical Society.

Raghnall Ó Floinn is a Curator in the Irish Antiquities Division of the National Museum of Ireland with particular responsibility for the early medieval collections. He has published widely on the subject of medieval Insular metalwork, the archaeology of the early Irish church, and bog bodies.

Orla Scully, MA MIAI, directed parts of the Waterford city centre excavations, including the final dig in 1992. Thereafter she worked as senior archaeologist with Waterford City Council, collating all the results and specialist reports, resulting in the publication of the book, *Late Viking Age & Medieval Waterford Excavations 1986-1992* in which she covered the domestic architecture, and did a report on the metal artefacts.

Julian Walton is a graduate of Oxford University. He is a Project Assistant at the Boole Library, University College, Cork. He has had a lifelong interest in the historic buildings and families of county Waterford on which he has written numerous articles. He contributed to *A History of Waterford and its Mayors* and was the author of *The Royal Charters of Waterford* (Waterford Corporation 1992). He is a former editor of *The Irish Genealogist* and *Decies*. He broadcasts a daily historical slot 'On This Day' on Waterford local radio.

LIST OF ILLUSTRATIONS

LIST OF ILLUSTRATIONS

END PAPERS

Wood engraved map of Europe with south orientation, by Sebastian Munster. Published by Sebastian Munster, Basle, c1550. It is notable that Waterford is the only place recorded in Ireland (Hibernia) being marked as *GARAFORDA*.

FOOTNOTES

NOTE

The editor would like thank Timothy O'Neill for the use of his article 'A Fifteenth Century Entrepreneur, Germyn Lynch fl.1441-1448' in the entry on the coinage of King Edward IV.

All measurements are in mm.

L length, W width, D depth, Th thickness, Dia diameter, H height.

PROVENANCE: Waterford excavations - this denotes the Waterford city centre excavations 1986-1992.

All objects are in Waterford Museum of Treasures unless otherwise stated.

Museum Origins

1. G. Smith, 'Thomas Wyse (1791-1862) and the origins of an Irish system of National Education', *Decies*, vol. 58, 2002, p 23.
2. *Journal of the Waterford and South East Archaeological Society*, (1897-1898). The annual report of 1897 records that Major Cusse, of Adelphi Quay, headed a large group in the society who wanted to see a museum set up in Waterford city (p xxi). A committee meeting was set up for April of that year and here the proposal was passed unanimously. In the annual report of 1898, Major Cusse reported that the museum had been established over the course of the previous year, and the society was passing control of the museum on to the 'Free' Library of the city.
3. Catalogue of Lady Lane Museum (now at Waterford Museum of Treasures).
4. T. O'Sullivan, 'Introduction', in M. Hurley, O. Scully with S. McCutcheon, *Late Viking Age and Medieval Waterford Excavations 1986-1992*, (Waterford, 1997) p xiii.

Reginald's Tower

1. T. N. Fewer, *I Was a Day in Waterford: An Anthology of Writing about Waterford City and County from the Eighteenth to the Twentieth Century,* (Waterford, 2001), p 132
2. J. Radner (ed), *Fragmentary Annals of Ireland*, (Dublin, 1978) pp 109-11.
3. S. MacAirt (ed), *Annals of Inisfallen*, MsRawlinson B503 (Dublin, 1951).
4. A. Scott and F. Martin (ed), *Expugnatio Hibernica: The Conquest of Ireland by Giraldus Cambrensis*, (Dublin, 1978) pp 67, 141.
5. J. Bradley et al, *Urban Archaeology Survey: Waterford: Part XIII* (ii), (Dublin 1988), p 195.
6. E. McEneaney, 'Mayors and Merchants in Medieval Waterford 1169-1495', in W. Nolan and T.P. Power (ed), *Waterford History & Society*, (Dublin, 1992), p 167.
7. Deeds in Waterford City Archives.
8. Reproduced in *Archaeologica*, vol. 20, 1824.
9. P. Kerrigan, 'The Fortifications of Waterford, Passage and Duncannon, 1495-1690' in *Decies* 39, 1985, p 12.
10. Ibid., p 14.
11. Ibid., pp 15-16.
12. J. Walton, 'Honest and Prudent Citizens: James Sherlock fitz John, Mayor-1580-81, 1590-91', in McEneaney, E, (ed) *A History of Waterford and its Mayors from the 12th to the 20th Century*, (Waterford 1995), p 121.
13. N. Byrne, 'Reformation in Elizabethan Waterford', *Decies*, vol. 57, 2001, p 49.
14. McEneaney, *Discover Waterford*, p 45.
15. Bradley et al, op. cit., p 197.
16. C. Smith, *The Ancient and present State of the County and City of Waterford*, (Dublin, 1746), p 172.
17. Ibid.., p 183.
18. McEneaney, *Discover Waterford*, (Dublin 2001), p 72.

Viking Age Waterford

1. James Graham-Campbell, *The Viking World*, (London, 2001), p 10.
2. M. Oftedal, 'Scandinavian place-names in Ireland', B.Almqvist and D. Greene (ed), *Proceedings of the seventh Viking Congress* (Dublin, 1976), p 133.
3. J. H. Todd, *Cogadh Gaedhel re Gallaibh, The War of the Gaedhil and the Gaill*, (London, 1867), p 292.
4. J. O'Donovan (ed), *Annals of the kingdom of Ireland by the Four Masters from the earliest period to the year 1616*, 7 vols (Dublin, 1851) reprint Dublin, 1991.
5. Radner, J. (ed), *Fragmentary Annals of Ireland*, (Dublin 1978), pp 109-11
6. W. M. Hennessy and B. McCarthy, *Annals of the Four Masters and Annals of Ulster*, 4 vols, (Dublin, 1887-1901).
7. Ibid.
8. J. Bradley and A. Halpin, 'The Topographical Development of Scandinavian and Anglo-Norman Waterford city' in *Waterford History and Society*, Nolan and Power (ed), (Dublin, 1992), p 106.

9. Ibid., p 107.
10. M. Dolley, 'The identity of the second (?) Hiberno-Norse mint in Ireland' *Irish Numismatics*, vol. xvi, 1983, pp 121-4; 'Coinage to 1534: the sign of the times' in A. Cosgrave (ed), *A New History of Ireland*, (Oxford, 1987), p 826.
11. Maire Ni Mhaonaigh in S. J. Connolly (ed), *The Oxford Companion to Irish History* (Oxford, 1998).
12. T. W. Moody et al, *A New History of Ireland: Vol 8*, Part 1, (Oxford, 1982) p 55.
13. S. Mac Airt, *The Annals of Inisfallen and Annals of the Four Masters*, MsRawlinson B503, (Dublin, 1951).
14. J. Bradley and A. Halpin, 'The Topographical Development of Scandinavian and Anglo-Norman Waterford city' in *Waterford History and Society*, Nolan and Power (eds), (Dublin 1992) p108.
15. S. J. Connolly (ed), *The Oxford Companion to Irish History,* (Oxford, 1998), p 334.
16. M. Hurley `The Defences' in M. Hurley, O. Scully with S. McCutcheon, op. cit., pp 20-33.
17. T. O'Keeffe, *Archaeology and Ideology in Twelfth Century Romanesque Ireland*, (Dublin, 2003), p 103.
18. M. Hurley and S. Mc Cutcheon, 'St. Peter's Church and Graveyard' and also B. Murtagh 'The Architecture of St. Peter's Church' in M. Hurley, O. Scully op. cit., pp 20-33.
19. Ibid.., pp 20-33
20. T. O'Keeffe, op. cit., pp 42-46.
21. Ibid., p 47.
22. T. O'Keeffe, op. cit., p 47.
23. P. Wallace, 'Viking Age Ireland' in P. Wallace and R. Ó Floinn (ed), *Treasures of the National Museum of Ireland: Irish Antiquities*, (Dublin, 2002), pp 220-1.
24. T. O'Keeffe, op. cit., p 47.

Anglo-Norman Waterford

1. C. A. Empey, 'County Waterford 1200-1300', in Nolan and Power (ed), op. cit., p 131.
2. T. O'Neill, *Merchants & Mariners in Medieval Ireland*, (Dublin, 1987) p 87.
3. McEneaney, 'Mayors and Merchants', pp 47-49.
4. Ibid., p 148.
5. Ibid., p 152.
6. E. McEneaney, 'Waterford and New Ross Trade Competition, c.1300', *Decies*, vol. 13, 1979.
7. McEneaney, 'Mayors and Merchants', p 45.
8. M. Bateson, 'Borough Customs of Waterford', Seldon Society, vol. XIXXXI, 1904-06.
9. E. McEneaney (ed), *A History of Waterford and its Mayors from the 12th to the 20th Century*, (Waterford, 1995), p 45.
10. M. Dolley, ' Coinage to 1534', in A. Cosgrave, (ed), *A New History of Ireland II: Medieval Ireland 1169-1534*, (Oxford, 1987), p 819.
11. McEneaney, 'Mayors and Merchants', p 175.
12. Ibid., pp 173-175.
13. M. D. O'Sullivan, *Italian Merchant Bankers in Ireland in the Thirteenth Century*, (Dublin, 1962), pp 72-76.
14. D. Smith, 'Peter Lombard (1554-1625) - Prelate, Politician, Pragmatist', *Decies*, vol. 56, 2000, pp 35-55.
15. G. MacNiocaill, *Na Buirgéisí, XII - AV Aois*, vol. 2, (Dublin, 1964), p 446.
16. J. F. Lydon, 'Three Exchequer Documents from the Reign of Henry III', *Proc RIA*, vol. LXV, 1966, p 14.
17. Smith, *History of Waterford*, p 102.
18. Bradley and Halpin, 'The Topographical Development of Scandinavian and Anglo-Norman Waterford city', p 121.
19. McEneaney, 'Mayors and Merchants', p 151.
20. J. F. Lydon, *The Lordship of Ireland in the Middle Ages*, (Dublin, 1972), pp 120-149.
21. McEneaney (ed), *A History of Waterford and its Mayors*, p 41.
22. Ibid., p 66.
23. Ibid., p 64.

Late Medieval Waterford

1. McEneaney (ed), *A History of Waterford and its Mayors*, p 61.
2. Ibid., p 75.
3. Ibid., p 75.
4. Ibid., p 75.
5. McEneaney, 'Mayors and Merchants', p 159.

6. Ibid., p 160.
7. Ibid., p 161.
8. Ibid., p 161.
9. McEneaney (ed), *A History of Waterford and its Mayors*, p 97.
10. Ibid., p 97.
11. O'Neill, *Merchants & Mariners*, pp 68-69.
12. Ibid., p 70.
13. McEneaney, 'Mayors and Merchants', p 162.
14. Ibid., p 162.
15. McEneaney (ed), *A History of Waterford and its Mayors*, p 52.
16. Ibid., p 88.
17. G. Mac Niocaill (ed), *St. Saviour's Chantry, Registrum Cantariae S. Salvatoris Waterfordensis*, (B.M. Harl. 3765), no. 23, 1966, pp 135-222.
18. N. J. Byrne (ed), *Liber Antiquissimus Civitatis Waterfordiae*, (forthcoming, 2004), p xi.
19. J. T. Gilbert (ed), *Archives of the Municipal Corporation of Waterford*, (London, 1885) p 318.
20. A. Halpin, 'Archery Material', in M. F. Hurley and O. M. B. Scully, op. cit., p 540.
21. I. Arthurson, *The Perkin Warbeck Conspiracy 1494-1499*, (Gloucestershire, 1994), p 113.
22. McEneaney, *A History of Waterford and its Mayors*, p 103.

Sixteenth Century Waterford
1. J. Walton, *The Royal Charters of Waterford*, (Waterford, 1992), p 38.
2. J. Walton 'Gifts of Sword and Cap' in E. McEneaney (ed), *A History of Waterford and its Mayors*, p 107.
3. Ibid., p 108.
4. Walton, 'Gift of Sword and Cap', p 107.
5. J. Walton, 'Honest and prudent Citizens', in E. McEneaney (ed), *A History of Waterford and its Mayors*, p 121.
6. J. J. Silke, 'Irish Scholarship and the Renaissance, 1580-1673', *Studies in the Renaissance*, vol. XX, 1973, p 183.
7. J. Walton, 'Church, Crown and Corporation' in Nolan and Power (ed), op. cit., p 186.
8. Ibid., p 188.
9. J. Bradley et al, op. cit., p 277.
10. N. J. Byrne, op. cit., p xxi.
11. Ibid., p xxi.

Seventeenth Century Waterford
1. N. J. Byrne, *Jacobean Waterford: Religion and Politics 1603-25*, Unpublished PhD, University College Cork, 2001.
2. D. Smith, 'Peter Lombard (1554-1625) - Prelate, Politician, Pragmatist', p 40.
3. G. Cleary, *Father Luke Wadding and St. Isidore's College Rome*, (Rome, 1925), p 22.
4. Original letter on display in Waterford Museum of Treasures, see also J. Graves, 'The Ancient Fabric, Plate & Furniture of Christ Church Cathedral Waterford', *Kilkenny Archaeological Society Journal*, vol. II, p 78.
5. G. D. Burtchaell, *Report on Franciscan Manuscripts*, (Dublin, 1906), p 235.
6. P. J. Corish, 'Cromwellian Conquest 1649-53', in Moody et al (ed), *A New History of Ireland: Early Modern Ireland 1534-1691*, p 342.
7. J. Walton, 'Agin the Government', in E. McEneaney (ed), *A History of Waterford and its Mayors*, p 134.
8. J. Walton, 'To Hell or to Connaught ... and Back', in E. McEneaney (ed), *A History of Waterford and its Mayors*, p 136.
9. J. Graves, 'The Ancient Fabric, Plate & Furniture of Christ Church Cathedral Waterford', p 78.
10. Ibid., p 81.
11. C. O'Brien, 'Some Misidentified Munster Goldsmiths', *The Silver Society Journal*, vol. XIII, (Dublin, 2001), p 38.
12. Walton, 'To Hell or to Connaught ... and Back', p 145.

Eighteenth Century Waterford
1. R. Ryan, 'The Wyses of Waterford', *Irish Arts Review*, vol. 21, no. 1, Spring 2004, p 111.
2. C. Smith, *The Ancient and Present State of the County and City of Waterford*, p 196
3. D. Cowman, 'Thomas ('Bullocks') Wyse: A Catholic Industrialist During Penal Laws', *Decies*, vol. 25, Jan 1984, pp 40-44.
4. A. Bilbao Acedos, *The Irish Community in the Basque Country c. 1700-1800,* (Dublin, 2003), p 9.
5. F. Maclean, *Bonnie Prince Charlie*, (London, 1988), p 32.

6. D. Cowman, 'The Beginnings of Modern Waterford', in E. McEneaney (ed), *A History of Waterford and its Mayors*, p 148.
7. C. Smith, op. cit., p 181.
8. Ibid., p 181.
9. T. Friedman, 'William Halfpenny's designs for an 'Early Christian' cathedral at Waterford', *Irish Architectural & Decorative Studies*, The Journal of the Irish Georgian Society, vol. I, 1998.
10. J. Walton, 'Classicism and Civility', *Irish Arts Review*, vol. 21, no. 1, 2004, p 103.
11. Ibid., p 106.
12. Diary of William Savery: Transcript in Library of the Society of Friends, Dublin.
13. Deed in Waterford City Archives.
14. E. McParland, *James Gandon Vitruvius Hibernicus*, (London, 1985).
15. C. O'Brien, 'The Goldsmiths of Waterford', forthcoming.
16. T. P. Power, 'Electoral Politics in Waterford City, 1692-1832', in Nolan and Power (ed), op. cit., p 249.
17. Walton, 'Classicism and Civility', p 107.
18. Ibid., p 107.
19. J. Mannion, 'Vessels, Masters and Seafaring', in Nolan and Power (ed), op. cit., p 394.
20. M. Dunlevy, *Penrose Glass*, National Museum of Ireland, (Dublin 1989), p 13, see also F. O'Dwyer, 'Making Connections in Georgian Ireland', *Bulletin of the Georgian Society*, vol. XXXVIII, 1996, pp 1-22.
21. Mannion, 'Vessels, Masters and Seafaring', p 391.
22. C. Byrne, 'The Waterford Colony in Newfoundland 1700-1850', in Nolan and Power (ed), op. cit., p 369.

Nineteenth Century Waterford

1. J. Mannion, 'From Comfortable Farms to Mercantile Commerce and Cultural Politics: The Social Origins and Family Connections of Thomas Francis Meagher', *Decies*, vol 59, 2003, p 16.
2. Ibid., p 2.
3. Ibid., p 22.
4. D. McCarthy, *The Dawning of Democracy: Ireland 1800-1870*, (Dublin, 1987), pp 110-16.
5. Ibid., pp 110-16.
6. G. Smith, 'Thomas Wyse (1791-1862) and the origins of an Irish system of National Education', pp 29-39.
7. Ibid., p 41.
8. B. Irish, *Shipbuilding in Waterford 1820-1882*, (Wicklow, 2001), pp 29-64, 58-64.
9. Ibid., pp 145-146.
10. O. Schmidt-Rutsch, 'Hibernia, Shamrock, Erin ...William Thomas Mulvany and the 'Irish mines' in the Ruhr', *Decies*, vol. 59, 2003, pp 203-207.
11. Dr. John M. Hearne. The editor would like to thank Dr. Hearne for his research on the Denny company. This section is based completely on a transcript of a lecture delivered by him on 4 March 2004 to mark the presentation of the Denny Medal to the museum by Mr. George Goodman junior.

BIBLIOGRAPHY

Anonymous:
Dennys 1820-1970: History to celebrate 150 years of private enterprise.
Gatchell Letters, 2 Vols, National Museumof Ireland.
'Portraits of Daniel O'Connell', *The Irish Builder,* Vol XII, No 254, 1870.
Waterford Crystal, Waterford Crystal (1968).

Armstrong, E C R, 'Some Matrices of Irish Seals', Proc RIA 30 (Dublin 1913), Section C.
Arthurson, I, *The Perkin Warbeck Conspiracy 1491-1499*, (Gloucestershire 1994).
Athearn, R G, *Thomas Francis Meagher: An Irish Revolutionary in America*, (Colorado, 1949).
Auchmuty, J J, *Sir Thomas Wyse 1791-1862*, (London 1939).

Ballard, A, 'British Boroughs in the Reign of King John', *English Historical Review*, no. 14, 1899.
Ballard, A, and Tait, J, *British Borough Charters, 1216-1307*, (Cambridge, 1923).
Bartlett, T, and Jeffery, K, (ed) *A Military History of Ireland*, (Cambridge, 1996).
Bateson, M, 'Borough Customs of Waterford', *Seldon Society*, vol. XIXXXI, 1904-06.
Bateson, M, 'The Law of the Bretuil', *English Historical Review*, vol. XV, 1900, Vol. XVI, 1901.
Beresford, M, *New Towns of the Middle Ages*, (London, 1967).
Bilbao Acedos, A, *The Irish Community in the Basque Country c1700-1800*, (Dublin 2003.)
Bonaparte Wyse, O, *The Issue of Bonaparte Wyse: Waterford's Imperial Relations*, (Waterford, 2004).
Bonaparte Wyse, O, *The Spurious Brood*, (London, 1969).
Bradley, J, 'The Ballyhale Madonna and Its Iconography', in Rynne, E, (ed) *Figures from the Past: Studies on Figurative Art in Christian Ireland,*
    (Dubin, 1987).
Bradley, J, Halpin, A, and King, H A, *Urban Archaeology Survey: Waterford: Part XIII* (ii), (Dublin 1988).
Bradley, J, *Walled Towns in Ireland*, (Dublin, 1995).
Brennan, M N, 'The Interlace Programme of the Waterford Kite Brooch', forthcoming.
Broderick, E, *Waterford's Anglicans: Religion and Politics, 1819-1872*, unpublished PhD thesis, UCC, 2000.
Broderick, E, *Irish Corporatism, 1931-39*, unpublished MA thesis, UCC, 1991.
Brodie, M, *The Irish Customs 1275-1327*, Unpublished BA thesis, Trinity College, (Dublin, 1966).
Burtchaell, G D, *Report on Franciscan Manuscripts*, (Dublin, 1906).
Burtchaell, J, 'A Typography of Settlement and Society in County Waterford c1850', in *Waterford History and Society* (Dublin, 1992).
Byrne, C, (ed), *Gentlemen-bishops and faction fighters: the letters of Bishops O'Donel, Lambert, Scallan, and other Irish Missionaries*, (St. John's, 1984).
Byrne, N J, *Jacobean Waterford: Religion and Politics 1603-25*, Unpublished PhD thesis, University College Cork, 2001.
Byrne, N, 'Reformation in Elizabethan Waterford', *Decies*, vol. 57, 2001.
Byrne, N J, (ed) *Liber Antiquissimus Civitatis Waterfordiae*, (forthcoming, 2004).

Caffrey, P, *Treasures to Hold: Irish & English Miniatures 1650-1850 from the National Gallery of Ireland Collection* (Dublin 2000).
Calligas, E, *Coincraft's Standard Catalogue of the Coins of Scotland, Ireland, Channel Islands & Isle of Man*, (London, 1999).
Canny, N P, 'The Formation of the Old English Elite in Ireland', *O' Donnell Lectures (18)*, University College Dublin, 1975.
Carlsson, D and Owen, O, *Follow the Vikings*, (Sweden, 1996).
Catton, B & McPherson, J M, *The American Heritage: New History of the Civil War* (2001).
Cavanagh, M, *Memoirs of Gen. Thomas Francis Meagher*, (Worcester, 1892).
Cleary, G, *Father Luke Wadding and St. Isidore's College Rome*, (Rome, 1925).
Cochran, J, MLitt thesis, Trinity College Dublin, forthcoming.
Colclough, B and O'Neill, W, *Waterford & Thereabouts*, (Waterford, 1993).
Connolly, S J, (ed), *The Oxford Companion to Irish History*, (Oxford, 1998).
Conlan, P, *Franciscan Ireland*, (Mullingar, 1988).
Cosgrave, A, (ed), *A New History of Ireland II: Medieval Ireland 1169-1534*, (Oxford, 1987).
Cowman, D, 'Thomas ('Bullocks') Wyse: A Catholic Industrialist During Penal Laws', *Decies*, vol. 25, Jan. 1984.
Crookshank, A & the Knight of Glin, *Ireland's Painters 1600-1940*, (London 2002).
Curtis, E, 'English and Ostmen in Ireland', *English Historical Review*, vol. XXIII, 1908.

Decies - the Journal of Waterford Archaeological & Historical Society, Vol 1-59.

Deevy, M B, *Medieval ring brooches in Ireland - A study of jewellery, dress and society*, (Wicklow, 1998).

Doherty, R, *The Williamite War in Ireland 1688-1691*, (Dublin, 1988).

Dolley, M, 'Irish Mints of Edward I in the light of the Coin-Hoards from Ireland and Great Britain', *Proc RIA*, vol. LXVI, 1967-68.

Dolley, M, 'The identity of the second (?) Hiberno-Norse mint in Ireland', *Irish Numismatics*, vol. xvi, 1983.

Dolley, M, 'Coinage to 1534: the sign of the times' in A. Cosgrave (ed), *A New History of Ireland*, (Oxford, 1987).

Dowling, D, 'Cardinal Wiseman and His Association with South Kilkenny', *Old Kilkenny Review*, (Kilkenny, 1974).

Dowling, D, *Waterford Streets Past and Present*, (Waterford, 1998).

Duffy, C G, *Four Years of Irish History*, (London, 1883).

Dunlevy, M, *Penrose Glass*, National Museum of Ireland, (Dublin 1989).

Edwards, R D, 'The Beginning of Municipal Government in Dublin', *Dublin Historical Record*, 1938-39.

Ellis, S G, 'Taxation and Defence in Late Medieval Ireland: the Survival of Scutage', *JRSAI*, vol CVII, 1977..

Elviller, E M, *English and Irish Cut Glass 1750-1950*, (London, 1953).

Fanning, H, O P, *The Waterford Dominicans, 1226-1990*, (Waterford, 1990).

Fanning, T, *Viking Age Ringed Pins from Dublin*, Proc RIA, (Dublin 1994).

Fewer, T N, *I Was a Day in Waterford: An Anthology of Writing about Waterford City and County from the Eighteenth to the Twentieth Century*, (Waterford, 2001).

Fletcher, A, *A Study of the Great Charter Roll of Waterford*, unpublished BA moderatorship thesis, Trinity College Dublin, (Dublin 1994).

FitzGerald, A, and O'Brien, C, 'The production of silver in late-Georgian Dublin', *Irish Architectural and Decorative Studies*, Irish Georgian Society 2001.

Friedman, T, 'William Halfpenny's designs for an 'Early Christian' cathedral at Waterford', *Irish Architectural and Decorative Studies* (the journal of the Irish Georgian Society) Vol I, 1998.

Gilbert, J T, (ed) *Archives of the Municipal Corporation of Waterford*, (London, 1885).

Gillespie, J L, *The Age of Richard II*, (London, 1997).

Graham-Campbell, J, *The Viking World*, (London, 2001).

Graves, J, 'The Ancient Fabric, Plate & Furniture of Christ Church Cathedral Waterford', *Kilkenny Archaeological Society Journal*, vol. II.

Graves, J, 'The discovery of treasure trove at Waterford', *Historical & Archaeological Association of Ireland Journal*, Series 3, vol. I, 1869.

Gras, N, *The Early English Customs System*, Harvard Economic Studies, Cambridge, (Massachusetts, 1918).

Grehan, I, *Waterford: An Irish Art*, (New York, 1981).

Griffith, A, (ed) *Meagher of the Sword*, (Dublin, 1916).

Gwynn, D, *Young Ireland and 1848*, (Cork, 1949).

Hamilton, H C, (ed) *Calendar of State Papers relating to Ireland of the reign of Elizabeth, August 1588 - September 1592* (London, 1885).

Hand, G, *English Law in Ireland*, (Cambridge, 1967).

Harris, G L, *King, Parliament and Public Finance in Medieval England*, (Oxford, 1975).

Harvey, P D A and McGuinness, A, *A Guide to British Medieval Seals*, The British Library and the Public Record Office (London, 1996).

Hearne, J M, *Waterford: Economy, Society and Politics, 1780-1852*, Unpublished PhD thesis, University College Cork, 2001.

Hearne, J M, *Thomas Francis Meagher, the Making of an Irish American*, forthcoming.

Hennessy, W M and McCarthy, B, *Annála Uladh, Annals of Ulster*, 4 vols, (Dublin, 1887-1901).

Hope, V, *My Lord Mayor*, (London, 1989).

Hore, J F, and Graves, J, (ed) *Social State of the Southern and Eastern Counties of Ireland in the Sixteenth Century*, (Dublin, 1870). (see maces)

Hore, P H, *History of the Town and County of Wexford*, 6 vols, (London, 1910).

Hourihane, C P, *The Iconography of Religious Art in Ireland 1250-1550, and a Catalogue of Architectural Sculpture, Metalwork, Wooden Sculpture, Seals, Alabasters, Mural Paintings and Miscellanea*, PhD Thesis, Courtauld Institute of Art, University of London 1984.

Hurley, M F, and Scully, O M B with McCutcheon, S W J, *Late Viking Age and Medieval Waterford Excavations 1986-1992*, (Waterford 1997).

Irish, B, *Shipbuilding in Waterford 1820-1882: A Historical, Technical and Pictorial Study*, (Wicklow, 2001).

Irish Arts Review, vol. 21, no. 1, spring 2004 (Dublin 2004).

James, M, *Studies in the Medieval Wine Trade*, (Oxford, 1971).

Kerrigan, P M, 'The Fortifications of Waterford, Passage and Duncannon 1495 to 1690', *Decies* 29, summer, 1985.

Kiernan, T J, *The Irish Exiles in Australia*, (Dublin, 1954).

Kissane, N, *Treasures from the National Library of Ireland*, (Dublin, 1994).

Langrishe, R, 'Irish church bells', *Journal of the Royal Society of Antiquaries of Ireland*, Part III, 1881.

Lee, G, *Leper Hospitals in Medieval Ireland*, (Dublin, 1996).

Lightbown, R. W., *Medieval European Jewellery*, (London 1992).

Lloyd, T, *The English Wool Trade in the Middle Ages*, (Cambridge, 1977).

Lyons, W F, *Brigadier General Thomas Francis Meagher*, (New York, 1870).

Lydon, J F, 'Consent and Taxation in Medieval Ireland', (unpublished paper), delivered to the International Commission for the History of Representative and Parliamentary Institutions, (October 1964).

Lydon, J F, 'Three Exchequer Documents from the Reign of Henry III', *Proc RIA*, vol. LXV, 1966.

Lydon, J F, *The Lordship of Ireland in the Middle Ages*, (Dublin 1972).

Lydon, J F, 'Survey of the Memoranda Rolls of the Irish Exchequer, 1294-1509', *Analecta Hibernica*, no. 23.

Lydon, J F, (ed) *The English in Medieval Ireland*, (Dublin, 1984).

Lydon, J F, 'The city of Waterford in the later middle ages', *Decies* 12, Sept. 1979.

Lyon, E, '15th-century manuscript yields first look at Nina', *National Geographic*, vol. CLXX, no. 5, 1986.

Maitland, F, *Domesday Book and Beyond*, (Cambridge, 1897).

Mannion, J, 'From Comfortable Farms to Mercantile Commerce and Cultural Politics: The Social Origins and Family Connections of Thomas Francis Meagher', *Decies*, vol 59, 2003.

MacAirt, S, (ed) *Annals of Inisfallen*, Ms Rawlinson B503 (Dublin, 1951).

Maclean, F, *Bonnie Prince Charlie*, (London, 1988).

MacLeod, C, 'Fifteenth Century Vestments in Waterford', *Journal of the Royal Society of Antiquaries of Ireland* Vol LXXXII, Part II, 1952.

MacLeod, C, 'Mediaeval Figure Sculpture in Ireland, Statues in the Holy Ghost Hospital, Waterford', *Journal of the Royal Society of Antiquaries of Ireland* July 1946.

MacCurtain, M, *Tudor and Stuart Ireland*, (Dublin, 1972).

MacNiocaill, G, *Na Buirgéisí, XII - AV Aois*, vol. 2, (Dublin, 1964).

Mac Niocaill, G, (ed) *St. Saviour's Chantry, Registrum Cantariae S. Salvatoris*, (B.M. Harl. 3765), no. 23,1966.

McCarthy, D, *The Dawning of Democracy: Ireland 1800-1870*, (Dublin, 1987).

McCormish, W A, *Irish Overseas Trade in the Later Middle Ages,* unpublished BA thesis, Trinity College Dublin, 1968.

McEneaney, E, *Edward I and the City of Waterford*, unpublished moderatorship thesis, Trinity College, Dublin, 1978.

McEneaney, E, 'Waterford and New Ross trade competition, c1300', *Decies*, 12, 1979.

McEneaney, E, 'The government of the municipality of Waterford in the thirteenth century', *Decies*, 13, 1980.

McEneaney, E, 'King John and the city of Waterford', *Decies* 26, 1984.

McEneaney, E, (ed) *A History of Waterford and its Mayors from the 12th to the 20th Century*, (Waterford, 1995).

McEneaney, E, *Discover Waterford*, (Dublin, 2001).

McKisack, M, *The Parliamentary Representation of the English Boroughs during the Middle Ages*, (Oxford, 1932).

McManus, M J, *Thomas Davis and Young Ireland: A Centenary Tribute*, (Dublin, 1945).

McParland, E, *James Gandon Vitruvius Hibernicus*, (London, 1985).

Moody, T W, Martin, F X, and Byrne, F J, (ed) *A New History of Ireland III: Early Modern Ireland 1534-1691*, (Oxford, 1976).

Moody, T W, Martin, F X, and Byrne, F J, (ed) *A New History of Ireland: A Chronology of Irish History to 1976*, Vol VIII, (Oxford, 1982).

Mooney, Rev Canice O F M, 'Franciscan Architecture in Pre-Reformation Ireland' (Part II), *JRSAI* 86, 1956.

Mooney, Rev Canice, O F M, 'The Franciscans in Waterford', *JRSAI* .

Morrissey, J F, (ed) *Statute Rolls of the Parliament of Ireland: Twelfth and Thirteenth to the Twenty-First and Twenty-Second Years of the Reign of King Edward the Fourth*, (Dublin, 1939).

Murtagh, B, 'The Watergate and the Excavations at Grady's Yard, Waterford', *Decies* 57, 2001.

Nolan, W and Power, T P (ed), Cowman, D (associate ed), *Waterford History & Society, Interdisciplinary Essays on the History of an Irish County*, (Dublin 1992).

O'Brien Papers (now in the National Library, Dublin), Correspondence of William Smith O' Brien.

O'Brien, C, 'Some misidentified Munster goldsmiths', *The Silver Society Journal*, vol. XIII, Autumn 2001.

O'Brien, C, *The Goldsmiths of Waterford*, forthcoming.

Ó Croinin, D, *Early Medieval Ireland: 400-1200*, (London, 1995).

O'Donovan, J, (ed) *Annals of the kingdom of Ireland by the Four Masters from the earliest period to the year 1616,* 7 vols, Dublin 1851, reprint Dublin 1991.

O'Dwyer, F, 'Making Connections in Georgian Ireland', *Bulletin of the Georgian Society*, vol. XXXVIII, 1996.

Ó Floinn, R, *Irish Shrines and Reliquaries of the Middle Ages*, Dublin 1994.

Ó Floinn, R, 'Schools of Metalworking in eleventh and twelfth-century Ireland', *Ireland and Insular Art A.D. 500-1200*, (Dublin, 1987).

O'Keeffe, T, *Archaeology and Ideology in Twelfth Century Romanesque Ireland*, (Dublin, 2003).

O'Meadhra, U, *Early Christian, Viking and Romanesque Art: motif-pieces from Ireland. An illustrated and descriptive catalogue* (vol 1 Stockholm 1979, vol 2 *A Discussion* Stockholm 1987).

O'Neill, T, *Merchants & Mariners in Medieval Ireland*, (Dublin, 1987).

O'Neill, T, 'A Fifteenth Century Entrepreneur, Germyn Lynch fl. 1441-1483', J Bradley (ed), *Settlement and Society in Medieval Ireland* (Kilkenny 1988).

O' Sullivan, M D, *Italian Merchant Bankers in Ireland in Thirteenth Century*, (Dublin, 1962).

O'Sullivan, T J, *The Young Irelanders*, (Tralee, 1944).

O'Sullivan, W, *The Earliest Anglo-Irish Coinage*, National Museum of Ireland, 1961.

Oftedal, M, 'Scandinavian place-names in Ireland', B Almqvist and D Greene (ed), *Proceedings of the seventh Viking Congress*, Dublin 1976.

Olden, M, *The Cathedral of the Most Holy Trinity Waterford*, (Waterford, 1993).

Orpen, G H, *New Ross in the Thirteenth Century*, (Dublin, 1911).

Orpen, G H, *Ireland Under the Normans I - IV*, (Oxford, 1911).

Otway-Ruthven, *A History of Medieval Ireland*, (London, 1968).

Parker, C, 'Paterfamilias and Parentela: The Le Poer Lineage in Fourteenth-Century Waterford', *Proc RIA*, vol. 95, no. 2, 1995.

Pender, S, 'Waterford Merchants Abroad', *O'Donnell Lectures* (8), University College Cork, 1964.

Pollock, Sir F, and Maitland, F W, *History of English Law before Edward I*, vols. I & II, 2nd edition, (Cambridge, 1898).

Power, P., 'The Cistercian Abbeys of Munster', *Journal of the Cork Historical and Archaeological Society*, vol. 43, 1938.

Powicke, Sir M, *Henry III and the Lord Edward*, (Oxford, 1947).

Radner, J, (ed) *Fragmentary Annals of Ireland*, (Dublin 1978).

Rae, E C, 'The Rice Monument in Waterford Cathedral', *Proc RIA*, LXIX (Dublin, 1970).

Records Office Ireland, *Calendar Justiciary Rolls Ireland 1308-1314*, (Dublin).

Richardson, H, and Sayles, G, 'The Irish Parliament of Edward I', *Proc RIA*, vol. XXXVIII, no. 6, 1928-29.

Richardson, H, and Sayles, G, 'Irish Revenue: 1278-1384', *Proc RIA*, vol. LXII, 1962.

Richardson, H, and Sayles, G, *The Administration of Ireland 1172-1377*, (Dublin, 1963).

Richardson, H, and Sayles, G, *Parliament in Medieval Ireland*, (Dundalk, 1964).

Roesdahl, E, *The Vikings*, (London, 1991).

Rogozinski, I, *Pirates! An A-Z Encyclopaedia: Brigands, Buccaneers, and Privateers in Fact, Fiction, and Legend*, (New York, 1996).

Ryan, M, (ed) *The Illustrated Archaeology of Ireland*, (Dublin, 1991).

Ryan, R, 'The Wyses of Waterford', *Irish Arts Review*, vol. 21, no. 1, Spring 2004.

Ryland, R H, *A History of Waterford*, (Dublin, 1824).

Salzman, L, *Edward I*, (London, 1968).

Schmidt-Rutsch, O, 'Hibernia, Shamrock, Erin...William Thomas Mulvany and the 'Irish Mines' in the Ruhr', *Decies*, vol. 59, 2003.

Scott, A. and Martin, F. (ed) *Expugnatio Hibernica: The Conquest of Ireland by Giraldus Cambrensis*, (Dublin, 1978).

Shields, H, *The Walling of New Ross: A Thirteenth Century Poem in French*, (Dublin, 1975).

Silke, John J., 'Irish Scholarship and the Renaissance, 1580-1673', *Studies in the Renaissance*, Vol. XX, 1973.

Smekens F, *Stad Antwerpen Oudheidkundige Musea Vleeshuis, Catalogus X: Koper en Brons* (Antwerp, n d), 18 and No 419.

Smith, C, *The Ancient and Present State of the County and City of Waterford,* (Dublin, 1746).

Smith, D, 'Peter Lombard (1554-1625) - Prelate, Politician, Pragmatist', *Decies*, vol. 56, 2000.

Smith, G, 'Thomas Wyse (1791-1862) & the origins of an Irish system of national education', *Decies*, vol. 58, 2002.

Smith, R D, 'Towards a New Typology for Wrought Iron Ordnance', *The International Journal of Nautical Archaeology and Underwater Exploration*, 1988.

Stalley, R, 'Three Irish Buildings with West Country Origins', *Medieval Art and Architecture at Wells and Glastonbury*, British Archaeological Association, 1981.

Stevens, C D, *Meagher of the Sword: A Dramatization of the Life of Thomas Francis Meagher*, (New York, 1967).

Strickland, W J, *A Dictionary of Irish Artists*, (Dublin, 1913)

Tait, J, *The Medieval Irish Borough*, (Manchester, 1936).

Terry and Durling, *The Romance of the Rose or Guillaume de Dole*, (London, 1993).

Thomas Francis Meagher letters to Charles Gavan Duffy from Tasmania, Waterford Municipal Library.

Todd, J H, (ed) *Cogadh Gaedhel re Gallaibh, The War of the Gaedhil and the Gaill*, (London, 1867).

Tóstal exhibition catalogue 1955, No 76, St Patrick's College Maynooth Museum 1955.

Tuck, A, 'Anglo-Irish Relations: 1382-1393', *Proc RIA*, vol. XX, 1964.

Wallace, P F, and O' Floinn, R, (ed) *Treasures of the National Museum of Ireland: Irish Antiquities*, (Dublin, 2002).

Walton, J C, *The Royal Charters of Waterford*, (Waterford, 1992).

Walton, J C, 'The Library of Christ Church Cathedral Waterford', *Decies*, 1989.

Walton, J and O'Flanagan, P, 'The Irish in the bay of Cadiz in the 18th century', *Studies in Historical Geography*, forthcoming.

Walton, J, 'Classicism and Civility', *Irish Arts Review*, vol. 21, no. 1, 2004.

Warren, C B, 'Notes on the Church Plate of Waterford Diocese', *Journal of the Royal Society of Antiquaries of Ireland* 97, 1967.

Watt, J, *The Church in Medieval Ireland*, (Dublin, 1972).

Westropp, M S D, *Irish Glass. An account of glass-making in Ireland from the XVIth century to the present day*, revised edition, Boydell, M, (ed), (Dublin, 1978).

Whelehan, T P, *The Irish Wines of Bordeaux*, (Dublin, 1990).

Williams, G, *Medieval London from Commune to Capital*, (London, 1963).

Wilson, E M C, *The Overseas Trade of Bristol*, (Bristol, 1967).

Wood, H, 'The Offices of Chief Governor of Ireland: 1172-1504', *Proc RIA*, vol. XXXVI, no. 12, 1923.

Wyse Jackson, R, 'Old Church Plate of Lismore Diocese', *Journal of the Royal Society of Antiquaries of Ireland* 85, 1955.

Sicilia
Aetna
Lipari
Mare Tyrrhenum
Morea
Pelopõ nesus
GRAECIA
Corfun
Nigropont
Parnasus
Brendiſiu
Calabria
Neapol
Albania
Roma
ITALIA
Apulia
Olympus
Ancona
Salonica
Mare Adriaticum
Florẽtia
Dalmatia
Macedonia
Bononia
winden
Padus fl:
Cõſtantinopel
Seruia
Boſſina
Coruatia
Venetiæ
Medio lanũ
Histria
Bulgaria
Croatia
Carinthia
Saus fl:
Draua fl:
Septem Caſtra
Buda
Stiria
Rhenus
VNGARIA
Vualachia magna
Auſtria
Bauaria
Conſtãtia
Danubius fl:
Auguſta
Sueuia
Tranſ ſiluania
Vienna
GERMA
Muldauia
Bohe mia
Morauia
Nurnberga
Ruſſia
Cracouia
Praga
Slesia
Polonia
Erfordia
Podolia
Maſouia
Miſ nia
Turingia
Odera fl:
Marca Bran denburgenſis
Volhinia
Viſtula fl:
Saxonia
Brunſuic
Albis fl:
Lituania
Pomeria
Meckelburg
Samogitia
Pruſſia
Dantzig
Liuonia
Lubeck
Mare Germanicum
Schleſwick
Selandia
DANIA